Theresa Tenebruso

# OPTIMIZATION METHODS FOR ENGINEERING DESIGN

**RICHARD L. FOX**
*Case Western Reserve University*

# OPTIMIZATION METHODS FOR ENGINEERING DESIGN

**ADDISON-WESLEY PUBLISHING COMPANY**
*Reading, Massachusetts*
*Menlo Park, California · London · Amsterdam · Don Mills, Ontario · Sydney*

This book is in the
ADDISON-WESLEY SERIES IN MECHANICS AND THERMODYNAMICS

Howard W. Emmons and Bernard Budiansky
*Consulting Editors*

 Printed in the United States of America. Published simultaneously in Canada. Library of Congress Catalog Card No. 78-127891.

ISBN 0-201-02078-5
DEFGHIJKLM-MA-89876543210

*To my parents Kitty and Harry Fox*

# PREFACE

Design education presents the engineering educator with a difficult dilemma. Since the traditional, highly specific design course is in disfavor at many institutions, what should we teach about design which is (a) learnable and (b) relevant to the inexperienced student? With rapidly changing technology, the older style courses did not directly prepare the student for the design work he would eventually be doing, although some argue that they may have helped to prepare him for the kind of *thinking* he would be doing. This recognition of a possible irrelevance of existing design education sparked a search for something which might be called the essence of design and a means of teaching it.

Emerging from this search are two almost antithetical points of view. One of these, in its extreme expression, treats design as pure art, practiced by engineers who possess and use creativity as their main tool. The other school of thought views design as a completely logical decision-making process. Somewhere in the middle, or perhaps superimposed upon these ideas, is the belief, strongly held by some, that one of the key problems in designing is the psychological one, involving the psyche, the individual, and his interaction with the working group and the company in varying degrees. I feel that the true nature of useful design lies in a variable combination of these concepts, plus the application of experience, judgment, and a thorough understanding of the technology of the particular problem.

This book, however, is essentially a text on computerized design methods or, seen another way, an introduction to mathematical programming for engineers. As such, it appears to champion a sterilized view of design, but this is not the intent. The older courses often dealt with the design of specific engineering systems or elements with the real purpose of teaching the student something of how one went about design in general; in the same way, this material provides a vehicle upon which to carry some of the more intangible aspects of the process. It has been prepared to fill the need for an up-to-date application-oriented presentation of the subject. Very little of the book is new, but the material has been consolidated and streamlined from a wide variety of sources in order to make it accessible to the engineer/designer. Many of the topics are in a "state-of-the-art" form, which is a way of hedging against the almost certain obsolescence or further illumination which many of the topics will see as time goes on. Certainly the whole field is in a dynamic state.

I am somewhat ambivalent about the intended level of the book. In the undergraduate engineering school of Case Institute of Technology at Case Western Reserve University, we have been teaching an abbreviated form of the course to senior civil and mechanical engineering students. The civil engineers have had as a prerequisite a semester course in structural design which runs along the more traditional lines, and the mechanical engineers have had a similarly oriented course in mechanical design. This constitutes at least their second course in design. I feel that it would be singularly inappropriate to use this material as a first or only exposure in design, because it is essential that the student have sufficient exposure to the range of real problems in design to see the present material in a proper perspective. Otherwise, he is likely either to seize upon it as the answer to all problems of design, which it certainly is not, or to find it totally irrelevant. Our abbreviated course in optimum design for undergraduates includes the material in Chapter 1, Sections 2.1 – 2.9 of Chapter 2, Sections 3.1 – 3.5 of Chapter 3, and Section 4.4 on linear programming. For this material the student needs only the standard background in college mathematics plus (or including) an acquaintance with matrix notation. In order to work problems on the computer the student should also have had a programming short course in a compiler language such as ALGOL or FORTRAN. About one-third of the work in the course is a computer term project in which the student formulates, codes, and operates a program to solve a design problem. Some typical project titles are:

1. Cam profile optimization for the flat-faced radial roller, offset roller, and oscillating follower.
2. Optimization of the design of a welded wide-flange section, based upon AISC code limitations.
3. Optimization of function generation, input shaft vs. output shaft, for the 4-bar mechanism.
4. Quick return design of the 4-bar mechanism.

5. Optimization of a single-span prestressed concrete beam, using ACI code requirements.
6. Optimization of a concrete retaining wall, using Coulomb equations.
7. Swedish circle, slope stability analysis.
8. Selection of alignment and grading of a highway so as to minimize cut and fill.
9. Optimum design of a wide-flange beam, using standard rolled shapes.
10. Locating stations along a rapid transit line.
11. Optimization of plate-girder flange welds.
12. A gear reducer optimization program.
13. A computer approximation for the minimum cost of a construction project, based on the network diagram of construction activities.

The student is encouraged to select and develop his project with his own ideas and along the lines of any special interests he may have.

At the graduate level, the entire book is used plus some reading in the references. The level of mathematical rigor in the book enables the students to cope with the methods presented. For many students this fulfills their needs, but for others the exposure whets their appetites for more formal courses in operations research and mathematical programming. Graduate students also benefit from a term project involving an application or modification of an optimization method, and often there is the beginning of a thesis or dissertation in this work.

The order of presentation of the material differs somewhat from the usual sequence in mathematical programming courses. We begin by presenting a number of simple but concrete examples of optimum design problems and by defining terms and introducing the concepts of design space, constraint surfaces, etc. In Chapter 2 we consider methods for solving the general unconstrained minimization problem. In Chapter 3 we present methods for converting the general constrained problem to an unconstrained one. This chapter makes little mention of distinctions among the various classes of mathematical programming problems such as linear vs. nonlinear, convex vs. nonconvex, separable, etc., because the methods tend to treat all of them alike. In Chapter 4 the direct methods are discussed, including the method of feasible directions, gradient projection, and linear programming. The section on the latter (Section 4.4) is independent and hence can be presented at any stage, but in my opinion it is logically placed because in this context it really is a special method. In Chapter 5 some special tricks and applications are discussed.

I am deeply indebted to Professor Lucien A. Schmit for introducing me to this fascinating and useful subject and for his encouragement, help, and criticism. My interest in the subject has been further heightened by my participation in research work supported by the National Aeronautical and Space Administration. There are many other colleagues whose help and discussion have been invaluable in preparing this book. Notable among these are Professor Leon Lasdon, who initially reviewed the material in class note form, and Professor Fred Moses, with whom I have had many productive (for me) discussions.

As everyone knows, we academics owe much to our students and especially to our graduate students; I would like to express my gratitude especially to Frank Cinadr, Mahesh Kapoor, Larry Moore, Milton Schrader, Ed Stanton, and Ken Willmert, who as graduate students helped me learn so much.

*Cleveland, Ohio* R. L. F.
*November 1970*

# CONTENTS

CHAPTER 1

# INTRODUCTION TO THE FORMULATION OF OPTIMIZATION PROBLEMS

Engineering is the activity through which designs for material objects are produced. The engineering design communicates to the agency of manufacture or construction not only the creative product of the designer, but the results of all scientific deductions and judgmental decisions which were rendered in developing the design. Of course, few engineers are engaged directly in the act of designing all the time and some engineers seldom design, but the majority of engineering tasks have as their ultimate goal the production of an engineering design or the provision of a means or aid to designing.

Aside from these broad statements, engineering design does not seem to have a universally accepted definition. To some its important aspect is a broad planning function in which the general outline and form of a project are decided. To others it has an inventive connotation, describing the process of devising or selecting a solution to an engineering problem. In other cases the words are used to describe the act of sizing, dimensioning, or selecting the detailed elements of the design. The goal of the design process may range from providing a practicable solution to a problem where none is previously known to improving on or replacing an existing design. We will not attempt to further define design, since agreement regarding its meaning is not essential to our present purposes.

A description of the material in this text might be "quantified optimum design." In many design problems there are several possible alternative *design concepts*: for example, a girder for a highway bridge can be concrete or steel, and once material is chosen, several approaches to using it are possible. In mechanical design, a desired motion output may be obtained by a cam or a linkage, etc. Within these design concepts, there are variables which specify the dimensions, proportions, and other details of the item.

Throughout this text, we will adopt the point of view that a range of designs exists within a selected design concept, and we will examine methods of choosing values for the quantities which prescribe the design. The *optimum* design aspect arises because we assume that these values are to be chosen in such a way that the design will be the one that satisfies all the limitations and restrictions placed on it and is best in some sense. Our approach is adaptable to those cases in which the major problem is to find any acceptable design in the presence of restrictions so severe or complicated that it is not clear how to proceed. The methods we will examine are numerical and hence, in most cases, practical only if programmed for the computer. We will be using the computer to do more than merely analyze engineering designs; we will also be relegating to it some of the quantitative design decisions.

The methods and algorithms that are presented will not enable the computer to arrive at new solutions to engineering problems; rather they will allow the computer to optimize preselected design concepts against preselected design limitations. This methodology therefore does not add directly to the creative development of solutions, but it can enhance the engineer's ability to arrive at the best version of an engineering design concept. These ideas form the basis of a design tool, the value of which will vary depending on the degree to which the important conflicts in a design problem are quantifiable.

Many of the techniques and ideas presented in this text are taken from the mathematical programming literature. This is a branch of operations research and mathematics that deals with the general problem of optimality. We will do more, however, than explore the mathematical programming techniques, because engineering design problems often involve special difficulties or have special properties with which the mathematical programming literature does not deal.

In this chapter we develop some of the concepts and language of mathematical programming that are related to engineering design. We assume here and throughout the text that the engineering design problem has already been idealized, in the same sense that problems in analysis are considered idealized in texts on engineering analysis. In other words, the discussion will assume that a design concept has already been selected, that an appropriate analysis formulation for this class of designs is available, and finally, that the design has been idealized into a mathematical model for the purpose of analysis.[1] While it may be said that this approach sidesteps some of the most important questions in engineering, it should be noted that we are talking about a design *tool* and not design itself. These methods are tools just as the matrix displacement method of structural analysis is a tool for predicting the behavior of structures and that the various geometric techniques used in mechanism analysis are tools for predicting the kinematical behavior of mechanisms. In studying analysis methods one often dismisses questions of idealization in order to get on with the study of the methods themselves. In the application of the methods, however, the techniques of idealization can play the decisive role. It is at this stage that the skill, judgment, and experience of the engineering analyst are brought to bear on the analysis problem. Similarly in the design problem it is the recognition of

[1] Morris Asimow (1962) refers to this idealization of the design problem as the formulation of an *archetype*. Asimow's book provides a good perspective for the material in this text. See also Middendorf (1969).

the true design goals and limitations and the selection of a design type that require the insight and talent of the modern designer.

In order to help the reader relate the ideas and methods to engineering design problems, we present a number of examples. Four of these, designated E.1 through E.4, are defined in this chapter and utilized for illustration purposes throughout the book. These examples represent some of the more common characteristics of problems arising in structures and mechanical design. They by no means depict the scope or complexity of design problems that are amenable to the methods described. An attempt was made to select problems with simple and widely understood theory and, as might be expected, most of these examples are of limited technical importance.

In addition to the formal examples E.1 through E.4, other illustrative cases are used. These are introduced as needed to demonstrate specific points and are often of a purely mathematical nature.

## 1.1 DESIGN VARIABLES

The numerical quantities for which values are to be chosen in producing a design will be called *design variables*. Other names have been used and, of course, the designation used here is merely the author's preference. Perhaps the most descriptive of the alternative names are "construction parameters" or "construction variables." A few simple examples should help to make the idea of design variables clear.

Consider the following: An automobile has been completely designed and a prototype built. A major problem with the prototype is its ride and handling characteristics, and as a first pass at a remedy it has been decided to try to select a "better" spring and damper set for the front suspension system.

If a linear spring[2] is to be used, then, its stiffness $k$ can be taken as a design variable. If the damper is a simple viscous dashpot,[3] then the damping coefficient $C$ can be used as a second design variable. Various values can be chosen for $k$ and $C$ and each combination can be called a "design" of the front end cushioning system. Clearly no choice of $k$ can produce a nonlinear spring design, should that be more effective; nor can any choice of $C$ determine the use of a more exotic damper than the linear viscous type.

A value of $k$ does not actually "design" the spring. However, in terms of the ride of the automobile it would probably adequately represent its important characteristics. On the other hand, some circumstances might require a breakdown of the problem into more detailed design variables. For example, in place of $k$ we might put $n$, the number of coils; $d$, the diameter of the wire; $D$, the mean diameter of the spring; and $h_f$, the free height of the spring (see

[2] Force $= k \times$ displacement.

[3] Force $= C \times$ velocity.

Fig. 1.1). To a greater extent than $k$ alone, a set of values for $n$, $d$, $D$, and $h_f$ "designs" the spring. The foregoing is, of course, predicated on the assumption of a coil spring, which is only one of many possibilities.

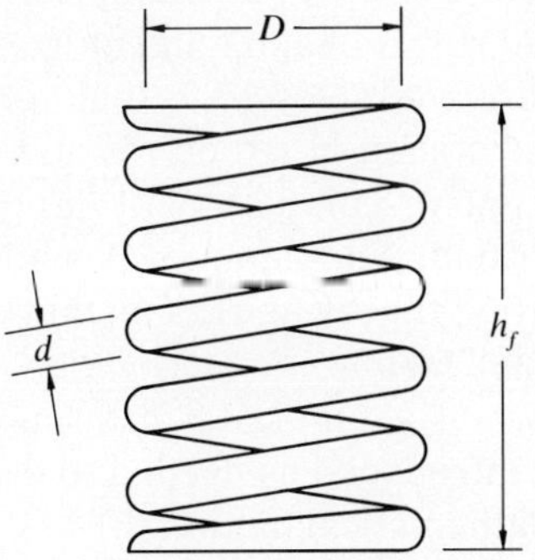


**Figure 1.1**

As another example, consider a three-dimensional truss structure which is fixed or "grounded" at certain points and loaded at certain other points (see Fig. 1.2). The truss is made up of straight members which are pin-connected at "nodes." Some nodes are the grounded points, others are the loaded points, and still others are neither.

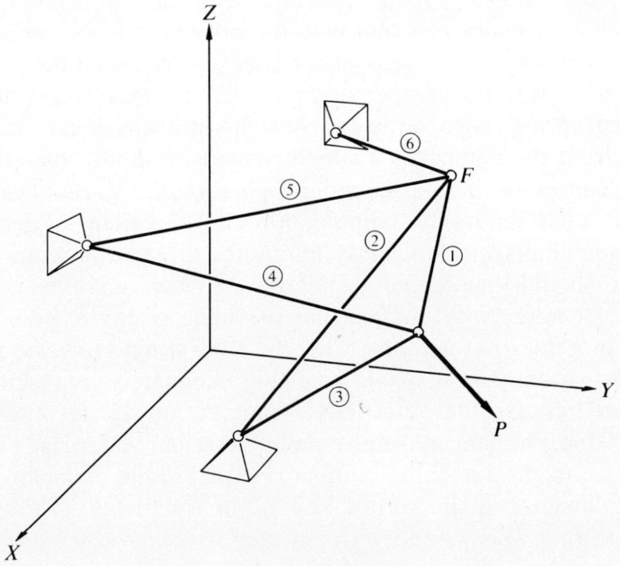


**Figure 1.2**

Suppose that the locations of all nodes have been chosen or are dictated by some prior consideration; then what remains is to "design" the members. An adequate set of design variables might be the areas $A_i$, $i = 1,2,\ldots, n$, of the $n$ members of the structure. A set of values for all the $A_i$ in a sense prescribes a design of the structure. However, just as with the spring in the previous example, a more detailed breakdown may be necessary. For instance, if axial buckling of the members is a consideration, the $A_i$ will not adequately characterize them. Perhaps the moments of inertia can be related to the areas through some approximate formula, but a more common situation is that a particular form of cross section has been chosen and its defining dimensions can be taken as the design variables. An example is the case of tubular members, the design variables of which are the mean diameter $d_i$ of the $i$th member and the wall thickness $t_i$ of the $i$th member (see Fig. 1.3).

The spatial locations of the unloaded nodes may also be varied in producing a design. In this case, a triplet of design variables for each such node would specify its location.

We will often refer to a *vector of design variables* $\boldsymbol{D}$, which is simply a column containing all the design variables in a particular problem. For example, if the truss shown in Fig. 1.2 is made up of tubular members and the location of the unloaded node $F$ is a variable in designing the structure, then the vector $\boldsymbol{D}$ might be defined[4] as

$$\boldsymbol{D} = \begin{Bmatrix} d_1 \\ t_1 \\ d_2 \\ t_2 \\ d_3 \\ t_3 \\ d_4 \\ t_4 \\ d_5 \\ t_5 \\ d_6 \\ t_6 \\ x \\ y \\ z \end{Bmatrix} \tag{1.1}$$

[4] Henceforth when the makeup of a vector is to be spelled out, it will be in the form $\boldsymbol{D} = (d_1, t_1, d_2, \ldots, z)$. This is to be taken to mean the column vector as shown in Eq. (1.1). The notation $\boldsymbol{D}^T$ will be used when a row form is intended.

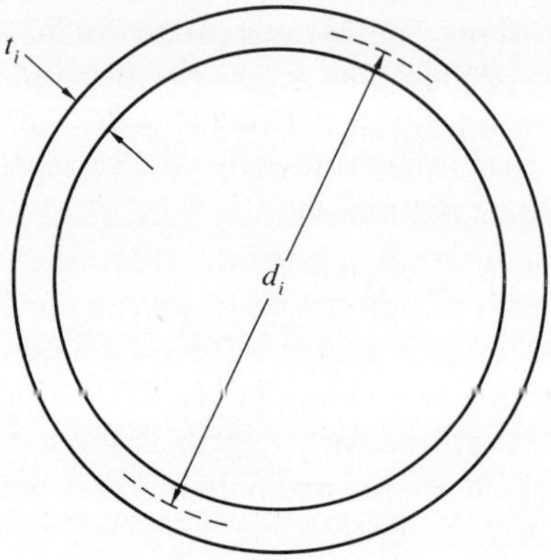


**Figure 1.3**

The order of the components is purely arbitrary, and any convenient scheme can be used. Once the makeup of such a vector is defined, any specific vector may be said to be a "design."[5] For instance,

$$\boldsymbol{D} = (1.0, 0.1, 1.0, 0.1, 2.0, 0.1, 1.0, 0.5, 1.5, 0.2, 2.5, 0.3, 1.0, 5.0, 3.5)$$

specifies a particular design of Fig. 1.2.

In many cases it is useful to choose quantities other than the obvious physical ones as design variables. An example of this idea is to use, for the truss, the design variables $r_i = d_i/t_i$ (the diameter-to-thickness ratio) and $A_i = \pi d_i t_i$ (the cross-sectional area). The two quantities $r_i$ and $A_i$ just as definitely determine the design of the $i$th member as do $d_i$ and $t_i$, since

$$d_i = (r_i A_i/\pi)^{1/2} \tag{1.2}$$

and

$$t_i = (A_i/\pi r_i)^{1/2}. \tag{1.3}$$

Such transformations of variables may not only simplify problem formulation but can also yield considerable advantage in the problem solution. Further discussion of the topic of transformations is deferred until Chapters 3 and 5.

In the discussions which follow, we will occasionally refer to certain quantities as *preassigned parameters*, or simply *parameters*. These quantities, together with the design variables, will completely describe a design but, for one reason or another, are to be considered invariant during the design process. In the truss example, if the node $F$ is taken as fixed at some point in space $(\bar{x}, \bar{y}, \bar{z})$, then $\bar{x}$, $\bar{y}$, and $\bar{z}$ are parameters.[6] Similarly, if $r_i$ is taken as

[5] Asimow (1962) refers to this as a "manifestation" of the design concept or archetype.

[6] The overbar is used occasionally to denote a specific constant value of a variable.

fixed at some value $\bar{r}_i$, then this quantity is a parameter. Quantities may be designated as parameters for a variety of reasons. It may be that the designer is simply not at liberty to change that particular element of the design, or it may be known from experience that a particular value of the parameter produces good results. Often an overriding reason is that by considering some quantities fixed, the problem is greatly simplified.

**Design Variable Studies, or "Grids"**

Our definition of parameters may cause some confusion for those familiar with the concept of a "parameter study." By the meaning adopted here, this useful design tool would be called a *design variable study*. The design variable study is the systematic examination of a range of designs done in order to choose a good or "best" design from among all those examined. Generally the characteristics of all the designs are studied and compared in order to choose a suitable one. Since these studies have some interesting relations to the more formalized methods we will be discussing later, a brief discussion of the approach will be undertaken now. One of the problems that will serve as a demonstration problem here and throughout the book will be used as an illustration.

**Example E.1** *The 2-Bar Truss.*

Consider the planar truss shown in Fig. 1.4. The members are tubular steel, pinned together at the point $F$, where the structure is to support the load $2P$. It is assumed that the wall thickness of the tubes is fixed at some value $\bar{t}$ and that the half span $B$ is fixed at $\bar{B}$. The problem of design is to select $d$ (the mean diameter of the tubes) and $H$ (the height of the truss) for minimum weight. The

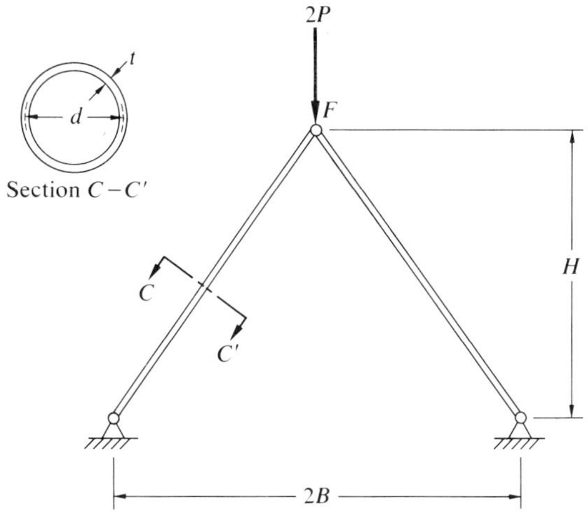


**Figure 1.4**

tubes must neither buckle nor yield, and there are maximum and minimum allowable values for $d$ and $H$. The load $P$ is taken to be 33 kips, $\bar{B}$ as 30.0 in. and $\bar{t}$ as 0.1 in. The strength of the material is taken as 100 ksi and the modulus as $3 \times 10^4$ ksi.

Suppose that after some preliminary study it is decided to survey those designs where $d$ lies between 1 and 3 inches in $\frac{1}{4}$ in. increments and where $H$ ranges from 10 to 35 inches in increments of 1 in. The member stress $\sigma$ for each design can be calculated from

$$\sigma = \frac{P}{\pi \bar{t}} \frac{(B^2 + H^2)^{1/2}}{Hd}. \tag{1.4}$$

The results of these calculations are given in Table 1.1. If we have chosen a particular steel for the design we can eliminate inadequate designs by compar-

**Table 1.1. Stress, psi × 10⁴**

| $H$ \ $d$ | 1.00 | 1.25 | 1.50 | 1.75 | 2.00 | 2.25 | 2.50 | 2.75 | 3.00 |
|---|---|---|---|---|---|---|---|---|---|
| 35 | 13.8 | 11.1 | 9.2 | 7.9 | 6.9 | 6.1 | 5.5 | 5.0 | 4.6 |
| 34 | 14.0 | 11.2 | 9.3 | 8.0 | 7.0 | 6.2 | 5.6 | 5.1 | 4.7 |
| 33 | 14.2 | 11.4 | 9.5 | 8.1 | 7.1 | 6.3 | 5.7 | 5.2 | 4.7 |
| 32 | 14.4 | 11.5 | 9.6 | 8.2 | 7.2 | 6.4 | 5.8 | 5.2 | 4.8 |
| 31 | 14.6 | 11.7 | 9.7 | 8.4 | 7.3 | 6.5 | 5.8 | 5.3 | 4.9 |
| 30 | 14.9 | 11.9 | 9.9 | 8.5 | 7.4 | 6.6 | 5.9 | 5.4 | 5.0 |
| 29 | 15.1 | 12.1 | 10.1 | 8.6 | 7.6 | 6.7 | 6.0 | 5.5 | 5.0 |
| 28 | 15.4 | 12.3 | 10.3 | 8.8 | 7.7 | 6.8 | 6.2 | 5.6 | 5.1 |
| 27 | 15.7 | 12.6 | 10.5 | 9.0 | 7.9 | 7.0 | 6.3 | 5.7 | 5.2 |
| 26 | 16.0 | 12.8 | 10.7 | 9.2 | 8.0 | 7.1 | 6.4 | 5.8 | 5.3 |
| 25 | 16.4 | 13.1 | 10.9 | 9.4 | 8.2 | 7.3 | 6.6 | 6.0 | 5.5 |
| 24 | 16.8 | 13.5 | 11.2 | 9.6 | 8.4 | 7.5 | 6.7 | 6.1 | 5.6 |
| 23 | 17.3 | 13.8 | 11.5 | 9.9 | 8.6 | 7.7 | 6.9 | 6.3 | 5.8 |
| 22 | 17.8 | 14.2 | 11.8 | 10.2 | 8.9 | 7.9 | 7.1 | 6.5 | 5.9 |
| 21 | 18.3 | 14.7 | 12.2 | 10.5 | 9.2 | 8.1 | 7.3 | 6.7 | 6.1 |
| 20 | 18.9 | 15.1 | 12.6 | 10.8 | 9.5 | 8.4 | 7.6 | 6.9 | 6.3 |
| 19 | 19.6 | 15.7 | 13.1 | 11.2 | 9.8 | 8.7 | 7.9 | 7.1 | 6.5 |
| 18 | 20.4 | 16.3 | 13.6 | 11.7 | 10.2 | 9.1 | 8.2 | 7.4 | 6.8 |
| 17 | 21.3 | 17.0 | 14.2 | 12.2 | 10.7 | 9.5 | 8.5 | 7.7 | 7.1 |
| 16 | 22.3 | 17.9 | 14.9 | 12.8 | 11.2 | 9.9 | 8.9 | 8.1 | 7.4 |
| 15 | 23.5 | 18.8 | 15.7 | 13.4 | 11.7 | 10.4 | 9.4 | 8.5 | 7.8 |
| 14 | 24.8 | 19.9 | 16.6 | 14.2 | 12.4 | 11.0 | 9.9 | 9.0 | 8.3 |
| 13 | 26.4 | 21.1 | 17.6 | 15.1 | 13.2 | 11.7 | 10.6 | 9.6 | 8.8 |
| 12 | 28.3 | 22.6 | 18.9 | 16.2 | 14.1 | 12.6 | 11.3 | 10.3 | 9.4 |
| 11 | 30.5 | 24.4 | 20.3 | 17.4 | 15.3 | 13.6 | 12.2 | 11.1 | 10.2 |
| 10 | 33.2 | 26.6 | 22.1 | 19.0 | 16.6 | 14.8 | 13.3 | 12.1 | 11.1 |

ing the values in Eq. (1.4) with the maximum allowable compressive stress. Taking the compressive strength of the material to be $\sigma_y = 100{,}000$ psi, we can eliminate the designs that are shaded in Table 1.1. We note that the members may buckle in some of the designs shown in Table 1.1, and we calculate the Euler buckling stress as

$$\sigma^{(e)} = \frac{\pi^2 EI}{l^2 A} = \frac{\pi^2 E}{8} \frac{(d^2 + \bar{t}^2)}{(\bar{B}^2 + H^2)}. \tag{1.5}$$

The results of these calculations, assuming that $E = 3.0 \times 10^7$ psi, are shown in Table 1.2, with the cross-hatched designs being the ones which are infeasible because of buckling. If we ignore any other possible failure modes, we are left with a number of acceptable designs from which to choose.[7]

**Table 1.2. Critical buckling stress, psi × 10⁴**

| H \ d | 1.00 | 1.25 | 1.50 | 1.75 | 2.00 | 2.25 | 2.50 | 2.75 | 3.00 |
|---|---|---|---|---|---|---|---|---|---|
| 35 | 1.8 | 2.7 | 3.9 | 5.4 | 7.0 | 8.8 | 10.9 | 13.2 | 15.7 |
| 34 | 1.8 | 2.8 | 4.1 | 5.5 | 7.2 | 9.1 | 11.3 | 13.6 | 16.2 |
| 33 | 1.9 | 2.9 | 4.2 | 5.7 | 7.5 | 9.4 | 11.6 | 14.1 | 16.8 |
| 32 | 1.9 | 3.0 | 4.3 | 5.9 | 7.7 | 9.8 | 12.0 | 14.6 | 17.3 |
| 31 | 2.0 | 3.1 | 4.5 | 6.1 | 8.0 | 10.1 | 12.4 | 15.1 | 17.9 |
| 30 | 2.1 | 3.2 | 4.6 | 6.3 | 8.2 | 10.4 | 12.9 | 15.6 | 18.5 |
| 29 | 2.1 | 3.3 | 4.8 | 6.5 | 8.5 | 10.8 | 13.3 | 16.1 | 19.2 |
| 28 | 2.2 | 3.5 | 5.0 | 6.8 | 8.8 | 11.1 | 13.8 | 16.6 | 19.8 |
| 27 | 2.3 | 3.6 | 5.1 | 7.0 | 9.1 | 11.5 | 14.2 | 17.2 | 20.5 |
| 26 | 2.4 | 3.7 | 5.3 | 7.2 | 9.4 | 11.9 | 14.7 | 17.8 | 21.2 |
| 25 | 2.5 | 3.8 | 5.5 | 7.5 | 9.7 | 12.3 | 15.2 | 18.4 | 21.9 |
| 24 | 2.5 | 3.9 | 5.7 | 7.7 | 10.1 | 12.7 | 15.7 | 19.0 | 22.6 |
| 23 | 2.6 | 4.1 | 5.9 | 8.0 | 10.4 | 13.1 | 16.2 | 19.6 | 23.3 |
| 22 | 2.7 | 4.2 | 6.0 | 8.3 | 10.7 | 13.6 | 16.7 | 20.3 | 24.1 |
| 21 | 2.8 | 4.3 | 6.2 | 8.5 | 11.1 | 14.0 | 17.3 | 20.9 | 24.9 |
| 20 | 2.9 | 4.5 | 6.4 | 8.7 | 11.4 | 14.4 | 17.8 | 21.6 | 25.7 |
| 19 | 3.0 | 4.6 | 6.6 | 9.0 | 11.8 | 14.9 | 18.4 | 22.2 | 26.4 |
| 18 | 3.1 | 4.8 | 6.8 | 9.3 | 12.1 | 15.3 | 18.9 | 22.9 | 27.2 |
| 17 | 3.1 | 4.9 | 7.0 | 9.6 | 12.5 | 15.8 | 19.5 | 23.6 | 28.0 |
| 16 | 3.2 | 5.0 | 7.2 | 9.8 | 12.8 | 16.2 | 20.0 | 24.2 | 28.8 |
| 15 | 3.3 | 5.2 | 7.4 | 10.1 | 13.2 | 16.7 | 20.6 | 24.9 | 29.6 |
| 14 | 3.4 | 5.3 | 7.6 | 10.4 | 13.5 | 17.1 | 21.1 | 25.6 | 30.4 |
| 13 | 3.5 | 5.4 | 7.8 | 10.6 | 13.9 | 17.6 | 21.7 | 26.2 | 31.2 |
| 12 | 3.6 | 5.6 | 8.0 | 10.9 | 14.2 | 18.0 | 22.2 | 26.8 | 31.9 |
| 11 | 3.7 | 5.7 | 8.2 | 11.1 | 14.5 | 18.4 | 22.7 | 27.5 | 32.7 |
| 10 | 3.7 | 5.8 | 8.4 | 11.4 | 14.8 | 18.8 | 23.2 | 28.0 | 33.3 |

[7] We are supposing, for the sake of simplicity, that the explicit upper and lower bounds on $d$ and $H$ are $1 < d < 3$ and $10 < H < 35$.

If for our purposes any one of these designs were as good as any other, we could pick one and be done with it. However, we have a reason for seeking the lightest weight design and we again calculate the indicated numbers from

$$\text{weight} = w = \rho 2\pi\, d\bar{t}(\bar{B}^2 + H^2)^{1/2}. \tag{1.6}$$

Taking the weight density $\rho$ as 0.3 lb/in$^3$ we obtain the schedule of weights given in Table 1.3. An examination of this table reveals that an approximation to the desired design is $d = 2.0$ and $H = 19.0$, for which the weight is 13.4 lb.

This method of "optimizing" is convenient for problems in which there are few design variables and each analysis can be performed quickly. By an "analysis" we mean a calculation of $\sigma$, $\sigma^{(e)}$ and $w$. Consider, however, a problem with 10 design variables and a design variable study, or *gridding*, consisting of an evaluation of 10 values for each variable. If an analysis consumes 0.001

**Table 1.3. Weight, lb**

| | | | | | | | | | |
|---|---|---|---|---|---|---|---|---|---|
| 35 | 8.7 | 10.9 | 13.0 | 15.2 | 17.4 | 19.6 | 21.7 | 23.9 | 26.1 |
| 34 | 8.5 | 10.7 | 12.8 | 15.0 | 17.1 | 19.2 | 21.4 | 23.5 | 25.6 |
| 33 | 8.4 | 10.5 | 12.6 | 14.7 | 16.8 | 18.9 | 21.0 | 23.1 | 25.2 |
| 32 | 8.3 | 10.3 | 12.4 | 14.5 | 16.5 | 18.6 | 20.7 | 22.7 | 24.8 |
| 31 | 8.1 | 10.2 | 12.2 | 14.2 | 16.3 | 18.3 | 20.3 | 22.4 | 24.4 |
| 30 | 8.0 | 10.0 | 12.0 | 14.0 | 16.0 | 18.0 | 20.0 | 22.0 | 24.0 |
| 29 | 7.9 | 9.8 | 11.8 | 13.8 | 15.7 | 17.7 | 19.7 | 21.6 | 23.6 |
| 28 | 7.7 | 9.7 | 11.6 | 13.5 | 15.5 | 17.4 | 19.3 | 21.3 | 23.2 |
| 27 | 7.6 | 9.5 | 11.4 | 13.3 | 15.2 | 17.1 | 19.0 | 20.9 | 22.8 |
| 26 | 7.5 | 9.4 | 11.2 | 13.1 | 15.0 | 16.8 | 18.7 | 20.6 | 22.4 |
| 25 | 7.4 | 9.2 | 11.0 | 12.9 | 14.7 | 16.6 | 18.4 | 20.2 | 22.1 |
| 24 | 7.2 | 9.1 | 10.9 | 12.7 | 14.5 | 16.3 | 18.1 | 19.9 | 21.7 |
| 23 | 7.1 | 8.9 | 10.7 | 12.5 | 14.3 | 16.0 | 17.8 | 19.6 | 21.4 |
| 22 | 7.0 | 8.8 | 10.5 | 12.3 | 14.0 | 15.8 | 17.5 | 19.3 | 21.0 |
| 21 | 6.9 | 8.6 | 10.4 | 12.1 | 13.8 | 15.5 | 17.3 | 19.0 | 20.7 |
| 20 | 6.8 | 8.5 | 10.2 | 11.9 | 13.6 | 15.3 | 17.0 | 18.7 | 20.4 |
| 19 | 6.7 | 8.4 | 10.0 | 11.7 | 13.4 | 15.1 | 16.7 | 18.4 | 20.1 |
| 18 | 6.6 | 8.2 | 9.9 | 11.5 | 13.2 | 14.8 | 16.5 | 18.1 | 19.8 |
| 17 | 6.5 | 8.1 | 9.7 | 11.4 | 13.0 | 14.6 | 16.2 | 17.9 | 19.5 |
| 16 | 6.4 | 8.0 | 9.6 | 11.2 | 12.8 | 14.4 | 16.0 | 17.6 | 19.2 |
| 15 | 6.3 | 7.9 | 9.5 | 11.1 | 12.6 | 14.2 | 15.8 | 17.4 | 19.0 |
| 14 | 6.2 | 7.8 | 9.4 | 10.9 | 12.5 | 14.0 | 15.6 | 17.2 | 18.7 |
| 13 | 6.2 | 7.7 | 9.2 | 10.8 | 12.3 | 13.9 | 15.4 | 16.9 | 18.5 |
| 12 | 6.1 | 7.6 | 9.1 | 10.7 | 12.2 | 13.7 | 15.2 | 16.7 | 18.3 |
| 11 | 6.0 | 7.5 | 9.0 | 10.5 | 12.0 | 13.6 | 15.1 | 16.6 | 18.1 |
| 10 | 6.0 | 7.5 | 8.9 | 10.4 | 11.9 | 13.4 | 14.9 | 16.4 | 17.9 |
| $H$ | | | | | | | | | |
| | $d$ 1.00 | 1.25 | 1.50 | 1.75 | 2.00 | 2.25 | 2.50 | 2.75 | 3.00 |

sec,[8] then the study would require $0.001 \times 10^{10}$ sec $= 10^7$ sec, or approximately 3000 hr! Certainly only extremely important problems can justify such an expenditure.

We might consider reducing the fineness of our grid, but it should be borne in mind that this will lessen our chances of obtaining the best possible design. For instance, even with the fine grid used in the previous example we have not obtained the lightest possible design, which is about 12.9 lb. Furthermore, it should be recognized that in complicated problems it is not always obvious what a fruitful range of design variables might be, and further effort must be expended to determine the range before a gridding can be undertaken.

Sometimes a design variable study is done to establish a qualitative feeling for the design problem. For example, we might not have known that we had to consider buckling until we had blocked out all designs which were unacceptable from the standpoint of material strength, or vice versa.

The methods presented in the following chapters are, in a sense, alternatives to the "try them all" approach of the design variable study. In some cases the computer programming effort may not be worth the trouble, but in many cases, if the problem is large and complex or must be solved often, the methods may be valuable.

## 1.2 DESIGN CONSTRAINTS

It should be emphasized at this point that "a design" is simply a set of values for the design variables (i.e., a particular design vector $\boldsymbol{D}$). Even if the design is patently absurd (e.g., negative areas) or inadequate in terms of function, it can still be called a design. Clearly some designs are useful solutions to the design problem and others are not. If a design meets all the requirements placed on it, it will be called a *feasible design* or an *acceptable design*; the complement of the set of feasible designs will be called *infeasible* or *unacceptable designs*.

The design restrictions that must be satisfied in order to produce an acceptable design are collectively called *constraints*. It is useful to identify two categories or kinds of constraints in engineering problems: side constraints and behavior constraints. These categories are not necessarily definitive, as it may not always be easy to classify constraints in this way. However, since the classifications are mainly for convenience of communication, this is not a serious difficulty.

A constraint that restricts the range of design variables for reasons other than the direct consideration of performance is called a *side constraint*. A constraint that derives from those performance or behavior requirements that are explicitly considered will be called a *behavior constraint*. Some examples may be useful. If, because of space limitations in the 2-bar truss problem, the

[8] This is about the time required on an IBM 7094 computer for each of the extremely simple analyses in the study just presented.

height of the truss $H$ is restricted to less than 25 in. and greater than 18 in, the limitations $18 \leqslant H \leqslant 25$ may be termed side constraints. As to the diameter of the tubes, clearly $d$ must be greater than $\bar{t}$ to make physical sense. The constraint $\bar{t} \leqslant d$ is also a side constraint. One might refer to such side constraints as constructibility constraints, since they derive from the physiognomy of the design.

Side constraints may also reflect other kinds of limitations, such as rules of thumb or the lack of adequate predictive techniques. For example, automotive cushioning systems may not operate properly if the damping ratio is subcritical (this would be a rule of thumb), and a constraint on $K$ and $C$ of the form $\sqrt{K} \leqslant \alpha C$ might be imposed. Or it may be that in the 2-bar truss problem the ratio $d/\bar{t}$ becomes so large that the simple buckling theory used here is insufficient.[9] Thus a limit of $d/\bar{t} \leqslant \beta$ might be imposed, where $\beta$ is some appropriate scalar.

An example of a behavior constraint in the 2-bar truss arises from the limit on maximum compressive stress. Taking Eq. (1.4) as the stress prediction we may write the constraint

$$100{,}000 \geqslant \frac{P}{\pi \bar{t}} \frac{(\bar{B}^2 + H^2)^{1/2}}{Hd}, \tag{1.7}$$

which provides an explicit limit on the ranges of $d$ and $H$. Clearly the constraint can be rewritten as

$$\frac{P}{\pi \bar{t}} \frac{(\bar{B}^2 + H^2)^{1/2}}{Hd} - 100{,}000 \leqslant 0, \tag{1.8}$$

which will be our standard form of writing inequality constraints. Similarly, we can avoid Euler buckling of the member by satisfying the constraint[10]

$$\frac{P}{\pi \bar{t}} \frac{(\bar{B}^2 + H^2)^{1/2}}{Hd} - \frac{\pi^2 E}{8} \frac{(d^2 + \bar{t}^2)}{(\bar{B}^2 + H^2)} \leqslant 0. \tag{1.9}$$

In many engineering problems it is not possible or practical to write explicit expressions for the constraints in terms of the design variables. For example, in a problem in which the stress is the final result of a finite difference

[9] See, for example, Shanley (1960).

[10] We are taking a few liberties with good practice here in allowing the stress to actually reach the theoretical Euler stress. One might prefer to see

$$\frac{P}{\pi \bar{t}} \frac{(\bar{B}^2 + H^2)^{1/2}}{H\,d} - \frac{\pi^2 E}{F_s 8} \frac{(d^2 + \bar{t}^2)}{(\bar{B}^2 + H^2)} \leqslant 0,$$

where $F_s$ is a factor of safety, $F_s > 1$.

computation or matrix inversion, the constraint cannot in general be put in an explicit form similar to Eq. (1.8) or (1.9). More will be said later about this question. It suffices for now to state that the function which is limited by the constraint must be a *computable* function of the design variables. This is not to say that the existence of explicit expressions for the behavior functions is immaterial. On the contrary, this consideration often dictates the choice of optimization method. At this stage, however, both situations look formally the same.

Another type of constraint which arises in some engineering problems is that of the discrete-valued design variable. In such cases the design variable is not to be selected from a continuous range of values but is permitted to take on only one of a discrete set of values. For example, suppose in the 2-bar truss example that the tubing from which the members were to be made comes only in sizes of $\frac{1}{2}$-in. increments, i.e.,

$$d = 1, 1\tfrac{1}{2}, 2, 2\tfrac{1}{2}, 3, 3\tfrac{1}{2}.$$

Such constraints can be very troublesome, but sometimes there are ways of handling or avoiding them. The problem will be briefly discussed in Chapter 5.

In formulating a design problem, the engineer must make a choice (or several choices) of what is often called a "design philosophy." This term usually means that a statement is made about how the design will fail when the design conditions are exceeded, and then this failure is designed against. For example, if a structure is to be designed so that no member exceeds its elastic limit, the term "elastic design philosophy" might be applied. On the other hand, a design based on the ultimate inelastic collapse of the structure is called "limit design," or "plastic design."

Traditionally, the design philosophy often explicitly dictates the design. Indeed, earlier design techniques have been worked out in conjunction with the formulation of design philosophy. The methods that we discuss in this text also require a design philosophy (or more correctly, a failure philosophy) to be selected. However, the presence of a number of inequalities in the formulation distinguishes the two approaches.

An interesting aspect of design is reliability. The design of systems for reliability is often called a reliability philosophy, although we must abstract the above concept of a design philosophy to use the term in this way. The basic idea is: Given that the aggregate probability of failure of the system over all "loads" and in all failure modes is $P$, where $P = P(\mathbf{D})$, design the system such that $P(\mathbf{D}) - P_{\max} < 0$. In other words, there is only one constraint on the problem, albeit a vastly complicated one.

Since the major effort in reliability-based design is in the computation of $P$, we will consider this topic beyond the scope of this text. On the other hand, some of the material covered is useful insofar as it enables us to attack problems of difficult analysis with increased efficiency.

## 1.3 THE OBJECTIVE FUNCTION

Of all feasible designs, some are "better" than others. If this is true, then there must be some quality that the better designs have more of than the less desirable ones do. If this quality can be expressed as a computable function of the design variables, we can consider optimizing to obtain a "best" design. The function with respect to which the design is optimized is called the *objective function*. We designate the objective function as $F$ or, to emphasize its dependence upon the design variables, as $F(\boldsymbol{D})$. We always assume that the objective function is to be minimized, which entails no loss of generality since the minimum of $F(\boldsymbol{D})$ occurs where the maximum of $-F(\boldsymbol{D})$ occurs.

The selection of an objective function can be one of the most important decisions in the whole optimum design process. In some situations, an obvious objective function exists. For example, a light fieldpack for a soldier is clearly better than a heavy one. In other cases, an objective function exists because the design is part of a larger, complicated system whose end use, it is *judged*, will be best satisfied by having parts which are optimized with respect to certain characteristics. Consider, "Light parts make good airplanes." Clearly *good* airplanes are not only light, but have high payloads, long range, are economical to operate, inexpensive to buy, use reasonable runway length, etc. The use of light components and subassemblies can be expected to further such goals, without being a specific attack on any one of them. Finally an objective function may exist because there is a specific requirement for some design property that is difficult to satisfy. Optimization with respect to this property is an artifice for solving the design problem. For example, suppose that a design requirement in the 2-bar truss problem was that the structure weigh less than $13\frac{1}{2}$ lb; optimizing with respect to weight would solve this problem.

In some design situations, there may appear to be two or more quantities which should be objective functions. For example, consider a product which must be designed so that two undesirable properties $A$ and $B$ are "at a minimum." It develops that there is no way to satisfy such requirements in general cases because they have no precise meaning unless the properties are dependent upon completely different sets of design variables, and all constraints are independent. Suppose we had two designs $\boldsymbol{D}_1$ and $\boldsymbol{D}_2$ such that $A(\boldsymbol{D}_1)$ is less than any other $A(\boldsymbol{D})$ over all acceptable $\boldsymbol{D}$, and $B(\boldsymbol{D}_2)$ is less than any other $B(\boldsymbol{D})$. Also suppose $A(\boldsymbol{D}_1) \ll A(\boldsymbol{D}_2)$ and $B(\boldsymbol{D}_2) \ll B(\boldsymbol{D}_1)$. Conceivably, neither design is the desired one. Such situations are usually handled in one of three ways: (1) a composite objective function is formulated, (2) a limit is set for one of the functions and it is used as a constraint, or (3) a trade-off study is done. Approach (3) is discussed in Section 3.5; approach (2) involves making some difficult decisions about the function to be held and the level to be set for it and often necessitates a trade-off study. Approach (1), the use of composite objective functions, consists of defining a function $F$ to be minimized as some combination of the properties involved. For example, some possibilities from the above case may be

$$F = A(\boldsymbol{D}) + B(\boldsymbol{D}),$$

or

$$F = A(\boldsymbol{D}) + 100\,B(\boldsymbol{D}).$$

In constructing such functions one should be sure to keep dimensional unit effects out of the picture. For example, if $A$ is in feet and $B$ is in dollars, $A + B$ may be perfectly acceptable as an objective function but would not be the same if $A$ were measured in inches.[11]

Much has been written about formulating objective functions, and in some disciplines this process is considered an essential part of the system modeling process. In engineering design we often feel that the objective functions are self evident. But there are pitfalls. Care must be taken to optimize with respect to the objective function which most nearly reflects the *true* goals of the design problem. Some examples of common errors in the constitution of objective functions should help to focus this point. In static structures, the fully utilized (fully stressed) design is not always the lightest weight; the lightest weight design is not always the cheapest; in mechanisms, the design with optimum transmission angle does not necessarily have the lowest force levels; minimization of acceleration level at the expense of jerk (third derivative) may result in inadequate dynamic response.

Simultaneous failure of all parts in service is often used as a condition of optimality but this One-Hoss Shay philosophy[12] ignores the fact that in com-

---

[11] See Starr (1963), Chapter 6, for examples.

[12] This amusing poem by Oliver Wendell Holmes describes a shay (a kind of wagon) so well built that it lasted 100 years, after which it went completely to pieces all at once.

. . .

But the Deacon swore (as Deacons do),
With an "I dew vum," or an "I tell *yeou*,"
He would build one shay to beat the taown
'N' the keountry 'n' all the kentry raoun';
It should be so built that it *couldn'* break daown:
—"Fur," said the Deacon, "'t's mighty plain
Thut the weakes' place mus' stan' the strain;
'N' the way t' fix it, uz I maintain,
Is only jest
T' make that place uz strong uz the rest."

. . .

You see, of course, if you're not a dunce,
How it went to pieces all at once,—
All at once, and nothing first,—
Just as bubbles do when they burst.
End of the wonderful one-hoss shay.
Logic is logic. That's all I say.

plex systems (and in some not so complex systems) elements may work together to prevent failure. In other words, an efficient design may have elements which would be considered overly strong individually, but this feature prevents other elements from failing.

As an example of a complicated objective function, consider the following problem:

**Example E.2** *The 4-Link Mechanism.*

Consider the 4-link mechanism shown in Fig. 1.5. The skeletal design is considered specified if the lengths $a$, $b$, $c$ and the shaft reference angles $\alpha$ and $\beta$ are given. The fixed pivot center distance will be taken to be 1 unit, since overall size does not affect the results in this particular problem. The object is to design the mechanism so that the output angle $\theta$ is some desired function of the input angle $\phi$, and so that certain geometric constraints among the $a$, $b$, and $c$ are satisfied.

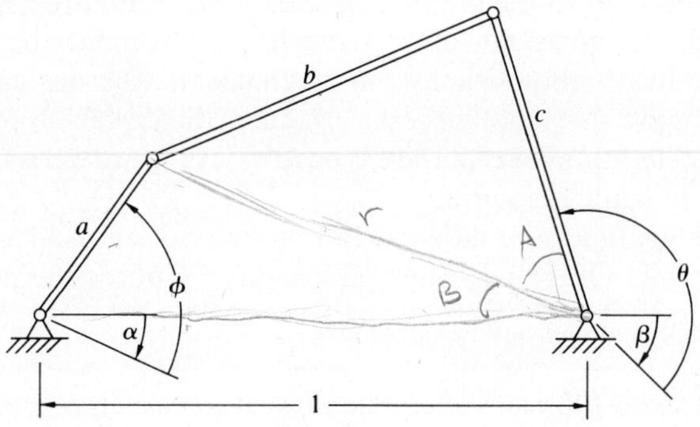


**Figure 1.5**

If we denote the desired output function as $\bar{\theta}(\phi)$ and the generated function for any particular design as $\theta(\phi)$ (see Fig. 1.6), a measure of the error can be formulated as

$$E = \int_0^{360} w(\phi)[\bar{\theta}(\phi) - \theta(\phi)]^2 d\phi, \tag{1.10}$$

where $w(\phi)$ is a prescribed, positive weighting function. The purpose of $w(\phi)$ is to emphasize certain portions of the curve in calculating the error. Using a trapezoidal rule approximation for the integral (see Section 3.6), we state the objective function to be used in succeeding chapters as

$$F(D) = \tfrac{1}{2}\{\sum_{i=1}^{n-1} [w_i(\bar{\theta}_i - \theta_i)^2 (\phi_{i+1} - \phi_{i-1})] \tag{1.11}$$
$$+ [w_0(\bar{\theta}_0 - \theta_0)^2 (\phi_1 - \phi_0) + w_n(\bar{\theta}_n - \theta_n)^2 (\phi_n - \phi_{n-1})]\},$$

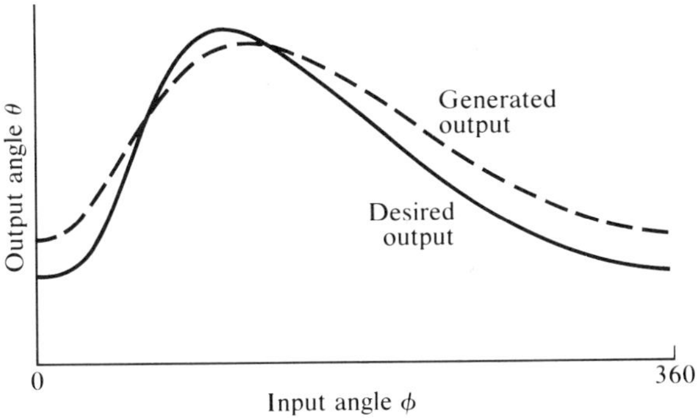

**Figure 1.6**

where $w_i$, $\bar{\theta}_i$, and $\theta_i$ are the values of these quantities for $\phi = \phi_i$. Note that $\phi_0 = 0$ and $\phi_n = 360$ and that the intermediate values can be selected as desired, although uniform spacing is most convenient. Here $F$ is a function of $D \equiv (a,b,c,\alpha,\beta)$ because $\theta_i = \theta(D,\phi_i)$.

From purely geometric considerations we find

$$\theta = \begin{cases} 180 - A - B + \beta, & \phi - \alpha \text{ in first 2 quadrants,} \\ 180 - A + B + \beta, & \phi - \alpha \text{ in third and fourth quadrants,} \end{cases} \tag{1.12}$$

where

$$b^2 = r^2 + c^2 - 2rc \cos A$$

$$A = \cos^{-1}\left[\frac{r^2 + c^2 - b^2}{2rc}\right], \tag{1.13}$$

$$a^2 = r^2 + 1 - 2r\cos B$$

$$B = \cos^{-1}\left[\frac{r^2 + 1 - a^2}{2r}\right], \tag{1.14}$$

$$a^2 + b^2 \cdot 2ab \cos\theta$$

and

$$r = [a^2 + 1 - 2a\cos(\phi - \alpha)]^{1/2}. \tag{1.15}$$

See Fig. 1.7.

We will consider only crank-rocker mechanisms, that is, only mechanisms for which the input crank $a$ can undergo a complete revolution and in which the output crank oscillates between two limits. This is assured if all the following inequalities are satisfied:

$$a < b, \tag{1.16}$$

$$a < c, \tag{1.17}$$

$$a < 1, \tag{1.18}$$

$$[(a + c) - (b + 1)][(c - a)^2 - (b - 1)^2] < 0. \tag{1.19}$$

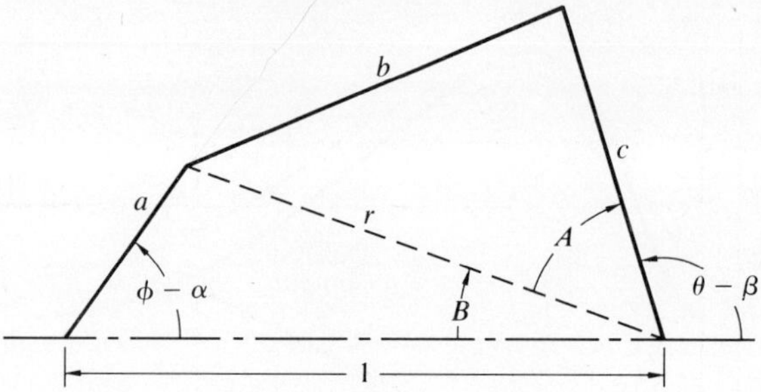


**Figure 1.7**

Two other simple design constraints will be considered. First, the maximum link length is required to be less than some predetermined value $L^U$. Thus

$$b < L^U , \tag{1.20}$$

$$c < L^U . \tag{1.21}$$

Second, the maximum deviation of the transmission angle $\mu$ from 90° is to be less than a predetermined value $T^U$. This is assured by satisfaction of the constraints:

$$|90 - \mu_{max}| < T^U , \tag{1.22}$$

$$|90 - \mu_{min}| < T^U , \tag{1.23}$$

where

$$\mu_{max} = \cos^{-1}\left[\frac{b^2 + c^2 - (1 + a)^2}{2bc}\right] \tag{1.24}$$

and

$$\mu_{min} = \cos^{-1}\left[\frac{b^2 + c^2 - (1 - a)^2}{2bc}\right] . \tag{1.25}$$

The desired output function to be used for illustration later (see Fig. 1.8) will be

$$\bar{\theta}(\phi) = \begin{cases} 20° + \phi/3 , & 0° < \phi \leqslant 240° , \\ \text{unspecified}, & 240° < \phi \leqslant 360° , \end{cases} \tag{1.26}$$

and the weighting function $w(\phi)$ will be

$$w(\phi) = \begin{cases} 10, & 0° < \phi \leqslant 30°, \\ 5, & 30° < \phi \leqslant 210°, \\ 10, & 210° < \phi \leqslant 240°, \\ 0, & 240° < \phi \leqslant 360°. \end{cases} \tag{1.27}$$

## 1.4 THE DESIGN SPACE

For problems in which the design variables are continuous, the preceding ideas can be visualized in a design space. Consider a cartesian space in which

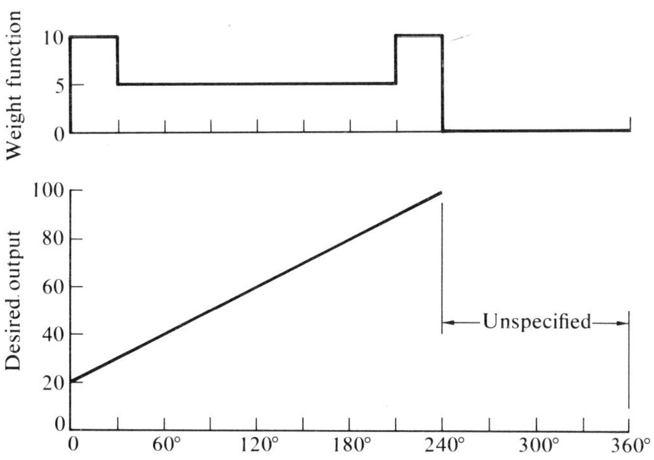


**Figure 1.8**

each coordinate axis corresponds to a component of the design vector ***D***. While this space will in general be $n$-dimensional, we can illustrate many of the concepts in 2- and 3-dimensional spaces. In Fig. 1.9 we see that every point in the space is a design, or alternatively can be expressed as the design vector ***D*** emanating from the origin of the design space.

All inequality constraints can be written in the form $g_j(\boldsymbol{D}) \leq 0$, as in Eqs. (1.8) and (1.9). Repeating the constraints of the 2-bar truss problem, we may define[13] the $g_j(\boldsymbol{D})$ as

$$g_1(\boldsymbol{D}) \equiv H - H^{(U)} \leq 0 \text{ (upper limit on } H) , \tag{1.28}$$

$$g_2(\boldsymbol{D}) \equiv -H + H^{(L)} \leq 0 \text{ (lower limit on } H) , \tag{1.29}$$

$$g_3(\boldsymbol{D}) \equiv d - d^{(U)} \leq 0 \text{ (upper limit on } d) , \tag{1.30}$$

$$g_4(\boldsymbol{D}) \equiv -d + d^{(L)} \leq 0 \text{ (lower limit on } d) , \tag{1.31}$$

$$g_5(\boldsymbol{D}) \equiv \frac{P}{\pi \bar{t}} \frac{(\bar{B}^2 + H^2)^{1/2}}{Hd} - 100{,}000 \leq 0 \quad \text{(strength constraint)} , \tag{1.32}$$

$$g_6(\boldsymbol{D}) \equiv \frac{P}{\pi \bar{t}} \frac{(\bar{B}^2 + H^2)^{1/2}}{Hd} - \frac{\pi^2 E}{8} \frac{(d^2 + \bar{t}^2)}{(\bar{B}^2 + H^2)} \leq 0 \quad \text{(buckling constraint)} , \tag{1.33}$$

where $\boldsymbol{D} = (d,H)$. These six functions are called the *constraint functions* for the problem, and for the purposes of this text they will always be defined so that negative and zero values of the $g_j$ are acceptable, and positive values are unacceptable.

[13] The symbol ≡ in this text is intended to be read, "is defined as."

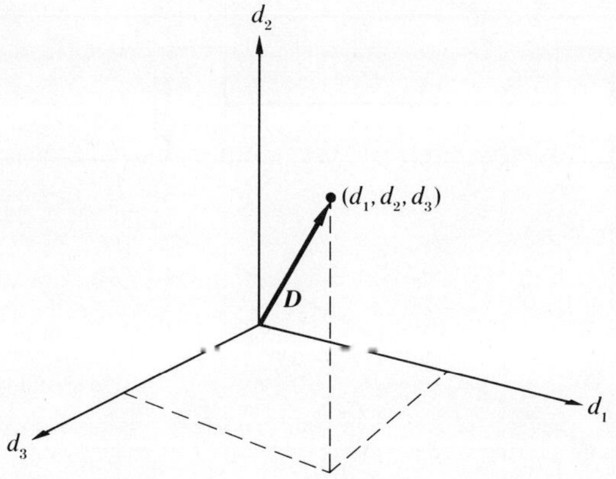


Figure 1.9

## Constraint Surfaces

The set, or locus, of values of $\boldsymbol{D}$ that satisfy the equation $g_i(\boldsymbol{D}) = 0$ forms a "surface" in the design space. Note that this is not a 2-dimensional subspace, but an $n - 1$ dimensional subspace where $n$ is the number of components in $\boldsymbol{D}$ (i.e., the number of design variables). It is a surface in the sense that it cuts the space into two regions: one where $g > 0$ and the other where $g < 0$. Thus a point is on one side of the surface or the other. These "surfaces" are shown in Fig. 1.10[14] for the 2-bar truss problem (E.1).

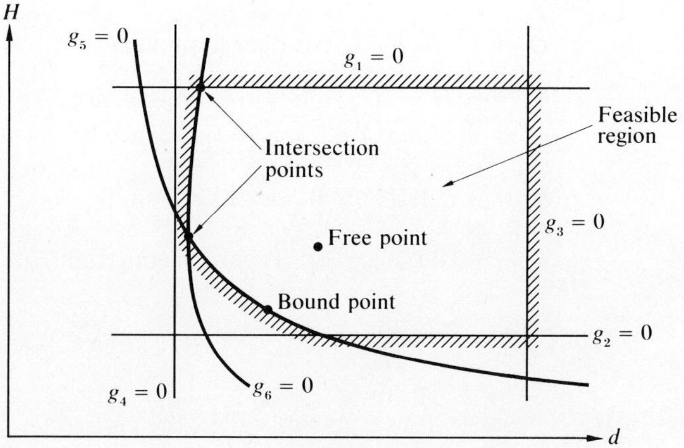


Figure 1.10

[14] In all the figures, the convention will be to hatch the unacceptable side of the constraints whenever they are shown.

The portions of the respective constraint surfaces that bound the feasible region form a patchwork of constraints called the *composite constraint surface.* Points within this region [i.e., where $g_j(\boldsymbol{D}) < 0$, $j = 1,2,\ldots,s$] are called *free points,* or *unconstrained designs*; points on the surface [i.e., feasible designs for which at least one $g_j(\boldsymbol{D}) = 0$] are called *bound points,* or *constrained designs.* It is possible for the acceptable region to be composed of two or more disjoint subregions, but this is rare in design problems.

The subspace where two or more $g_j(\boldsymbol{D}) = 0$ is called an *intersection.* Note that in 3-space, the intersection of three constraints defines a point; in 2-space, two constraints intersect in a point. The dimension of an intersection is $n - r$, where $r$ distinct constraints intersect.

In order to illustrate further characteristics of constraints, we introduce at this point our third illustrative example.

**Example E.3** *The Planar Truss.*

Consider the redundant planar truss shown in Fig. 1.11. The members, which are pinned together at the numbered nodes, are characterized by their cross-sectional areas. The structure must sustain two different load systems: (1) the

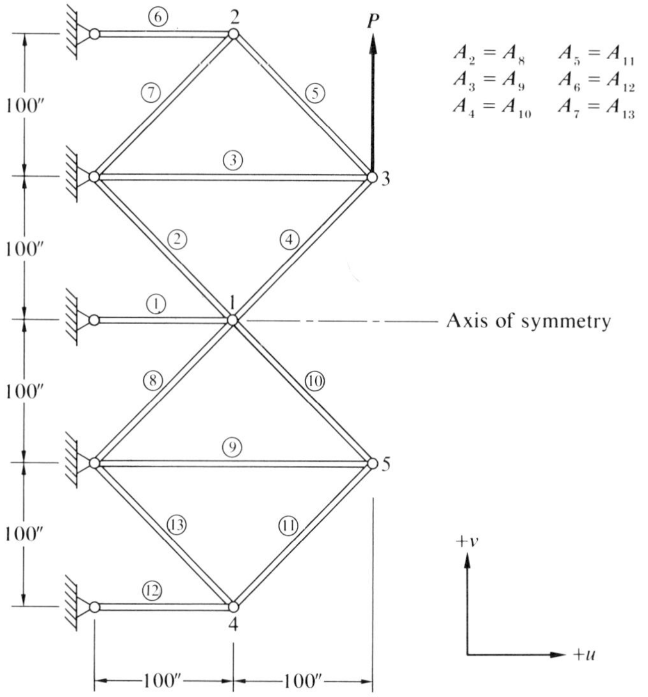


**Figure 1.11**

load $P = 20$ kips acting upward at node 3, and (2), at a different time, the load $P$ acting downward at node 5. Clearly, this requirement can be met by making the truss symmetric as shown and considering only the load application of $P$ at node 3.

The design problem is to select the areas $A_1, A_2, \ldots, A_7$ (from which, due to symmetry, $A_8, A_9, \ldots, A_{13}$ can be determined) for minimum weight. The stress in every member must be less than the tension yield and greater than the compression yield,[15] which are respectively $+20$ ksi and $-15$ ksi.

Strictly speaking we should call the dimensions locating the nodes "parameters" and denote them by letters, but this would unnecessarily complicate the equations and discussion which follow.

There are several ways to formulate the analysis of this problem, and the one chosen here is the displacement method. Since there are only three redundant members as opposed to ten displacement unknowns, the displacement method is perhaps a poor choice, but it will emphasize the fact that in many problems the performance of an analysis is a major complication.

The displacement formulation leads to the following ten modified equilibrium equations in which $A_8$ through $A_{13}$ have been replaced by their equivalents:

$$2(\sqrt{2}A_1+A_2+A_4)u_1-A_4u_3-A_4v_3-A_4u_5+A_4v_5=0, \tag{1.34a}$$

$$2(A_2+A_4)v_1-A_4u_3-A_4v_3+A_4u_5-A_4v_5=0\,, \tag{1.34b}$$

$$(A_5+2\sqrt{2}A_6+A_7)u_2+(-A_5+A_7)v_2-A_5u_3+A_5v_3=0\,, \tag{1.34c}$$

$$(-A_5+A_7)u_2+(A_5+A_7)v_2+A_5u_3-A_5v_3=0\,, \tag{1.34d}$$

$$-A_4u_1-A_4v_1-A_5u_2+A_5v_2+(\sqrt{2}A_3+A_4+A_5)u_3+(A_4-A_5)v_3=0\,, \tag{1.34e}$$

$$-A_4u_1-A_4v_1+A_5u_2-A_5v_2+(A_4-A_5)u_3+(A_4+A_5)v_3=\frac{200\sqrt{2}}{E}P\,, \tag{1.34f}$$

$$(A_5+2\sqrt{2}A_6+A_7)u_4+(A_5-A_7)v_4-A_5u_5-A_5v_5=0\,, \tag{1.34g}$$

$$(A_5-A_7)u_4+(A_5+A_7)v_4-A_5u_5-A_5v_5=0\,, \tag{1.34h}$$

$$-A_4u_1+A_4v_1-A_5u_4-A_5v_4+(\sqrt{2}A_3+A_4+A_5)u_5+(-A_4+A_5)v_5=0\,, \tag{1.34i}$$

$$A_4u_1-A_4v_1-A_5u_4-A_5v_4+(-A_4+A_5)u_5+(A_4+A_5)v_5=0\,, \tag{1.34j}$$

[15] In this problem we have adopted the convention that tension is positive, whereas in E.1 we took compression to be positive.

In matrix form, these would be expressed as

$$\mathbf{K}\boldsymbol{W} = \boldsymbol{P}\,, \tag{1.35}$$

where

$$\boldsymbol{W} = (u_1, v_1, u_2, v_2, u_3, v_3, u_4, v_4, u_5, v_5),$$

$$\boldsymbol{P} = (0, 0, 0, 0, 0, 200\sqrt{2}\,P/E, 0, 0, 0, 0),$$

and $\mathbf{K}$ is the stiffness matrix which can be read from Eqs. (1.34). Note that $\mathbf{K}$ is a function of the design variables $A_1, A_2, A_3, A_4, A_5, A_6$, and $A_7$.

Having determined the displacement vector $\boldsymbol{W}$ for a given design from

$$\boldsymbol{W} = \mathbf{K}^{-1}\boldsymbol{P}\,, \tag{1.36}$$

we can calculate the stresses from

$$\sigma_1 = (E/100)u_1, \tag{1.37a}$$

$$\sigma_2 = (E/100)\,[\tfrac{1}{2}u_1 - \tfrac{1}{2}v_1]\,, \tag{1.37b}$$

$$\sigma_3 = (E/100)\,[\tfrac{1}{2}u_3]\,, \tag{1.37c}$$

$$\sigma_4 = (E/100)\,[\tfrac{1}{2}(u_3 - u_1) + \tfrac{1}{2}(v_3 - v_1)]\,, \tag{1.37d}$$

$$\sigma_5 = (E/100)\,[\tfrac{1}{2}(u_3 - u_2) - \tfrac{1}{2}(v_3 - v_2)]\,, \tag{1.37e}$$

$$\sigma_6 = (E/100)u_2\,, \tag{1.37f}$$

$$\sigma_7 = (E/100)\,[\tfrac{1}{2}u_2 + \tfrac{1}{2}v_2]\,, \tag{1.37g}$$

$$\sigma_8 = (E/100)\,[\tfrac{1}{2}u_1 + \tfrac{1}{2}v_1]\,, \tag{1.37h}$$

$$\sigma_9 = (E/100)\,\tfrac{1}{2}u_5\,, \tag{1.37i}$$

$$\sigma_{10} = (E/100)\,[\tfrac{1}{2}(u_5 - u_1) - \tfrac{1}{2}(v_5 - v_1)] \tag{1.37j}$$

$$\sigma_{11} = (E/100)\,[\tfrac{1}{2}(u_5 - u_4) + \tfrac{1}{2}(v_5 - v_4)]\,, \tag{1.37k}$$

$$\sigma_{12} = (E/100)\,u_4\,, \tag{1.37l}$$

$$\sigma_{13} = (E/100)\,[\tfrac{1}{2}u_4 - \tfrac{1}{2}v_4]\,. \tag{1.37m}$$

In matrix form, these would be

$$\boldsymbol{\sigma} = \mathbf{R}\boldsymbol{W}\,, \tag{1.38}$$

where $\mathbf{R}$ is the $13 \times 10$ matrix associated with Eqs. (1.37).

The weight of the structure is a linear function of the design variables:

$$\mathrm{F}(\boldsymbol{D}) = \rho_w\left[l_1A_1 + 2\sum_{i=2}^{7} l_iA_i\right], \tag{1.39}$$

where $\rho_w$ is the weight density and $l_j$ is the length of the $j$th member.

We can define the constraint functions as

$$g_j(\boldsymbol{D}) \equiv \sigma_j - \sigma^t \leqslant 0, \qquad j = 1,2,\ldots,13 \text{ upper bound on stress,} \tag{1.40a}$$

$$g(\boldsymbol{D})_{j+13} \equiv \sigma^c - \sigma_j \leqslant 0, \qquad j = 1,2,\ldots,13 \text{ lower bound on stress,} \tag{1.40b}$$

$$g(\boldsymbol{D})_{j+26} \equiv w_j - u^U \leqslant 0, \qquad j = 1,2,\ldots,10 \text{ upper bound on displacement,} \tag{1.40c}$$

$$g(\boldsymbol{D})_{j+36} \equiv u^L - w_j \leqslant 0, \qquad j = 1,2,\ldots,10 \text{ lower bound on displacement,} \tag{1.40d}$$

$$g(\boldsymbol{D})_{j+46} \equiv A_j - A^U \leqslant 0, \qquad j = 1,2,\ldots,7 \text{ upper bound on area,} \tag{1.40e}$$

$$g(\boldsymbol{D})_{j+53} \equiv -A_j \leqslant 0, \qquad j = 1,2,\ldots,7 \text{ nonnegativity of area.} \tag{1.40f}$$

The optimization of this problem will be examined in subsequent chapters;[16] however, we will mention here some of the special formulation difficulties that problems of this type possess.

While for this problem we may still write the abstract expression $g_j(\boldsymbol{D})$ for the stress and displacement constraints, we cannot easily write the explicit dependence of $g_j$ on the components of $\boldsymbol{D}$, as in Example (E.1). However, given any vector $\boldsymbol{D}$ we can *calculate* $g_j(\boldsymbol{D})$, and we can still imagine the locus $g_j(\boldsymbol{D}) = 0$, even though it might be quite a task to construct even an approximation to it. In such cases, the analysis algorithm (in this case, a simultaneous equation solution) can be considered a computational rule for relating the value of the constraint function to the design vector. Many engineering design problems possess this characteristic: the response or behavior to be limited cannot, for all practical purposes, be expressed explicitly in terms of the design variables. In some cases the relationship between $g_j$ and $\boldsymbol{D}$ can be expressed through a set of equality constraints; such problems are amenable to some of the methods discussed in Chapter 3.

In some extreme situations, the connection between the value of the constraint function and the design variables is so abstruse and complicated that an experiment or simulation is necessary to evaluate the $g_j$. In these problems, a fair amount of uncertainty is often associated with the outcome of the experiment and hence in the resulting value of $g_j$. Problems like these are probably best approached by methods from the statistical design of experiments,[17] which are beyond the scope of this text.

**Parametric Constraints**

Parametric constraints, which represent a departure from those already discussed, are illustrated by the following example.

**Example E.4** *The 3-bar Truss with Loading Envelope.*

Consider the 3-member planar truss shown in Fig. 1.12. The structure is to support a load applied to the free node, which can act in any direction and

[16] See especially Chapter 4.

[17] For an introduction to stochastic approximation, see Wilde and Beightler (1967). Also see Box and Hunter (1959) and Box and Youle (1955).

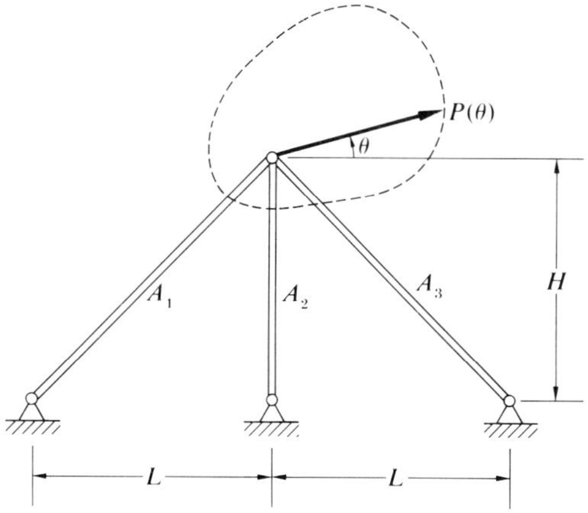


**Figure 1.12**

whose magnitude varies as some known function of the angle $\theta$ it makes with the horizontal. Two separate loading envelopes are to be considered and hence there are two distinct design problems:

$$P_1(\theta) = |20.0 \sin(2\theta)| \text{kips}, \qquad 0 \leq \theta \leq \pi, \tag{1.41}$$

$$P_2(\theta) = 10.0/[1 - 0.5 \cos(\theta - \pi/6)] \text{kips}, \qquad 0 \leq \theta \leq 2\pi. \tag{1.42}$$

These are illustrated in Figs. 1.13(a) and 1.13(b).

The failure mode to be guarded against is yielding of the members, and for simplicity the tension and compression stress limits are equal in magnitude. The design variables are the areas of the members $A_1$, $A_2$, and $A_3$, and the objective function is the volume of material in the structure. The dimensions of the truss are $L = H = 1$, and the yield stress is 20 ksi.

The stresses in the members are

$$\sigma_1(\theta) = \frac{1}{2A_1}\left[\frac{L_1 P(\theta)}{H}(\sin\theta + \cos\theta) - \frac{L_1}{H} F_2\right], \tag{1.43}$$

$$\sigma_2(\theta) = \frac{1}{A_2} F_2, \tag{1.44}$$

$$\sigma_3(\theta) = \frac{1}{2A_3}\left[\frac{L_1 P(\theta)}{H}(\sin\theta - \cos\theta) - \frac{L_1}{H} F_2\right], \tag{1.45}$$

where

$$F_2 = \frac{A_2 L_1^3 H \left[\frac{\sin\theta}{H}(A_1 + A_3) + \frac{\cos\theta}{L}(A_3 - A_1)\right] P(\theta)}{L_1^3 A_1 A_2 + 4H^3 A_1 A_3 + L_1^3 A_2 A_3} \tag{1.46}$$

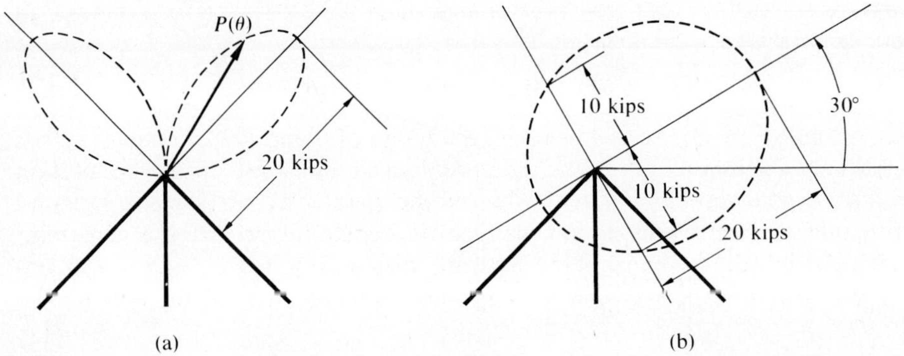


**Figure 1.13**

and

$$L_1 = (L^2 + H^2)^{1/2}. \tag{1.47}$$

The design problem can be stated as follows. Find $\boldsymbol{D} = (A_1, A_2, A_3)$ such that $F = L_1(A_1 + A_3) + A_2 \to \min$, and

$$g_1 \equiv \sigma_1{}^2(\theta) - \sigma_y{}^2 \leqslant 0\,, \qquad 0 \leqslant \theta \leqslant \theta^{(u)}\,, \tag{1.48a}$$

$$g_2 \equiv \sigma_2{}^2(\theta) - \sigma_y{}^2 \leqslant 0\,, \qquad 0 \leqslant \theta \leqslant \theta^{(u)}\,, \tag{1.48b}$$

$$g_3 \equiv \sigma_3{}^2(\theta) - \sigma_y{}^2 \leqslant 0\,, \qquad 0 \leqslant \theta \leqslant \theta^{(u)}\,, \tag{1.48c}$$

$$g_4 \equiv -A_1 \leqslant 0\,, \tag{1.48d}$$

$$g_5 \equiv -A_2 \leqslant 0\,, \tag{1.48e}$$

$$g_6 \equiv -A_3 \leqslant 0\,. \tag{1.48f}$$

The first three $g_j$ represent a different kind of constraint from those previously discussed in that it must be satisfied for a range of some parameter (in this case $\theta$). Such constraints are referred to as *parametric constraints*.

More realistic examples of such constraints are found in highway bridge specifications, where the loadings move across the structure, and their critical locations and spacing depend on the design. Other problems with parametric constraints are those in which dynamic response is to be limited and the parameter of the constraint is time.

Parametric constraints can have more than one parameter, e.g., the stress in a plate $\sigma(x,y)$. In this case we might have a constraint of the form

$$g = \sigma(x,y)^2 - \sigma_u{}^2 \leqslant 0\,, \qquad a \leqslant x \leqslant b\,, c \leqslant y \leqslant d \tag{1.49}$$

in the two parameters $x$ and $y$.

We can deal with such constraints by replacing what may be considered an infinite number of constraints with a finite but sufficiently restrictive set of constraints. In the 3-bar truss, the constraint could be written for a number of specific angles as

$$g_j(\theta_i) \leq 0\ , \qquad i = 1,2,\ldots,R\ , \tag{1.50}$$

where the $\theta_i$ are values of $\theta$ between the limits of 0 and $\theta^{(u)}$. If enough values are taken, a solution to the substitute problem should approximate the solution to the original problem. Each value of the parameter produces a separate constraint surface, whereas the parametric constraint produces a constraint surface that is the envelope of the separate surfaces (see Fig. 1.14).

In Section 3.6, we discuss a penalty function method for solving the original problem.

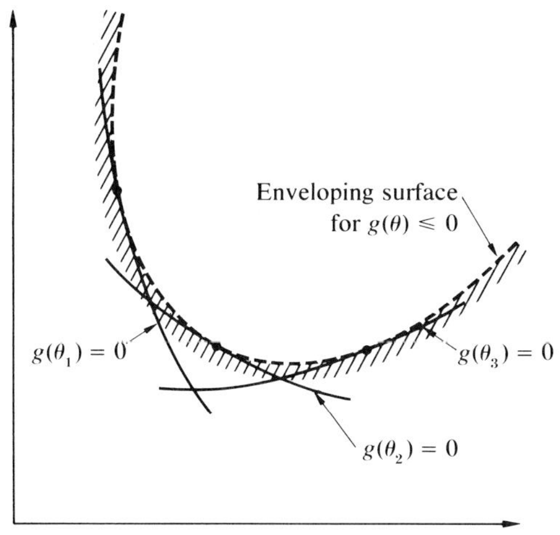


**Figure 1.14**

**Objective Function Contours**

In addition to the constraint surfaces, we can imagine another set of surfaces in the design space: the *level surfaces* of $F(\boldsymbol{D})$. The locus of all points satisfying $F(\boldsymbol{D}) = \text{const} \equiv C$ forms a surface, and for each value of the constant $C$ there corresponds a different member of a family of surfaces. Figure 1.15 shows the family of constant weight contours and constraints for the 2-bar truss (Example E.1). Every design on a particular contour has the same weight. These surfaces are called *objective function contours.*

Examination of Fig. 1.15 reveals that the least weight design occurs at point $P$. Figure 1.16 shows the constraints and weight contours for the same problem as in Fig. 1.15 except that the material strength has been lowered to 60,000 psi. In this case, we see that the least weight design occurs at point $P'$.

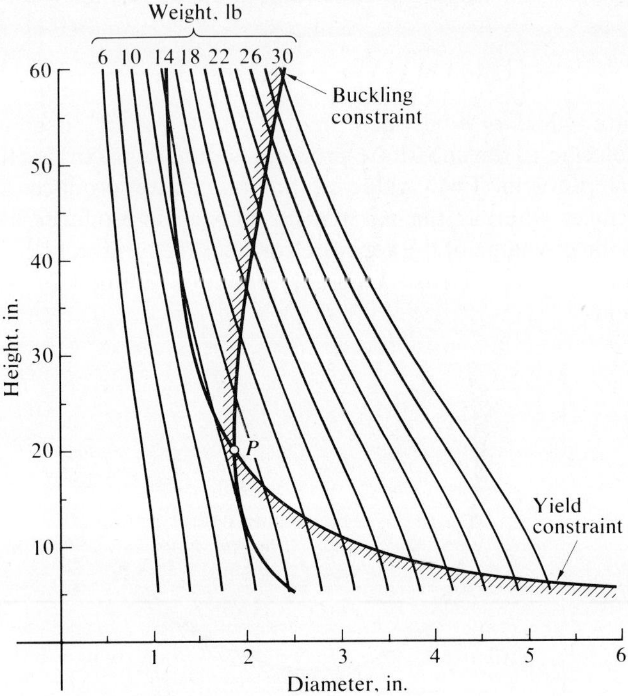


**Figure 1.15**

## Mathematical Programming Problems

We now consider a standard form of problem statement. This formalism allows a generalization of the solution techniques to be presented and provides a uniform framework for discussion.

After making the appropriate engineering judgments and defining all the necessary functions and limitations, we state an optimization problem as follows. Find the design $\boldsymbol{D}_m$ such that

$$F(\boldsymbol{D}_m) \rightarrow \min,$$ [18]

$$g_j(\boldsymbol{D}_m) \leqslant 0\,, \qquad j = 1,2\,\ldots\,,S.$$

The problem is said to be stated in the design space since the only variables are the components of $\boldsymbol{D}$. This form of problem is called a *mathematical programming problem,* or a *mathematical program.*

[18] The notation $F(\boldsymbol{D}_m) \rightarrow \min$ is read $F$ "goes to a minimum" or "is a minimum" at $\boldsymbol{D}_m$.

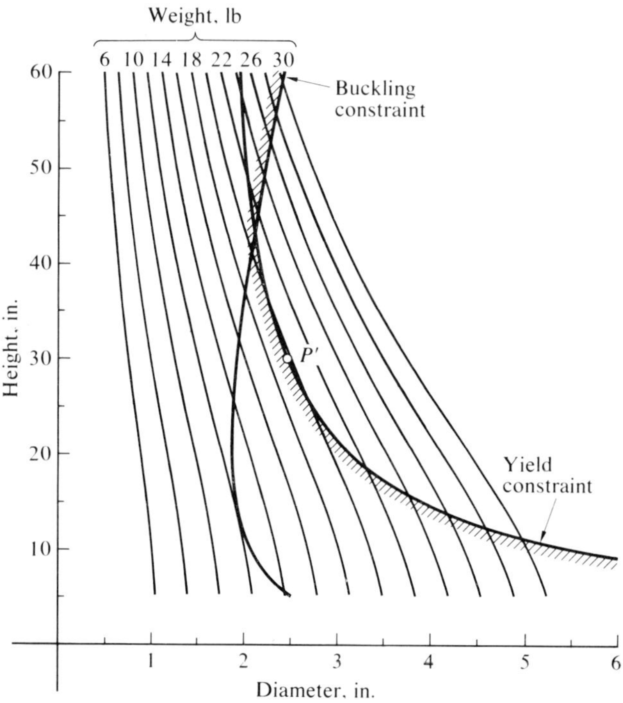


**Figure 1.16**

## 1.5 THE INTEGRATED PROBLEM STATEMENT

The redundant planar truss (E.3) presents an additional complication, as we mentioned before. The system of Eqs. (1.34) (the equilibrium equations in terms of nodal displacements) distinguishes the complicated structure of E.3 from that of E.1. Once the displacements are known from a solution of Eqs. (1.34), the stresses and hence the constraint function values are computed by a mere substitution into Eqs. (1.37), the stress-displacement equations. Equations (1.37) are thus only "depth of notation," but Eqs. (1.34) have to be solved for the $u_j$ and $v_j$. Theoretically, of course, there is really no distinction between these, because by applying Cramer's rule or by direct elimination we could write the formulas for the displacements $u_j = u_j(\mathbf{D})$, $v_j = v_j(\mathbf{D})$, but it is easy to conceive of problems where this step is impractical or even impossible. In such cases, numerical algorithms are used to obtain $u_j$ and $v_j$ (or their counterparts in the given problem) for specific values of the design variables. This step is often called the "analysis" and usually consumes the most computer time. Consider the difference between analyzing $10^{10}$ designs where each design requires 0.001 sec and analyzing a case involving a matrix inversion that requires 10 min.

We can state many design problems so that the solution of the analysis and the determination of the optimum design occur at the same time. This form of problem statement will be called the *integrated formulation.*

Conceptually the most difficult aspect of the integrated formulation is the idea of the system vector. This vector is defined as the concatenation of the design variable vector $\boldsymbol{D}$ and a vector of some of the behavior variables.[19] For the planar truss problem (E.3), we might define

$$\boldsymbol{Y} \equiv (\boldsymbol{D}, \boldsymbol{W}) = (A_1, A_2, \ldots, A_7, u_1, v_1, u_2, \ldots, v_5) = (y_1, \ldots, y_{17}). \tag{1.51}$$

In what may now be called the optimization/analysis process, all components of $\boldsymbol{Y}$ have equal standing. The meaning of this should become clear as we proceed.

Define each of Eqs. (1.34) as a function $l_j(\boldsymbol{Y}) = 0$. Thus for the first equation of the set (1.34) we have

$$l_1(\boldsymbol{Y}) \equiv \sqrt{2}(y_1 + y_2 + y_4)y_8 - y_4y_{12} - y_4y_{13} - y_4y_{15} - y_4y_{17} = 0. \tag{1.52}$$

There will be ten such equations, and if a $\boldsymbol{Y}$ vector satisfies

$$l_j(\boldsymbol{Y}) = 0, \qquad j = 1, 2, \ldots, 10, \tag{1.53}$$

then $\boldsymbol{Y}$ is a design (given by $y_1, \ldots, y_7$) and its correct analysis (given by $y_8, \ldots, y_{15}$).

Even though the weight function involves only $y_1, \ldots, y_7$, we may still write $F(\boldsymbol{Y})$. Furthermore, if we substitute the stress-displacement relations (Eq. 1.37) into the constraint functions (Eq. 1.40), we may still write the $g_j$ as $g_j(\boldsymbol{Y})$.

The mathematical programming problem may now be stated in this way: Given the preassigned parameters and side constraints, find the $\boldsymbol{Y}_{\text{opt}}$ for which

$$\begin{aligned} &F(\boldsymbol{Y}_{\text{opt}}) \to \min, \\ &g_j(\boldsymbol{Y}_{\text{opt}}) \leqslant 0, \qquad j = 1,2, \ldots, S, \\ &l_j(\boldsymbol{Y}_{\text{opt}}) = 0, \qquad j = 1,2, \ldots, T. \end{aligned} \tag{1.54}$$

If this form of problem statement is confusing, it is probably because we do not think of design variables as being in the same league with behavior variables. It may be helpful in this regard to consider the following mathematical example, which will subsequently be shown to correspond to a simple design problem.

---

[19] By behavior variables we mean, loosely, quantities that are the *result* of an analysis, such as stress, velocity, force, natural frequency, etc. Sometimes the terminology "behavior function" is used to connote more abstract quantities that determine the adequacy of a design, for example, the value of a complicated buckling expression used as a go–no-go test for design acceptability.

Given that $\boldsymbol{Y}$ is composed of the three components $y_1, y_2, y_3$, and given the values $C_i$ and $a_i$, find $\boldsymbol{Y}$ such that

$$F(\boldsymbol{Y}) \equiv C_1 y_1 + C_2 y_2 \to \min, \tag{1.55}$$

$$g_1(\boldsymbol{Y}) \equiv y_3 - a_1 \leqslant 0, \tag{1.56}$$

$$g_2(\boldsymbol{Y}) \equiv y_2 - a_2 y_1 \leqslant 0, \tag{1.57}$$

$$l(\boldsymbol{Y}) \equiv y_2 - a_3/y_3 = 0. \tag{1.58}$$

This problem says, "Find the point $(y_1, y_2, y_3)$ lying on the surface $y_2 - a_3/y_3 = 0$ and inside the region enclosed by the planes $y_3 = a_1$ and $y_2 = a_2 y_1$ that minimizes $C_1 y_1 + C_2 y_2$" (see Fig. 1.17). Clearly, we could use $l(\boldsymbol{Y}) = 0$ to eliminate $y_3$ from the problem, but the reader is asked to ignore this fact.[20]

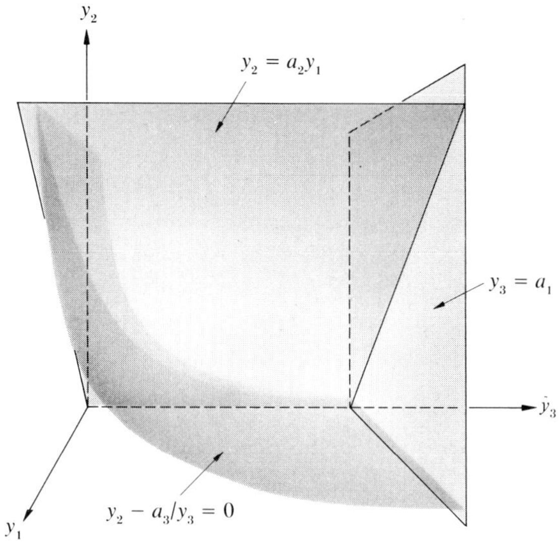


**Figure 1.17**

This problem corresponds to the following design problem. A cable is to span a distance $L$ and support a load $P$ at its center (see Fig. 1.18). We are to choose the cable cross-sectional area $A$ and the cable tension $T$ such that the deflection under the load is less than $\delta$ and the stress in the cable is less than $\sigma_w$.

The objective function $F(Y)$ is to represent the cost of the installation. This cost is assumed to have two parts: $C_1 A$, the cost of the cable, and $C_2 T$, the cost of maintaining and supporting the tension by the structure at the ends.

[20] See Exercise 1.4, in which the corresponding physical problem is formulated nonlinearly.

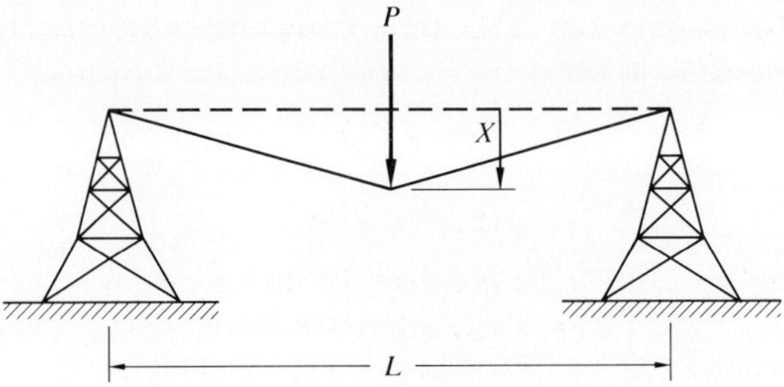


**Figure 1.18**

In other words, $C_2T$ is an approximation to the cost of the support structure.

Assuming the deflection $x$ to be small compared to $L$, we have the equilibrium equation

$$x = \frac{PL}{4T}. \tag{1.59}$$

The design constraints, in terms of the physical quantities, are

$$x \leq \delta, \tag{1.60}$$

$$\frac{T}{A} \leq \sigma_w. \tag{1.61}$$

Equations (1.59), (1.60), and (1.61) can be written in the form

$$T - \frac{PL}{4x} = 0, \tag{1.59a}$$

$$x - \delta \leq 0, \tag{1.60a}$$

$$T - A\sigma_w \leq 0. \tag{1.61a}$$

If we identify $A \equiv y_1$, $T \equiv y_2$, $x \equiv y_3$, and $\delta \equiv a_1$, $\sigma_w \equiv a_2$, $PL/4 \equiv a_3$, we see the equivalence to the original problem.

A note of caution regarding equalities is in order. It sometimes occurs that we will, *ab initio*, feel that some of the behavior variables or constraint functions must attain their limiting values in order for a design to be optimum. We may do so on the basis of experience or intuition and we may often be right, but such assumptions should be carefully examined. In the 2-bar truss problem (E.1), the value of $\sigma_y$ may allow an optimum in which $\sigma = \sigma_y$ and $\sigma > \sigma^{(e)}$ or in which $\sigma > \sigma_y$ and $\sigma = \sigma^{(e)}$, as well as an optimum in which $\sigma = \sigma^{(e)} = \sigma_y$.[21] In those cases where such assumptions are *valid*, the resulting equations would become part of the set of $l_j = 0$.

[21] Figure 1.16 shows $\sigma = \sigma_y$, $\sigma > \sigma^{(e)}$ at the optimum. In this case, the false application of the "constraint" $\sigma = \sigma_y = \sigma^{(e)}$ results in a design which is overweight by about 8%.

Equality constraints can also arise from the transformation of an inequality constraint into an equality. This is always possible, since

$$g(Y) \leqslant 0 \tag{1.62}$$

is equivalent to

$$g(Y) + \eta^2 = 0, \tag{1.63}$$

where $\eta$ is a new variable in the problem. In such a case we could define $Y' = (Y, \eta) = (y_1, \ldots, y_n, \eta)$. These *slack variables* have several theoretical and practical applications which will be discussed in Chapter 4.

The integrated problem statement can be a useful form in some problems; we will examine its character in Section 3.7.

## EXERCISES

**1.1** Produce a set of tables for aluminum similar to Tables 1.1, 1.2, and 1.3 (take $\sigma_y = 50$ ksi, $E = 1.0 \times 10^7$, $\rho = 0.1$). Assuming $P = 10$ kips, find the minimum weight design. Do this exercise by writing a computer program. [*Answer:* Using $\Delta H = 1$ and $\Delta d = \frac{1}{4}$, $d = 2.0$, $H = 11$.]

**1.2** Reformulate Example (E.1), taking as design variables $S \equiv (\bar{B}^2 + H^2)^{1/2}/(Hd)$ and $V \equiv d^2/(\bar{B}^2 + H^2)$. Assuming that $d >> t$, show that the constraint functions $g_5$ and $g_6$ (see Eqs. 1.32 and 1.33) are linear and that the weight is proportional to $(\bar{B}^2 S^2 V + 1)/(S^2\sqrt{V})$. Sketch the constraints $g_5$ and $g_6$ and the contours of the weight in the "design space" in terms of $V$ and $S$. [*Hint:* Verify that $H = 1/(\sqrt{V}S)$, $d = [\bar{B}^2 S^2 V + 1]^{1/2}/S$.]

**1.3** A classical approach to the design of linkages like those of Example (E.2) is to use the Freudenstein equations (see Mabie and Ocvirk, 1963):

$$-R_1 \cos(\phi_i - \alpha) + R_2 \cos(\phi_i - \beta) + R_3 = \cos(\phi_i - \alpha - \theta_i + \beta), \qquad i = 1, 2, 3,$$

where

$$R_1 = \frac{1}{C}, \qquad R_2 = \frac{1}{a}, \qquad R_3 = \frac{a^2 - b^2 + c^2 + 1}{2ac}.$$

The procedure for doing this is as follows:

a) Pick three pairs of angles $(\phi_1, \theta_1)$, $(\phi_2, \theta_2)$, $(\phi_3, \theta_3)$ where you would like the output to exactly match the desired curve and guess at probable values for $\alpha$ and $\beta$.

b) Solve the system of linear equations

$$-R_1 \cos(\phi_i - \alpha) + R_2 \cos(\theta_i - \beta) + R_3 = \cos(\phi_i - \alpha - \theta_i + \beta), \qquad i = 1, 2, 3,$$

for $R_1$, $R_2$, and $R_3$, and thence solve for $a$, $b$, $c$.

c) Check the design for "acceptability" and "desirability."

d) If it is not acceptable, modify $\alpha$, $\beta$, and the $\phi_i$ to "improve" the design.

In the traditional application of the method, the solution is developed by hand and a few different designs are tried until a suitable one is found.

Write a computer program that will read in a number of different values of $\alpha$, $\beta$, and $(\phi_i, \theta_i)$, $i = 1, 2, 3$. Solve the Freudenstein equations, determine $a$, $b$, $c$, and finally either print data for each set from which $\theta$ vs. $\phi$ can be plotted or, if a plotter or other graphical output device is available, have the computer plot the curves.

**1.4** In the stretched cable, Eqs. (1.59), (1.60), and (1.61) represent the linearization for $x << L$ and the assumption that the tension remains constant at $T$ as the cable is deflected. Drop these assumptions and show that the problem is represented by:

$$F = C_1 A + C_2\left\{T_0 + 2\frac{EA}{L}\left[\left(x^2 + \frac{L^2}{4}\right)^{1/2} - \frac{L}{2}\right]\right\},$$

$$x - \delta \leq 0,$$

$$T_0 + 2\frac{EA}{L}\left[\left(x^2 + \frac{L^2}{4}\right)^{1/2} - \frac{L}{2}\right] - A\sigma_w \leq 0,$$

$$T_0 + 2\frac{EA}{L}\left[\left(x^2 + \frac{L^2}{4}\right)^{1/2} - \frac{L}{2}\right] - \frac{P}{2x}\left(x^2 + \frac{L^2}{4}\right)^{1/2} = 0,$$

where $T_0$ is the tension in the cable before deflection and $E$ is the modulus of elasticity of the cable material. The design variables are $A$ and $T_0$, and the behavior variable is $x$.

**1.5** Given the uniformly loaded "propped" cantilever beam in Fig. 1.19, supported at one end by a cable as shown. Consider the design variables to be $b$, $H$, and $A$ (the cross-sectional area of the cable); assume that $h$ is preassigned. The moment in the beam is

$$M(x) = -\frac{wx}{2}\left[x - \frac{1}{4}\left\{\frac{3AH^2L^4}{AL^3H^2 + 3I_z(H^2 + L^2)^{3/2}}\right\}\right];$$

we assume that the cable and the beam have the same modulus of elasticity. The compressive stress in the extreme fiber of the beam is

$$\sigma(x) = \left|\frac{Mh}{2I_z}\right| + \frac{F_a}{bh},$$

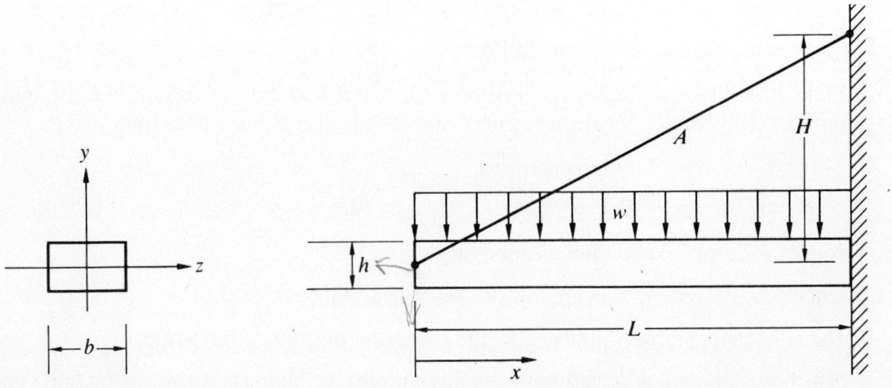


**Figure 1.19**

where $F_a$ is the axial force in the beam due to the horizontal component of the tension in the cable, and $I_z$ is the moment of interia of the beam about a horizontal axis. The downward deflection of the beam is

$$\Delta = \frac{w}{2EI_z}\left[\frac{x^4}{12} - \frac{L^3x}{3} + \frac{L^4}{4}\right] - \frac{P_r}{EI_z}\left[\frac{x^3}{6} - \frac{L^2x}{2} + \frac{L^3}{3}\right],$$

where $P_r$ is the vertical component of the reaction of the cable on the beam

$$P_r = \frac{wL^4}{8}\left[\frac{3AH^2}{AL^3H^2 + 3I_z(H^2 + L^2)^{3/2}}\right].$$

For buckling in the horizontal plane, if the ends are simply supported (not shown), the critical load is

$$F_{\text{crit}} = \frac{\pi^2 EI_y}{L^2},$$

where $I_y$ is the moment of inertia about a vertical axis. Assume that the beam is restrained against buckling in the vertical plane.

Calling the working stress of the beam material $\sigma_b$, that of the cable $\sigma_c$, and the maximum allowable deflection $\Delta_m$, complete the analysis of the system and write all necessary constraint functions $g_j(b, H, A)$. Eliminate $x$ from the constraint equations by solving for the points where $\sigma_{\text{max}}$ and $\Delta_{\text{max}}$ occur. Assuming that the cable material is $\alpha$ times as costly as the beam material, write a cost function for the system. Ignore the cost of connections, as they are constant.

**1.6** The quantities defining a specific design of a spring are $d$, $D$, $n$, and $h_f$ (see Fig. 1.20), where $n$ is the number of coils and $h_f$ is the free height of the spring. Ignoring certain complexities of spring technology, we can write some simplified basic relations for spring analysis [see Faires (1965) for elucidation of these].

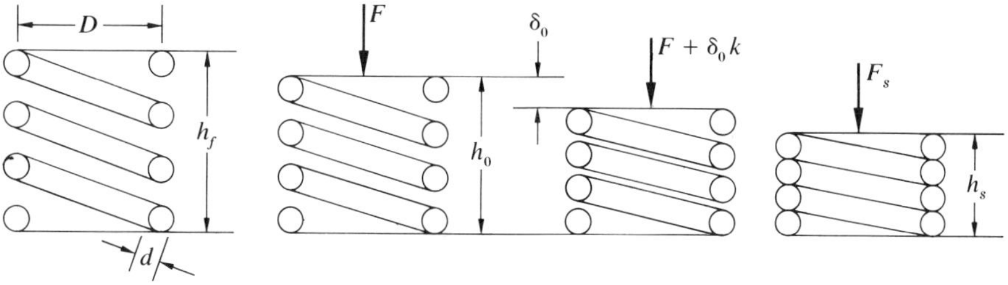


**Figure 1.20**

The spring stiffness (rate) is

$$k = \frac{Gd^4}{8D^3n},$$

where $G$ is the shear modulus of the material. The stress in the spring with an axial load of $F$ is

$$\sigma = \frac{8FD}{\pi d^3}K,$$

where $K$ is the Wahl factor that accounts for stress concentration due to curvature of the spring as well as direct shear:

$$K = \frac{4D - d}{4(D - d)} + 0.615\frac{d}{D}.$$

Solid height is the height at which the coils of the compressed spring close up. It is simply

$$h_s = nd.$$

If the spring is to operate an indefinite number of times through a deflection $\delta_0$, it must be designed so that the material does not fail in fatigue. A fatigue criterion for compression spring design is

$$\left(\frac{\sigma_m - \sigma_a}{\sigma_w} + \frac{\sigma_a}{\sigma_e}\right) S_f \leqslant 1,$$

where $\sigma_m$ is the mean (average) stress in operation, $\sigma_a$ is the alternating stress $[\sigma_a = (\sigma_{\max} - \sigma_{\min})/2]$, $\sigma_w$ is a working stress (strength), $\sigma_e$ is the endurance limit for completely reversed stress, and $S_f$ is a factor of safety. Both $\sigma_w$ and $\sigma_e$ vary with wire diameter in a manner approximated by $Q/d^x$, where $Q$ and $x$ are given constants for the material and differ, of course, for $\sigma_w$ and $\sigma_e$. Finally, both $\sigma_w$ and $\sigma_e$ have maximum values. That is, for $\sigma_w$

$$\sigma_w = \begin{cases} \dfrac{Q_1}{d^{x_1}}, & d \geqslant \bar{d}_1, \\[2ex] \dfrac{Q_1}{\bar{d}_1^{\,x_1}}, & d < \bar{d}_1, \end{cases}$$

where $\bar{d}_1$ is a given constant for the material. Sketch $\sigma_w$ or $\sigma_e$ vs. $d$ to see how this function looks. Write all expressions for the following two optimization problems:

a) Maximize the force available from the spring at a compressed length of $h_0$. The spring is to operate an indefinite number of times through a deflection $\delta_0$ measured as additional compression from $h_0$. The stress at solid height must be less than $\sigma_w$ to protect the spring from inadvertent damage, and the O.D. of the spring is to be no greater than $D_m$.

b) Minimize the length at which the spring will supply a specific force $F_0$ and satisfy all the above requirements.

## REFERENCES

Asimow, M., *Introduction to Design*, Prentice-Hall, Englewood Cliffs, N.J. (1962)

Box, G. E. P., and J. S. Hunter, "Condensed Calculations for Evolutionary Operation Programs," *Technometrics* **1**, 77–95 (1959)

Box, G. E. P., and P. V. Youle, "The Exploration and Exploitation of Response Surfaces: An Example of the Link between the Fitted Surface and the Basic Mechanism of the System," *Biometrics* **11**, 287 (1955)

Faires, V. M., *Design of Machine Elements*, 4th ed., Macmillan (1965)

Mabie, H. H., and F. W. Ocvirk, *Mechanisms and Dynamics of Machinery*, 2nd ed., Wiley, New York (1963)

Middendorf, W. H., *Engineering Design*, Allyn and Bacon, Boston (1969)

Shanley, F. R., *Weight Strength Analysis of Aircraft Structures*, Dover, New York (1960)

Starr, M. K., *Product Design and Decision Theory*, Prentice-Hall, Englewood Cliffs, N.J. (1963)

Wilde, D. J., and C. S. Beightler, *Foundations of Optimization*, Prentice-Hall, Englewood Cliffs, N.J. (1967)

CHAPTER 2

# UNCONSTRAINED MINIMIZATION

In this chapter we will examine methods of solving the following problem. Find $X$ such that $F(X) \rightarrow \min$ where there are no restrictions on the choice of $X$. In light of Chapter 1, we might suppose that there are few practical applications in which a design problem is unconstrained. It will be seen in Chapter 3, however, that some of the most powerful and convenient methods of solving *constrained* problems involve the conversion of the problem to one of unconstrained minimization. In addition there are, of course, some design problems that are either unconstrained or that can be treated as unconstrained except very close to the final minimum. Still another reason for the study of unconstrained minimization is that familiarity with unconstrained minimization methods provides a good conceptual base from which to study the direct constrained methods (see Chapter 4).

An additional utility of unconstrained minimization methods is that they are emerging as powerful solution methods for certain engineering analysis problems. While these applications are tangential to the subject of this text, some allusions will be made to them because of the intimate connection between analysis and optimization methods. As we mentioned in Section 1.6, some problems can be cast in the form of optimization problems, and the analysis (i.e., the numerical solution) can be streamlined in the bargain.[1]

In this chapter, some important properties and concepts of a minimum are discussed first, and then several methods of numerically searching a multivariable function for its minimum are described. The techniques presented become more advanced and powerful as the chapter proceeds, and in some discussions, the reader may feel that the engineering viewpoint has been left far behind. This situation, while lamentable, seems hard to avoid in this chapter. The reader is assured that we will eventually come at least part way back.

## 2.1 SOME PROPERTIES OF MINIMA

The usual notion of a minimum is a point where a function has its least value, i.e., $X_M$ such that $F(X_M) \leqslant F(X)$ for all $X$. In elementary calculus, we discover

[1] See Section 3.7 for a discussion of some of these ideas. See also Fox and Stanton (1968), Fox and Kapoor (1968), Daniel (1967a) and (1967b), Bradbury and Fletcher (1966), Broyden (1965), Kowalik (1966), and Case Western Reserve University (1968).

that for a function of the $n$ variables $(x_1, x_2, \ldots, x_n)$ with continuous derivatives, the minimum will be a point where

$$\frac{\partial F}{\partial x_i} = 0, \qquad i = 1,2, \ldots, n. \tag{2.1}$$

A point satisfying Eq. (2.1) is guaranteed to be a relative minimum if the quadratic form

$$Q = \sum_{i=1}^{n} \sum_{j=1}^{n} \left( \frac{\partial^2 F}{\partial x_i \partial x_j} \right)_{X_0} a_i a_j \tag{2.2}$$

is positive for all choices of the arbitrary constants $a_1, a_2, \ldots, a_n$, except that $Q = 0$ only when $a_i = 0$, $i = 1, \ldots, n$. The second derivatives are evaluated at $X_0$, a point where $\partial F / \partial x_i = 0$. The usual statement of this property is that the matrix

$$\mathbf{J} \equiv \begin{bmatrix} \dfrac{\partial^2 F}{\partial x_1{}^2} & \dfrac{\partial^2 F}{\partial x_1 \partial x_2} & \cdots & \dfrac{\partial^2 F}{\partial x_1 \partial x_n} \\ \cdot & & & \cdot \\ \cdot & & & \cdot \\ \cdot & & & \cdot \\ \dfrac{\partial^2 F}{\partial x_n \partial x_1} & \dfrac{\partial^2 F}{\partial x_n \partial x_2} & \cdots & \dfrac{\partial^2 F}{\partial x_n{}^2} \end{bmatrix} \tag{2.3}$$

must be *positive definite*.[2] This matrix is sometimes called the Hessian matrix of $F$.

Geometrically, this property indicates that the quadratic function that approximates the original function at the point has its minimum there.[3] Consider the Taylor series expansion of $F$ about $X_M$ up to quadratic terms:

$$\begin{aligned} F(X) \simeq F(X_M) &+ \sum_{i=1}^{n} \left( \frac{\partial F}{\partial x_i} \right)_{X_M} (x_i - x_{Mi}) \\ &+ \frac{1}{2} \sum_{j=1}^{n} \sum_{i=1}^{n} \left( \frac{\partial^2 F}{\partial x_i \partial x_j} \right)_{X_M} (x_i - x_{Mi})(x_j - x_{Mj}). \end{aligned} \tag{2.4}$$

In matrix form,[4] this becomes

$$F(X) \simeq F(X_M) + (X - X_M)^T \, \nabla F(X_M) + \tfrac{1}{2}(X - X_M)^T \mathbf{J}_M (X - X_M). \tag{2.5}$$

---

[2] The matrix will be positive definite if all its eigenvalues are positive. A test for positive definiteness which may be practical for small problems and involves only determinants is given in Exercise 2.1.

[3] This concept will be taken up again in Sections 2.6 and 2.10.

[4] For the reader unfamiliar with matrix and vector operations we suggest keeping handy a copy of *Theory and Problems of Matrices*, by Frank Ayres, Jr., in the Schaum Outline Series (New York: Schaum Pub. Co., 1962).

If $\mathbf{J}_M$ is positive definite, as defined above, and $\partial F/\partial x_i = 0$, then for all "small" steps away from $X_M$, $F$ will increase. For example, the function

$$F_1(X) = x_1^4 - 2x_2x_1^2 + x_2^2 + x_1^2 - 2x_1 + 5 \tag{2.6}$$

has a minimum of 4.0 at the point (1,1). This function has continuous derivatives of all orders and hence at the minimum

$$\frac{\partial F_1}{\partial x_1} = 4x_1^3 - 4x_2x_1 + 2x_1 - 2 = 0\,,$$

$$\frac{\partial F_1}{\partial x_2} = -2x_1^2 + 2x_2 = 0\,.$$

Furthermore, the matrix of second derivatives

$$\mathbf{J}_M = \begin{Bmatrix} 12x_1^2 - 4x_2 + 2 & -4x_1 \\ -4x_1 & 2 \end{Bmatrix}_{(1,1)} = \begin{Bmatrix} 10 & -4 \\ -4 & 2 \end{Bmatrix}$$

is positive definite at (1,1). (See Exercise 2.1.) Contours of $F_1$ are shown in Fig. 2.1. Notice that near the minimum point the contours are approximately ellipses. This is because the function can be approximated by a quadratic near (1,1). (See Section 2.6 and Exercise 2.2.)

In many cases, these properties of minima are useful. However, there are large classes of problems in which only our first notion of a minimum (i.e., $X_M$ such that $F(X_M) \leqslant F(X)$ for all $X$) is applicable. First of all, we may have to deal with functions that do not possess even continuous *first* derivatives. For example, the function

$$F_2(X) = \max\,[(x_1 - 1)^2\,, x_1^2 + 4(x_2 - 1)^2] \tag{2.7}$$

has a minimum of $\frac{1}{4}$ at the point ($\frac{1}{2}$, 1), but the derivatives $\partial F_2/\partial x_1$ and $\partial F_2/\partial x_2$ are undefined there. The contours of this function are shown in Fig. 2.2. Functions of this type are not unusual in engineering problems, since we often want to minimize the largest of several outputs or responses and we may not know in advance which will be the controlling responses at the optimum.[5,6]

[5] In Schmit and Fox (1964), a shock isolator is optimized in which the objective is to minimize the maximum acceleration. This function has discontinuous first derivatives.

[6] We can always find the unconstrained minimum of a function of the form

$$F = \max_{i=1}^{r}\,[f_i(X)]$$

without dealing with discontinuous functions if we use inequalities. For example, find $X$ and $s$ such that

$$s \to \min\,, \qquad f_i(X) - s \leqslant 0\,, \qquad i = 1,2\ldots,r\,.$$

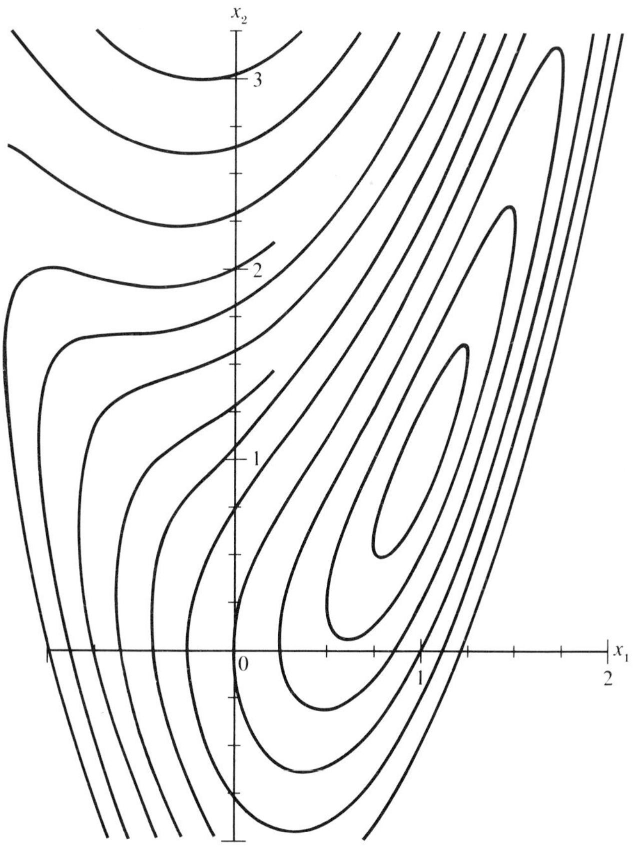


**Figure 2.1**

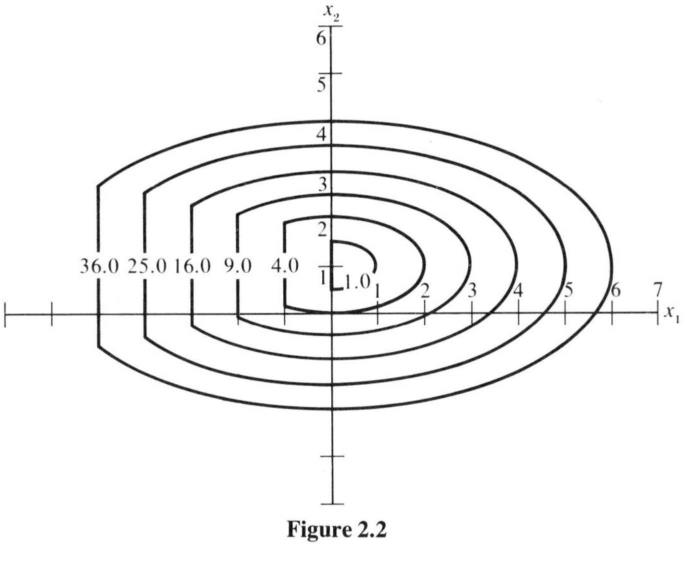


**Figure 2.2**

In other cases, the criteria of Eqs. (2.1) and (2.2) do not answer the need because they only ensure that a point is a relative minimum. That is, they ensure that a point has the least function value in its neighborhood, but not necessarily the least function value for all $\boldsymbol{X}$. For example, the function

$$F_3(X) = 4 + \tfrac{9}{2}x_1 - 4x_2 + x_1^2 + 2x_2^2 - 2x_1x_2 + x_1^4 - 2x_1^2x_2 \qquad (2.8)$$

has relative minima of 0.9855 at (1.941, 3.854) and −0.5134 at (−1.053, 1.028). The contours of this function are shown in Fig. 2.3. Note also that there is a *saddle point* at (0.61173, 1.4929) where $\partial F_3/\partial x_1 = \partial F_3/\partial x_2 = 0$, but where $\mathbf{J} = [\partial^2 F_3/\partial x_i \partial x_j]$ is not positive definite (see Exercise 2.3).

The problem of relative minima is one of the most vexing in optimum design methodology. This is because most of the viable methods can seek

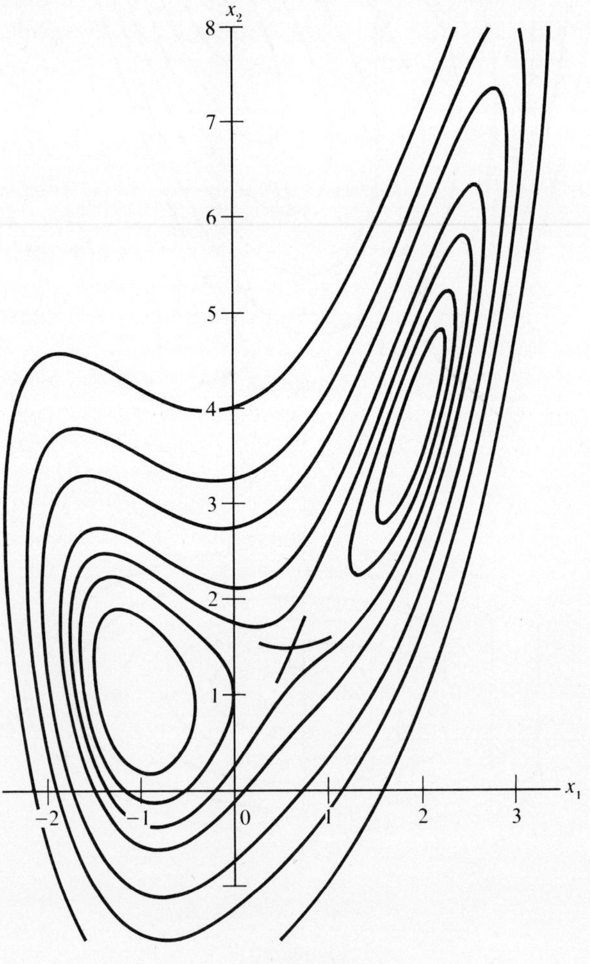


**Figure 2.3**

only a relative minimum and cannot be relied on in the general case to converge to the least minimum. The consequences of this are clearly serious; the proposed "solution" to an optimum design problem may in truth be only the best of all similar designs, while superior designs may exist undiscovered because they require gross changes from the relative minimum design.

One of the most common methods of attempting to deal with this problem is to re-solve the problem, using various starting points. The minimum obtained will in a sense be the one nearest to the starting point, and the use of multiple starting points increases the likelihood of finding the lowest minimum. In engineering problems, we seldom need to use arbitrary starting points, because the relative minima often have physical significance. The situation occurs as a manifestation of alternative subconcepts within a major design concept. The engineer may be called upon to select the most promising design subtype for a starting point. Except for an occasional example, the possibility of relative minima will be ignored in this text.

## 2.2 GRID AND RANDOM METHODS

These sampling methods are almost trivial in concept and, as suggested earlier, they can be extremely wasteful of computer time. Their principal utility is in small problems where the effort of programming and applying the more efficient methods overshadows the gains. It has also been suggested that these sampling methods might be used to compute a good starting point for one of the more efficient methods.

The random search is nearly as simple as the grid, but it has the advantage that on each successive sample, every point in the space is equally likely to be tested. It consists of generating a set of $X$'s, each component of which is a random number in some preselected range. Most computer libraries have random number generators and so this can be done quite conveniently. The method was applied to $F_2$ (Eq. 2.7) by generating $x_1$ and $x_2$ as random numbers from 0 to 4.5. The results are shown in Table 2.1. Only the trials which produced improvement are shown in the table.

**Table 2.1. Random search of $F_2$**

| Trial | $x_1$ | $x_2$ | $F_2$ |
|---|---|---|---|
| 1 | 1.608 | 0.644 | 3.090 |
| 6 | 1.136 | 1.298 | 1.648 |
| 14 | 0.887 | 0.895 | 0.831 |
| 32 | 0.792 | 1.175 | 0.751 |
| 136 | 0.425 | 1.342 | 0.648 |
| 161 | 0.785 | 0.999 | 0.617 |
| 200 | No improvement | | |
| Exact | 0.500 | 1.000 | 0.250 |

Of course, we could now use a smaller range about the point (0.785, 0.999) and continue the search. Comparison between the two methods (grid and random) is probably fruitless, inasmuch as the results depend on the function being searched and the methods are used only when efficiency is no object.

A random-based method that is somewhat more sophisticated is the *random walk*. The version that we will discuss is based on a sequence of improved approximations to the minimum, each derived from the preceding approximation. The sequence is determined from the prescription

$$X_{q+1} = X_q + \rho \hat{e}_r , \tag{2.9}$$

where $X_q$ is the "old" approximation to the minimum and $X_{q+1}$ is the "new" approximation, $\rho$ is a scalar step length, and $\hat{e}_r$ is a unit random vector. The algorithm is based on the following steps.

1. Choose a starting point $X_0$ and a step length $\rho$ that is large in relation to the final accuracy desired.
2. Generate $\hat{e}_r$.
3. Calculate $\tilde{F} \equiv F(X_q + \rho\hat{e}_r)$.
4. If the result of step 3 is less than $F(X_q)$, then set $X_{q+1} = X_q + \rho\hat{e}_r$ and repeat steps 2, 3, and 4. Otherwise, just repeat steps 2, 3, and 4.
5. If a sufficient number of trials produces no acceptable $X_{q+1}$, reduce $\rho$ and continue steps 2, 3, and 4.
6. When $\rho$ has been reduced below the accuracy desired, terminate.

The algorithm is described by the flow diagram shown in Fig. 2.4.[7] Figure 2.5 shows part of a random walk on a contour plot of $F_3$. The numbers at each point represent the total number of trials needed to obtain the point. The initial point was (5,4), $\rho$ was 1, and $N$ was 40. It took about 400 function

[7] Throughout this text, flow diagrams are utilized to help the reader follow the logic of the various algorithms. The computational detail displayed in these diagrams will fluctuate, and in many or even most cases it cannot serve alone as a coding guide.

The conventions used are simple: "$\leftarrow$" means that the value indicated by the expression on the right is to be stored or recorded in the variable or place indicated by the symbol on the left (this is commonly referred to as a replacement or assignment statement). This notation will be used for scalar quantities, vector quantities, matrix quantities, and evaluated functions.

If the contents of a box are to be executed for a range of values of some index, this will be signified by the usual mathematical notations (e.g., $i = 1,2,\ldots, m$).

Conditional control statements (logic statements) are contained in ovals and have only two outcomes: true or false.

In many cases, programs written from fleshed-out versions of these diagrams would be singularly inefficient, as no use has been made of computation or code-economizing tricks because of their tendency to obscure the computational flow. The joy of inventing these tricks is perhaps the only thing that makes the task of coding bearable, and the author would not rob the reader of that small solace.

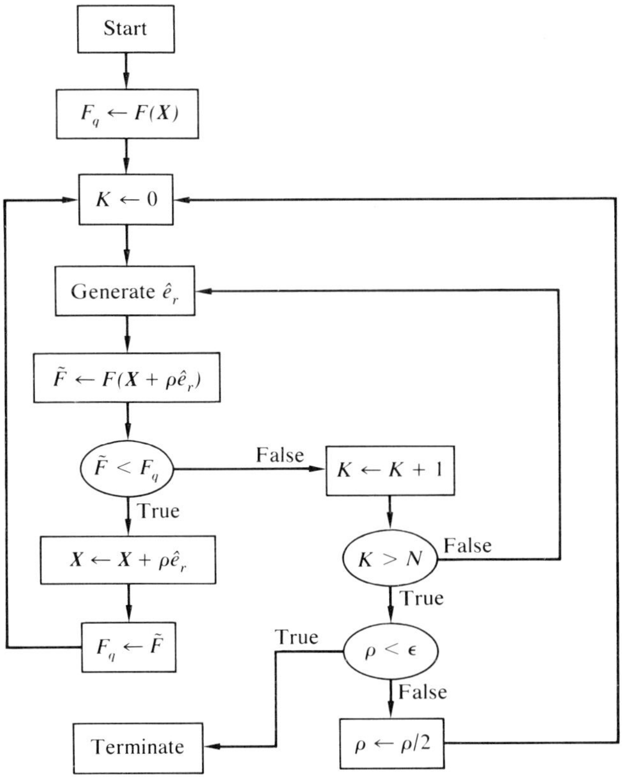


**Figure 2.4**

evaluations to obtain the answer to three significant figures, but this could be reduced somewhat by choosing a smaller $N$. Note that this starting point resulted in convergence to the higher of the two relative minima of the problem; other starting points produce convergence to the lower minimum. The method can be improved if each successful direction is exploited until it fails to be useful. The flow diagram in Fig. 2.6 shows this modification.

A note of caution on the generation of random unit vectors is in order. In two dimensions: if $R$ is a random number between 0 and $2\pi$, then $\hat{e}_r = (\cos R, \sin R)$ is a unit vector with random direction, but if $R_1$ and $R_2$ are random between $+1$ and $-1$, then the unit vector

$$\hat{e} = \frac{1}{(R_1^2 + R_2^2)^{1/2}} \begin{pmatrix} R_1 \\ R_2 \end{pmatrix}$$

is not random in direction but biased on the diagonals of the unit square. In three dimensions, even the two angles of spherical coordinates cannot be used to generate a random unit vector. One suggestion is to generate a vector with random components between $+1$ and $-1$ and compute its length:

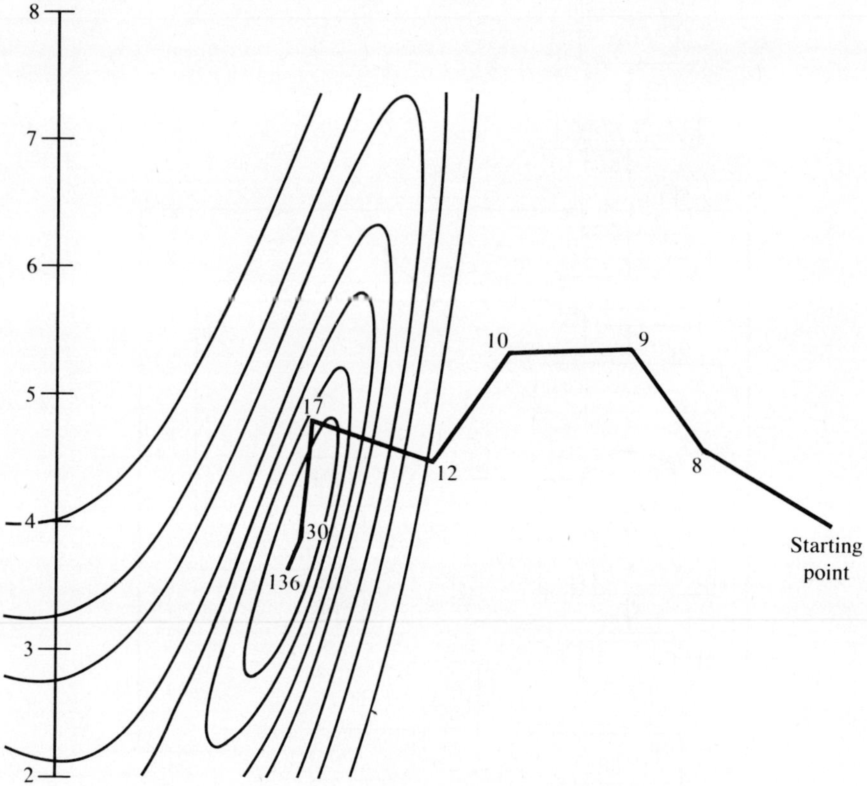


**Figure 2.5**

if it is greater than 1 discard it; otherwise normalize it to unit length. Vectors so produced have random direction in any number of dimensions, but may be costly to generate. It is, of course, not absolutely essential to produce a random unit vector so long as the vectors used provide a more or less uniform distribution of directions.

This latter idea suggests methods which merely probe in a number of directions in some cyclic order. Such methods have received attention in the literature,[8] but for unconstrained minimization they are often far more complicated than other methods which will be discussed subsequently.

## 2.3 UNIVARIATE METHODS

In the random walk method, we produced a succession of approximations to a minimum by adding a fixed scalar multiple of a random unit vector to a

[8] One interesting system is a subprogram called RIDGE, which is part of the program called by its developer the "poor man's optimizer." See Mugele (1962).

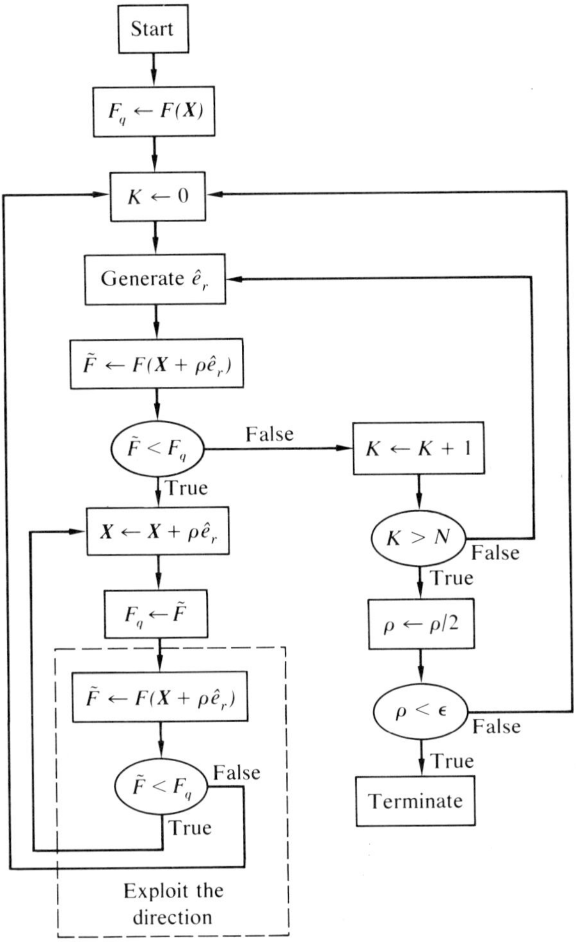


**Fig. 2.6.** Random walk with direction exploitation.

previous approximation. In this section, we discuss a method which proceeds according to a similar prescription:

$$X_{q+1} = X_q + \alpha_q S_q \,, \tag{2.10}$$

where the $S_q$ are a cyclic ordering of the unit vectors $S_1 = (1,0,0,\ldots,0)$, $S_2 = (0,1,0,\ldots,0),\ldots,$ $S_n = (0,0,0,\ldots,1)$, $S_{n+1} = (1,0,0,\ldots,0)$, etc., and the $\alpha_q$ are positive or negative step lengths chosen so that $F(X_{q+1}) < F(X_q)$. With this choice for the $S_q$, Eq. (2.10) is a glorified statement of "change one variable at a time."

A number of variations of the simple univariate method are possible, depending on the rationale used to choose $\alpha_q$. In this section, an accelerated incremental scheme is described; in the next section, a minimizing step is described.

The accelerated incremental scheme operates according to the following steps.

1. Determine whether $\alpha_q$ should be positive or negative. In other words, for the particular $S_q$ in question, does the function decrease in the plus or minus direction?
2. Take a step of $\pm t$, where $t$ is some preselected step length, and calculate $F_t = F(X_q \pm tS_q)$.
3. If $F_t$ is less than $F_q \equiv F(X_q)$, then replace $F_q$ by $F_t$, increase $t$ to $t_p$ (e.g., double it), and repeat steps 2 and 3. Otherwise set $X_{q+1} = X_q \pm t_p S_q$, where $t_p$ is the last "successful" value. Choose the next $S_q$ and repeat steps 1, 2, and 3 for the new direction.
4. Stop when no direction $S_q$ produces an improvement in the function.

The flow diagram of Fig. 2.7 defines a possible version of the algorithm. In this version, $K$ is an indicator that is zero until some direction of the cycle is successful in reducing the function value, $J$ is an indicator that is zero until a particular direction is successful, $\epsilon$ is a small number used as a probe length to determine the direction of decrease of $F$, and $t_0$ is the minimum step length to be used. Each direction is probed at $t_0, 2t_0, 4t_0$, etc. (where $t_0$ is an "original" trial step length), until the function begins to increase. Then the last successful step length is used to compute the new $X$ (i.e., $X_{q+1}$).[9]

There are many possible variations of the algorithm shown in Fig. 2.7, and this one was chosen merely for its simplicity. The reader has, no doubt, already thought of alternatives for some of the steps. For example, $t_0$ could be used in place of $\epsilon$, saving some function evaluations, or perhaps the minimum step length should be different for each $S_q$; this can be handled by using different $t_0$'s or by incorporating the differences into the lengths of $S_q$ themselves. Further, the step can be accelerated differently and a successive reduction of the minimum step length can be used.

The method applied to $F_3$ is illustrated in Fig. 2.8. The starting point was $(-2.5, 4.25)$, $\epsilon$ was 0.0625, and $t_0$ was 0.25. The reader is cautioned that the 2-dimensional examples shown in the figures are chosen for illustrative purposes and that, in general, the efficiency of all methods decreases rapidly with an increase in dimensionality. Note that the method just described, applied to a 10-variable function, requires 10 single variable searches just to try all variables once. Suppose it takes 10 complete sweeps through the directions and

[9] If the $S_q$ are the univariate directions, then only one component of $X$ is changed at each step and we would probably code the method to take advantage of this fact. However, since the algorithms shown in this and some succeeding figures are equally applicable to other sets of directions, this specialization has been omitted.

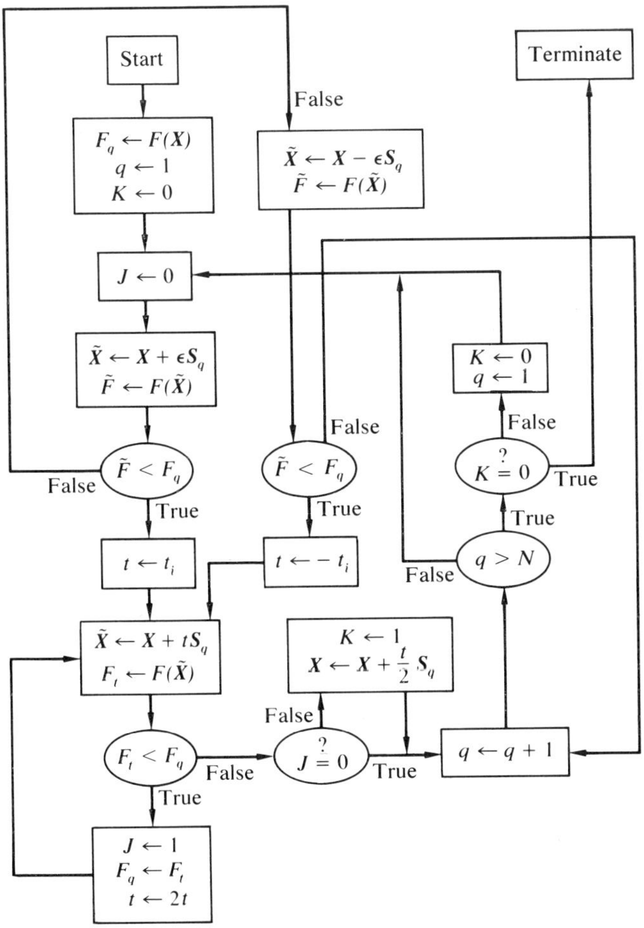


**Figure 2.7**

that each single variable search requires 5 function evaluations; this amounts to 500 function evaluations. If the function is at all ill-conditioned (i.e., elongated), it can require 100 or more sweeps (i.e., 5000 function evaluations) to get reasonably close to the minimum.

Theoretically, any function with continuous derivatives can be minimized by the univariate method.[10] However there are functions without derivatives that will foil even the most careful version of the method. This situation is depicted in Fig. 2.9, where a hypothetical function with a "ridge" is shown.

[10] A direction $\boldsymbol{S}$ will have decreasing function value locally if $\boldsymbol{S}^T\nabla F < 0$, and hence if $|\nabla F| \neq 0$. Then either $\boldsymbol{S}$ or $-\boldsymbol{S}$ is a direction of descent unless $\boldsymbol{S}^T\nabla F = 0$, which cannot be true for all the coordinate directions.

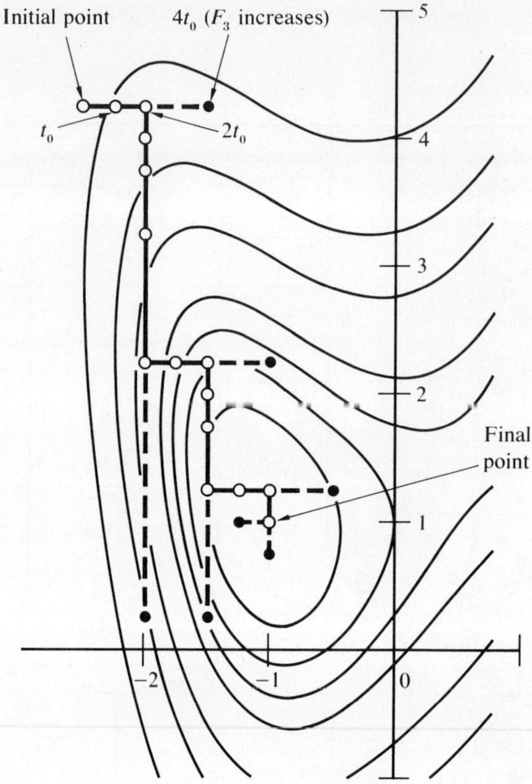


Figure 2.8

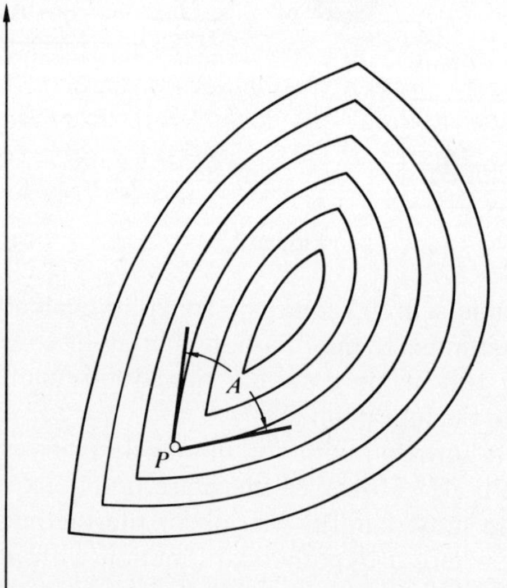


Figure 2.9

At the point $P$ none of the univariate directions are "downhill." In fact, only directions within the sector $A$ are minimizing directions. Figure 2.10 illustrates a similar function with continuous derivatives, but one that for all practical purposes possesses the same character, since the distance of travel that is possible may be less than the number of working significant figures of the computer.

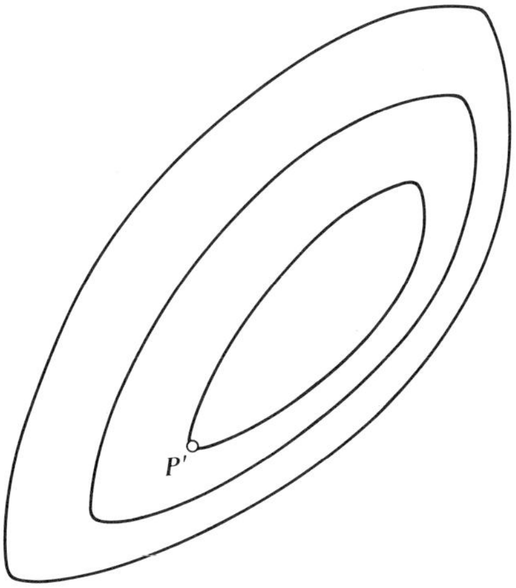


**Figure 2.10**

Many approaches to these difficulties are possible, but they are mostly special heuristic search methods and/or they are problem dependent. When such functions are encountered and the methods available for them[11] are either inapplicable or too cumbersome, the best approach is to construct special methods based on the properties of problems at hand.

## 2.4 MINIMIZING STEPS: QUADRATIC INTERPOLATION

The methods we have discussed for selecting the step length $\alpha_q$ are simple and easy to apply; however with only a slight increase in algorithm complexity, it is possible to choose the $\alpha_q$ which *minimizes* $F$ in the particular direction. An obvious advantage of this approach is that each step will produce the greatest possible reduction in $F$, and hence we would expect the process to converge faster. Another advantage, which we will discuss in later sections, is that by taking the minimizing step at each iteration, a pattern of moves emerges that can be used to improve the choice of subsequent directions.

[11] See, for example, Mugele (1962) and Wilde and Beightler (1967).

Consider *any* vector $S_q$ and the move prescription

$$X = X_q + \alpha S_q, \tag{2.11}$$

where, if $\alpha$ is considered a variable, the locus of $X$ for a range of values of $\alpha$ is a straight line.

Substituting this formally into $F(X)$, we obtain

$$F(X) = F(X_q + \alpha S_q) = F(\alpha), \tag{2.12}$$

since $F$ can be considered a function of $\alpha$ alone ($X_q$ and $S_q$ are considered fixed). We seek here the value of $\alpha$ which minimizes $F(\alpha)$. (See Fig. 2.11.) Note that this value, denoted $\alpha^*$, does not produce the global minimum of $F$ unless the line $X = X_q + \alpha S_q$ contains the global minimum point.

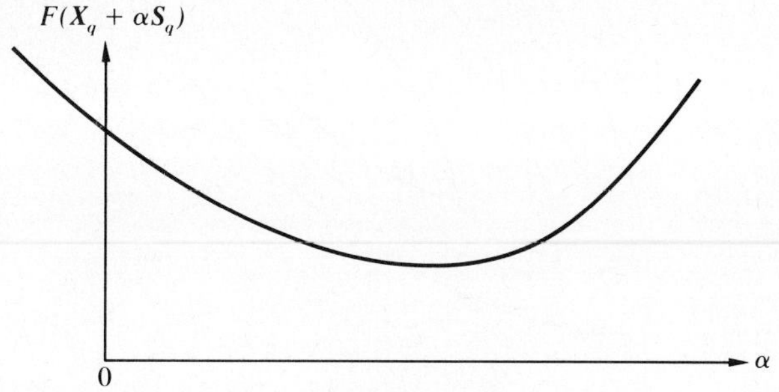


**Figure 2.11**

With this concept, the problem of minimizing $F(X)$ can be reduced to a succession of 1-dimensional minimization problems regardless of the dimensionality of $X$. If $F$ is a simple, explicit function of $X$, Eq. (2.11) can be written directly in terms of the variable $\alpha$, and the quantities $(x_{i,q})$, $(s_{i,q})$, and perhaps $\alpha^*$ can be computed exactly.[12] However, in practice we rarely have the good fortune or patience to carry out the operation and must usually resort to numerical means for finding $\alpha^*$.

Consider approximating the function $F(\alpha)$ by a function $H(\alpha)$ which has an easily determined minimum point. The simplest 1-variable function possessing a minimum is the quadratic

$$H(\alpha) = a + b\alpha + c\alpha^2, \tag{2.13}$$

the minimum of which occurs where

$$\frac{dH}{d\alpha} = b + 2c\alpha = 0 \tag{2.14}$$

[12] See Exercises 2.5 and 2.6 for examples.

or

$$\alpha^* = -\frac{b}{2c}. \tag{2.15}$$

The constants $b$ and $c$ for the approximating quadratic ($a$ is not needed) can be determined by sampling the function at three different $\alpha$ values, $\alpha_1$, $\alpha_2$, and $\alpha_3$, and solving the equations

$$\begin{aligned} f_1 &= a + b\alpha_1 + c\alpha_1^2, \\ f_2 &= a + b\alpha_2 + c\alpha_2^2, \\ f_3 &= a + b\alpha_3 + c\alpha_3^2, \end{aligned} \tag{2.16}$$

where $f_1$ denotes the value $F(\alpha_1)$, etc. If we use 0, $t$, and $2t$ for $\alpha_1$, $\alpha_2$, and $\alpha_3$, where $t$ is a preselected trial step, Eqs. (2.16) are particularly easy to solve and we can save one function evaluation.[13] Note that if $F$ at $\alpha = 0$ is presumed known from the previous iteration, only two function evaluations are required. With this choice, Eqs. (2.16) become

$$\begin{aligned} f_1 &= a, \\ f_2 &= a + bt + ct^2, \\ f_3 &= a + 2bt + 4ct^2. \end{aligned} \tag{2.17}$$

From these we obtain

$$\begin{aligned} a &= f_1, \\ b &= \frac{4f_2 - 3f_1 - f_3}{2t}, \\ c &= \frac{f_3 + f_1 - 2f_2}{2t^2}, \end{aligned} \tag{2.18}$$

$$\alpha^* \simeq \frac{4f_2 - 3f_1 - f_3}{4f_2 - 2f_3 - 2f_1}\, t. \tag{2.19}$$

For $\alpha^*$ to correspond to a minimum and not a maximum of $H(\alpha)$, it must satisfy

$$\left.\frac{d^2H}{d\alpha^2}\right|_{\alpha=\alpha^*} > 0. \tag{2.20}$$

The case in which $H$ is quadratic requires $c > 0$, or

$$f_3 + f_1 > 2f_2. \tag{2.21}$$

This means that the value of $f_2$ must be below the line connecting $f_1$ and $f_3$ (see Fig. 2.12).

[13] See Exercise 2.7 for the general case.

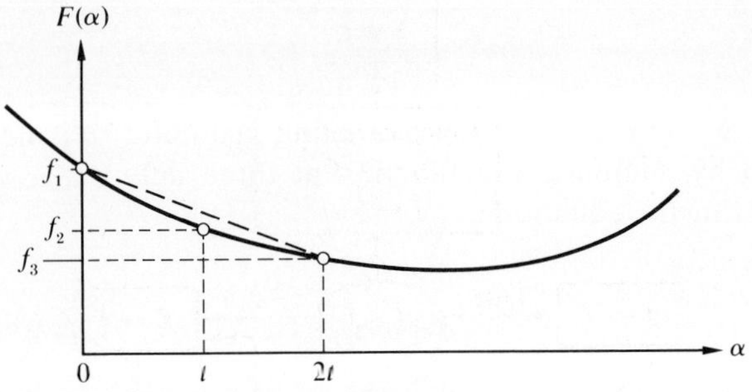


**Figure 2.12**

A scheme for ensuring that Eq. (2.21) is satisfied and that the minimum lies in the interval $0 < \alpha < 2t$ is as follows:

1. Choose an initial value for $t$ based on previous iterations or other information regarding a reasonable value for the step length. Ideally $t$ would be on the order of $\alpha^*$.
2. Compute $F(t)$.
3. If $F(t) > F(0) \equiv f_1$, then set $f_3 = F(t)$, cut $t$ in half, and repeat step 2; otherwise set $f_2 = F(t)$, double $t$, and repeat step 2.
4. When a value $t$ has been obtained such that $f_2 < f_1$ and $f_3 > f_2$, compute $\alpha^*$ according to Eq. (2.19). (The two final acceptable situations are illustrated in Fig. 2.13 a, b).

The logic for the *quadratic interpolation* algorithm described above is given in the flow diagram shown in Fig. 2.14. If the initial $t$ has the wrong sign (i.e., if $F$ *increases* in the direction $\mathbf{X}_q + t\mathbf{S}_q$, $t > 0$), the process will not terminate.

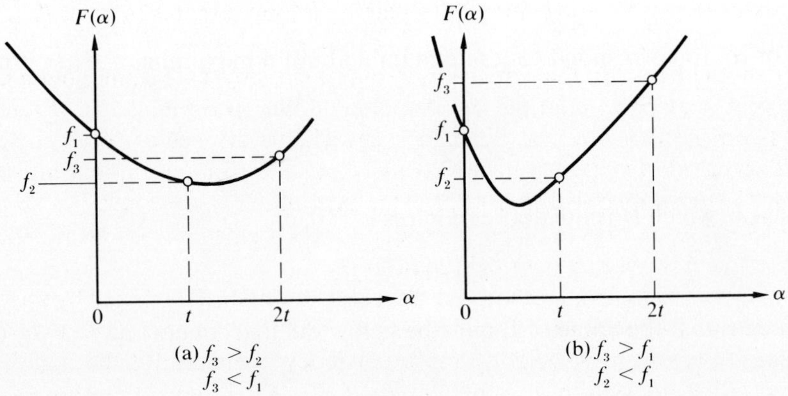


**Figure 2.13**

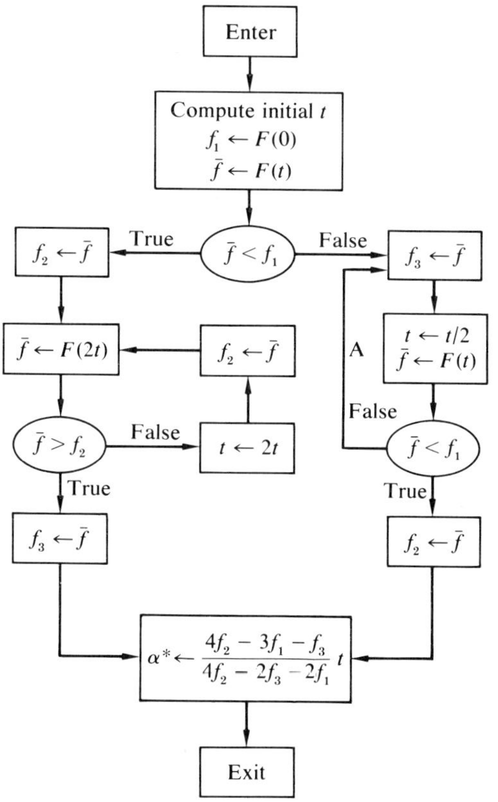


**Figure 2.14**

Therefore if the correct sign of $t$ is in doubt, the algorithm should be provided with a stop criterion, for example by placing a loop counter in loop A of Fig. 2.14.

It should be noted that even a function possessing a single minimum in the space of $X$ may have multiple minima along a line (see Fig. 2.15). If a test is made to ensure that $F(\alpha^*) < f_1$, the process will not diverge or cycle; however, it is a good rule to try to select $t$ so that only the nearest minimum to $X_q$ is included in the interval $0 < \alpha < 2t$. This precaution is wise because some of the methods to be discussed later depend for their efficiency on a smooth progression along the contours of the function.

With the univariate method, the approximation of $\alpha^*$ obtained by applying Eq. (2.19) will be sufficient for progress if $F(\alpha^*) < f_1$; a test should certainly be made to ensure this. Slightly more efficiency is ensured if the logic is arranged so that the step to $\alpha^*$ is taken only if $F(\alpha^*) < f_2$, and otherwise the step to $t$ is taken (since $f_2 < f_1$ and $f_3$, the step to $t$ is to the minimum of $f_1, f_2, f_3$).

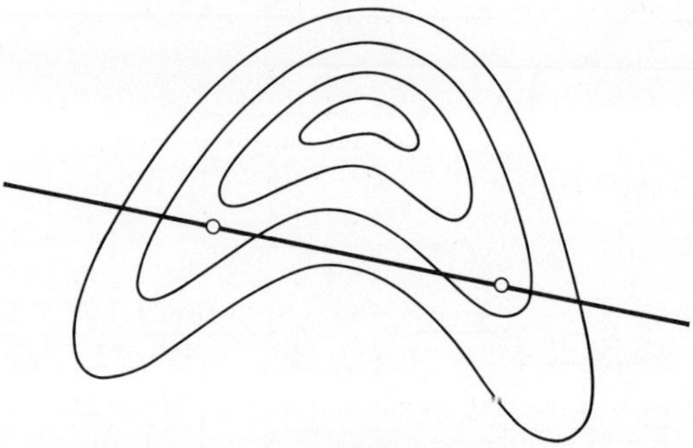

**Figure 2.15**

The methods which follow in this chapter, however, depend on $\alpha^*$ being a good approximation to the *minimum* of $F(\alpha)$. Several tests are possible to ascertain whether the approximation to the minimum, which we will denote $\tilde{\alpha}^*$, is a sufficiently good approximation to the exact $\alpha^*$. A sort of ultimate criterion is

$$F(\tilde{\alpha}^*) \leqslant \begin{cases} F(\tilde{\alpha}^* + \epsilon) \equiv f^+, \\ F(\tilde{\alpha}^* - \epsilon) \equiv f^-, \end{cases} \tag{2.22}$$

where $\epsilon$ is the minimum significant change of the variable in the direction under consideration. Computationally, this criterion has two main disadvantages: first, it requires two extra function evaluations, and second, it is not really as certain as it seems since the values $f^+$ and $f^-$ may be contaminated by roundoff noise, rendering the results of the tests inconclusive. An alternative is to compute an approximation to $dF/d\alpha$ at $\alpha = \tilde{\alpha}^*$ as

$$\tilde{f}' \equiv \frac{F(\tilde{\alpha}^* + \Delta) - F(\tilde{\alpha}^* - \Delta)}{2\Delta}, \tag{2.23}$$

where $\Delta$ is a numerically significant but still small change in $\alpha$. Then compare this with zero. The range of the derivative of $H$ in the interval 0 to $2t$ can be used as a basis of comparison; in other words, the maximum value of $dH/d\alpha$ is either $b$ (at $\alpha = 0$) or $b + 4ct$ (at $\alpha = 2t$), and these can be used to determine whether $\tilde{f}'$ is sufficiently small. For example, we might require

$$\tilde{f}' < \frac{2b + 4ct}{200}, \tag{2.24}$$

which is one-hundredth of the average of $H'(0)$ and $H'(2t)$. This criterion still requires two additional function evaluations, and it is not foolproof.

An alternative that is practically "free" is the following: Compare $F(\tilde{\alpha}^*)$ with $H(\tilde{\alpha}^*)$ and consider $\tilde{\alpha}^*$ a sufficiently good approximation if they differ by a small amount. It can be shown that

$$H(\tilde{\alpha}^*) = f_1 - \frac{(4f_2 - 3f_1 - f_3)^2}{8(f_1 - 2f_2 + f_3)} = a - \frac{b^2}{4c}. \tag{2.25}$$

For example, we might require

$$\frac{|H(\tilde{\alpha}^*) - f(\tilde{\alpha}^*)|}{|H(\tilde{\alpha}^*)|} < \epsilon, \tag{2.26}$$

where $\epsilon$ is a small fraction, say 0.01 (1%).

If the criterion chosen for the accuracy of the minimum is not satisfied, the original algorithm can be reapplied at $\tilde{\alpha}^*$ or $t$, whichever is a better approximation, or a general quadratic fit (see Exercise 2.7) can be made using the "best" 3 of the points $0, t, 2t$, and $\tilde{\alpha}^*$.

It is easy to concoct numerous function interpolation schemes based on higher-order polynomials, using more sample points or finite approximations to derivatives. Such algorithms may have advantages in certain problems, but in giving rein to our imagination, we should be careful to avoid excessive function calculation and algorithm complication. It is usually better to apply the same simple algorithm repeatedly in successive approximations, if refinement of the minimum is necessary in ill-behaved problems, than to attempt to construct an air-tight technique that will secure it in one trial.

In some cases, a higher-order interpolation for the 1-dimensional minimization *is* appropriate. In particular, if the function has continuous first partial derivatives, a 2-point cubic fit can be used economically; however, since this approach requires the use of the gradient $\nabla F$ of the function, its discussion will be deferred until after the section on gradient methods (Section 2.8).

Several types of schemes for 1-dimensional minimization have been omitted in this discussion, and the reader is referred to the literature.[14] Most of these are highly organized hunt-and-peck schemes with elegant logic behind them; however their usefulness is usually limited to problems in which the interpolation methods fail: for example, in some of the discontinuous derivative cases.

The algorithm of univariate directions combined with minimizing steps is illustrated in Fig. 2.16. An interesting feature of minimizing steps which can be seen in the figure is that the minimum points occur where the contours of the function are tangent to the direction vector. This is true regardless of the dimensionality of the space and the direction of the vector $\mathbf{S}_q$. The geometric

---

[14] One method in particular deserves mention: the Fibonacci search, which is based on the fascinating Fibonacci numbers. It is a sampling method that traps the minimum in successively smaller intervals. For a lucid explanation of this and certain related techniques, see Wilde and Beightler (1967). For the case in which the computed value of $F$ has some uncertainty associated with it, see Wilde (1965).

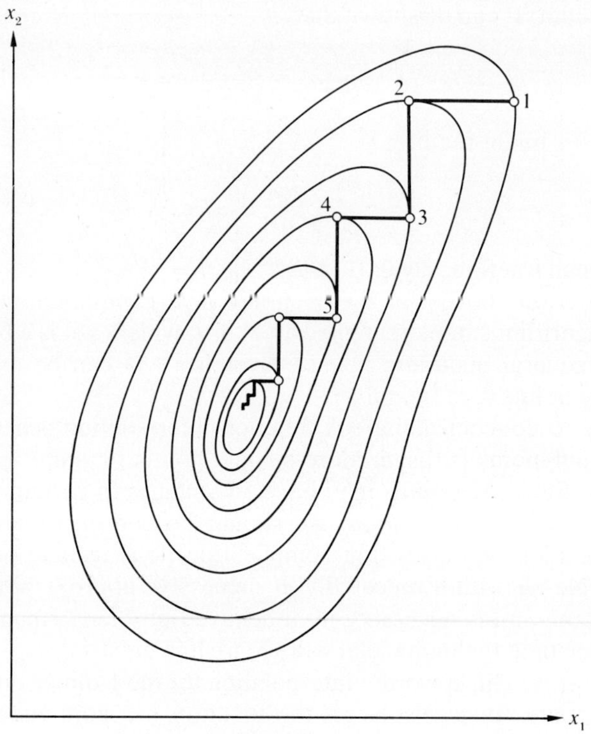


Figure 2.16

plausibility of this fact may be intuitively evident to the reader. It will be demonstrated analytically in Section 2.7.

## 2.5 THE PATTERN MOVE

As we saw in the previous illustration, the univariate directions may become bogged down even with minimizing steps. A useful technique for improving the convergence of this class of methods is the *pattern move*.

Note that in Fig. 2.16 the alternate points in the iteration (1, 3; 2, 4; 3, 5; etc.) define lines which lie in the general direction of the minimum (see Fig. 2.17). This property is so strong in 2 dimensions that if the function being minimized is quadratic, all such lines pass through the minimum; in other words, they pass through the common center of the family of ellipses that are the contours of the quadratic. Unfortunately, this property does not carry through directly to higher dimensions even for quadratic functions, but the idea can still greatly speed convergence in these problems.

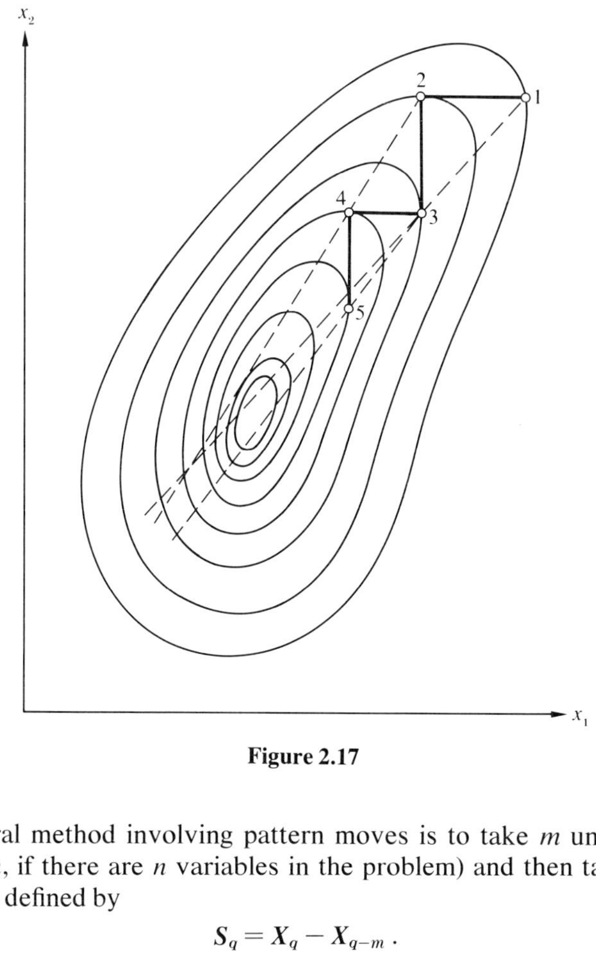


**Figure 2.17**

A general method involving pattern moves is to take $m$ univariate steps (often $m = n$, if there are $n$ variables in the problem) and then take a move in the direction defined by

$$\boldsymbol{S}_q = \boldsymbol{X}_q - \boldsymbol{X}_{q-m} \,. \tag{2.27}$$

Actually, the directions used prior to taking a pattern move need not be the univariate directions, a fact that we will exploit in the next section.

The algorithm for $m = n$ is defined by the flow diagram in Fig. 2.18. Blocks A and B of Fig. 2.18 imply the whole sequence of steps required to determine $\alpha^*$; this sequence may be in the form of the flow diagram in Fig. 2.14.

Notice that the pattern move direction may not always lie in a direction of descent. In other words, it is possible that the point $\boldsymbol{X}_q$ may already be a minimum on the line $\boldsymbol{S}_q$, and block B of Fig. 2.18 can produce no improvement. It may also be that $\boldsymbol{S}_q$ is in a direction of ascent and that the $\alpha^*$ for block A is negative. This situation should cause no trouble if the one-dimensional minimization algorithm is provided with logic for determining the "downhill" direction of $\boldsymbol{S}_q$ before it proceeds with the quadratic interpolation.

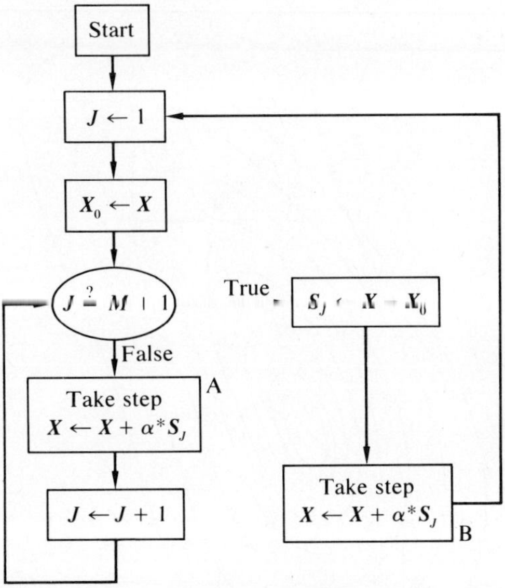


**Figure 2.18**

## 2.6 POWELL'S METHOD: CONJUGATE DIRECTIONS

An extension of the idea of a pattern move was presented by M. J. D. Powell in 1964.[15] We first describe his method in more or less geometric terms and note its characteristics. Then we briefly discuss its theoretical basis and show it to be a method of *conjugate directions*. This classification, which will be defined later in this section, ensures that the method will minimize a quadratic function in a finite number of steps; hence it can be said to converge *quadratically*.

Powell's method can be understood intuitively as follows: Given that the function has been minimized once in each of the coordinate directions and then in the associated pattern direction, discard one of the coordinate directions in favor of the pattern direction for inclusion in the next $m$ minimizations, since this is likely to be a better direction than the discarded coordinate direction. After the next cycle of minimizations, generate a new pattern direction and again replace one of the coordinate directions. The process is illustrated in Fig. 2.19.

Theoretically, a little more is required to make the method truly efficient, but the idea is contained in the above description. The flow diagram shown

[15] See Powell (1964). For an evaluation and discussion of related methods, see Fletcher (1965).

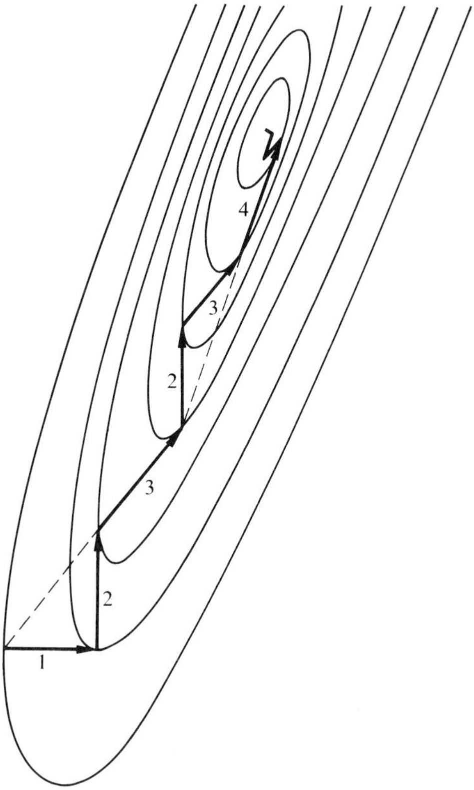


**Figure 2.19**

in Fig. 2.20 is a codification of the simplest version of the method. Note that a pattern direction is constructed (block A), then used for a minimization step (blocks B and C), and then stored in $\boldsymbol{S}_n$ (block D) as all of the directions are up-numbered and $\boldsymbol{S}_1$ is discarded. The direction $\boldsymbol{S}_n$ will then be used for a minimizing step just before the construction of the next pattern direction. Consequently, in the second cycle both $\boldsymbol{X}$ and $\boldsymbol{Y}$ in block A are points that are minima along $\boldsymbol{S}_n$, the last pattern direction. This sequence will impart special properties to $\boldsymbol{S}_{n+1} = \boldsymbol{X} - \boldsymbol{Y}$ that are the source of the rapid convergence of the method. These properties will be discussed subsequently, but first we will examine an example application.

**An Example Application**

Consider the 4-link mechanism (Example E.2) without all the constraints in Eqs. (1.16) through (1.23). This means that we are admitting designs in

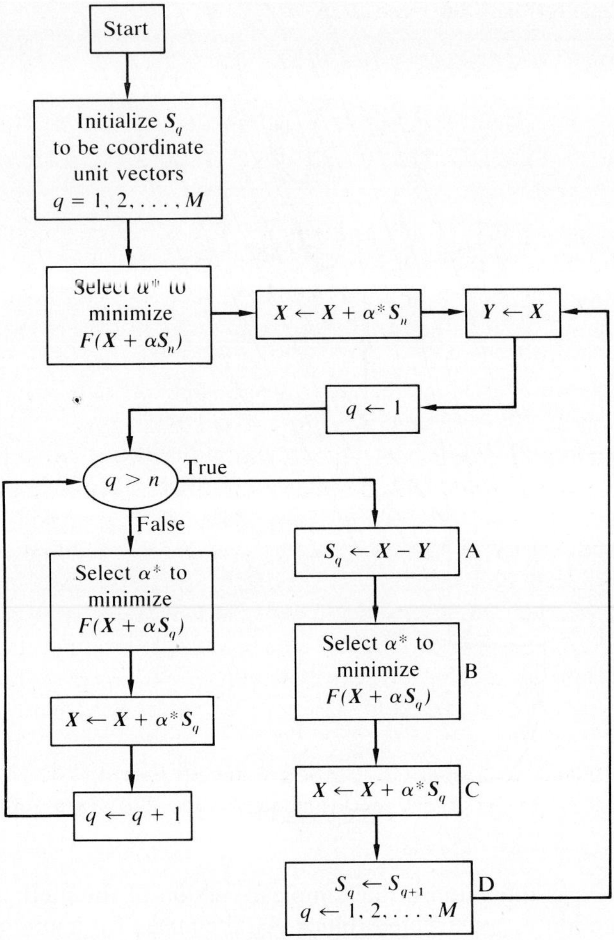


**Figure 2.20**

which the input member cannot make a complete revolution and we are placing no restrictions on member lengths or transmission angles. In the absence of these constraints, the optimization problem of finding $a$, $b$, $c$, $\alpha$, and $\beta$ such that $F$, as defined by Eq. (1.11), is a minimum can be solved by Powell's method.

In order to accomplish this the computer must be supplied with a subroutine, or procedure, for computing $F$, given any $\boldsymbol{D}$ [i.e., $(a, b, c, \alpha, \beta)$].[16] This is a straightforward process using the recipes given in Eq. (1.11) through (1.15), although it is possible to come up with a design for which the argument

[16] The vector $\boldsymbol{D}$ takes the place of the vector $X$ used in the general discussion.

**Table 2.2. Designs for the 4-link mechanism**

| | $a$ | $b$ | $c$ | $\alpha$ | $\beta$ | $F$ |
|---|---|---|---|---|---|---|
| Initial design | 0.4450 | 1.4450 | 1.000 | $-20.0°$ | $-20.0°$ | 76394 |
| Final design | 0.5451 | 2.4870 | 2.9493 | $-107.25°$ | $-78.46°$ | 171 |

of the arccosine in Eq. (1.14) exceeds $\pm 1$ for some positions of the input member in the range of interest, $0 \leqslant \phi \leqslant 240°$.

Even though the constraint that the mechanism be a crank-rocker has been removed, it is still necessary to require continuous motion in the active range of the device in order for the results to have any meaning at all. Indeed, if the mechanism cannot even theoretically traverse some portion of its active range, what error value can be assigned over the excluded portion?

This dilemma is resolved computationally by testing the argument of the arccosine for each $\phi_i$ in the active range and immediately setting the function $F$ to the largest possible computer number if this quantity exceeds 1 in absolute value. The philosophy of this approach is that if some portion of the desired motion is geometrically impossible, then the error is infinite and we set $F$ equal to the nearest thing to infinity we have in the computer. Practically speaking, the technique avoids the need for special programming of the minimization method to account for this possibility. The reader is invited to consider the implications of this approach used in conjunction with the quadratic interpolation algorithm of Fig. 2.14.

An example case is given in Table 2.2 and the results are plotted in Figs. 2.21 and 2.22. Note that there is a very good fit of the optimum design to the

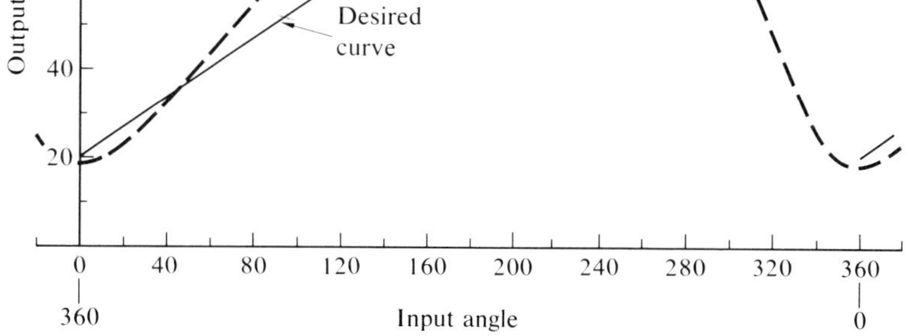

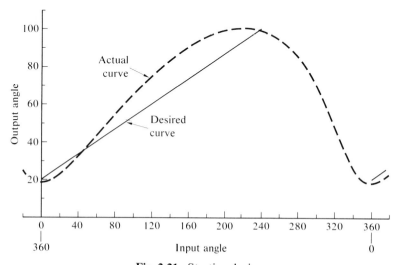

**Fig. 2.21.** Starting design.

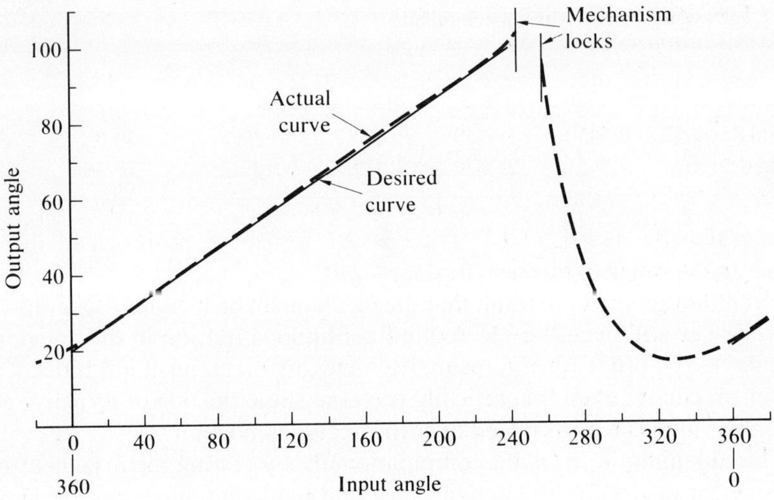


**Fig. 2.22.** Final design.

desired curve, but the device locks at about 243° and 258°. While these results appear to be satisfactory, we note that for a substantial portion of the active range the mechanism is in an extremely cramped configuration that makes tolerances critical, to say nothing of possible large forces. This problem will be repeated in the next chapter with the constraints imposed, and a more practical but geometrically less accurate design will result.

## Quadratic Convergence and Conjugate Directions

We now take up a theoretical discussion of Powell's method in which we consider its application to the minimization of a function $Q$ which is quadratic, i.e., of the form

$$Q(X) = \sum_{i=1}^{n} \sum_{j=1}^{n} a_{ij} x_i x_j + \sum_{k=1}^{n} b_k x_k + c\,, \tag{2.28}$$

or, in matrix notation,[17]

$$Q(X) = X^T \mathbf{A} X + X^T B + c\,. \tag{2.29}$$

The importance of the quadratic is not so much that it is a frequently occurring function, but that many functions are closely approximated by a quadratic near their minima.

---

[17] The superscript $T$ represents the *transpose* of the vector or matrix. If $X$ and $Y$ are two $n$ component vectors, then $X^TY$ means $\sum_i^n x_i y_i$. Another common notation for this product is $X \cdot Y$. Note also that the product $\mathbf{A}X$ is a vector, the $i$th component of which is $\sum_{j=1}^{n} a_{ij} x_j$.

In this regard, consider the Taylor series expansion of a general function $F$ about its minimum point $X_M = (x_{M1}, x_{M2}, \ldots, x_{Mn})$:

$$F(X) = F_M + \sum_{k=1}^{n} \left[\frac{\partial F}{\partial x_k}\right]_M (x_k - x_{Mk}) + \frac{1}{2!} \sum_{i=1}^{n} \sum_{j=1}^{n} \left[\frac{\partial^2 F}{\partial x_i \partial x_j}\right] (x_i - x_{Mi})(x_j - x_{Mj})$$

$$+ \frac{1}{3!} \sum_{r}^{n} \sum_{s}^{n} \sum_{t}^{n} \left[\frac{\partial^3 F}{\partial x_r \partial x_s \partial x_t}\right]_M (x_r - x_{Mr})(x_s - x_{Ms})(x_t - x_{Mt}) + \ldots . \quad (2.30)$$

Writing it in matrix form up to the quadratic terms, we obtain

$$F(X) = F_M + \nabla F_M{}^T (X - X_M) + \tfrac{1}{2}(X - X_M)^T \mathbf{J}_M (X - X_M) + \ldots , \quad (2.31)$$

where the subscript $M$ denotes that the quantity is evaluated at $X_M$, and $\mathbf{J}$ is the matrix of second derivatives as in Eq. (2.3). Note that $\nabla F_M = \mathbf{0}$ at the minimum point $X_M$, and as $|X - X_M|$ approaches zero, $F(X)$ approaches a quadratic. Moreover, if $\mathbf{J}_M$ is positive definite, then the approximating quadratic has its minimum at $X_M$.

If a minimization method always locates the minimum of a general quadratic function in no more than a predetermined number of operations and if the limiting number of operations is directly related to the number of variables $n$, then the process is said to be *quadratically convergent.* If we apply a quadratically convergent method to a general function for which the Taylor series is dominated by the quadratic terms near the minimum, then we can expect it to converge rapidly in the neighborhood of $X_M$.

In practice, it develops that a surprising number of functions are well approximated by a quadratic even at points moderately distant from $X_M$. Hence quadratically convergent methods are usually far more efficient for general applications than those lacking this property.

Most quadratically convergent methods are based, in one way or another, on the concept of *conjugate directions.* In the context of the minimization of a quadratic function (Eq. 2.29), a set of $n$ directions $\{S_q\}$ are said to be *conjugate*, or more accurately **A**-*conjugate*, if

$$S_i{}^T \mathbf{A} S_j = 0 , \qquad \text{for all } i \neq j , \quad (2.32)$$

where $\mathbf{A}$ is an $n \times n$ symmetric matrix.

A set of such directions possesses an extremely powerful property:[18] *If a quadratic function $Q$ is minimized sequentially, once along each direction of a set of $n$ linearly independent,* **A**-*conjugate directions, the global minimum of $Q$ will be located at or before the* $n$th *step regardless of the starting point.* Note that the order in which the directions are used is immaterial to this property.

There is an interesting geometrical interpretation of the property. Starting

[18] For a proof of this property, see Powell (1964) or Fletcher and Reeves (1964).

from the point $X_1$, if we minimize $Q$ along $S_1$, and then from the resulting point $X_2$ minimize along $S_2$ (which is $\mathbf{A}$-conjugate to $S_1$), then the resulting point is the minimum of $Q$ in the plane containing $S_1$ and $S_2$ and passing through $X_1$. In other words, it is the minimum in the plane

$$X = \alpha_1 S_1 + \alpha_2 S_2 + X_1 . \tag{2.33}$$

To see this, first note that in the plane

$$\begin{aligned} Q = Q(\alpha_1,\alpha_2) &= (\alpha_1 S_1 + \alpha_2 S_2 + X_1)^T \mathbf{A} (\alpha_1 S_1 + \alpha_2 S_2 + X_1) \\ &\quad + (\alpha_1 S_1 + \alpha_2 S_2 + X_1)^T B + c , \end{aligned} \tag{2.34}$$

but due to the conjugacy of $S_1$ and $S_2$, this reduces to

$$\begin{aligned} Q = {} & \alpha_1{}^2 S_1{}^T \mathbf{A} S_1 + \alpha_2{}^2 S_2{}^T \mathbf{A} S_2 + \alpha_1 S_1{}^T (2\mathbf{A} X_1 + B) \\ & + \alpha_2 S_2{}^T (2\mathbf{A} X_1 + B) + X_1{}^T B + c . \end{aligned} \tag{2.35}$$

In the plane, since the minimum is located where $\partial Q / \partial \alpha_1 = 0$, $\partial Q / \partial \alpha_2 = 0$, then

$$2\alpha_1 S_1{}^T \mathbf{A} S_1 + 2S_1{}^T \mathbf{A} X_1 + S_1{}^T B = 0 , \tag{2.36}$$

$$2\alpha_2 S_2{}^T \mathbf{A} S_2 + 2S_2{}^T \mathbf{A} X_1 + S_2{}^T B = 0 , \tag{2.37}$$

which implies

$$\alpha_1^* = -\frac{S_1{}^T (2\mathbf{A} X_1 + B)}{2 S_1{}^T \mathbf{A} S_1} , \tag{2.38}$$

$$\alpha_2^* = -\frac{S_2{}^T (2\mathbf{A} X_1 + B)}{2 S_2{}^T \mathbf{A} S_2} . \tag{2.39}$$

Note that $\alpha_1^*$ does not depend on $S_2$, and $\alpha_2^*$ does not depend on $S_1$. Thus if we minimized along $S_1$ from $X_1$ we would take a step $\alpha_2^*$ as calculated from the formula above. Further, if we then took a step from $X_2 = X_1 + a_1^* S_1$, we would have

$$\alpha_2^* = -\frac{S_2{}^T [2\mathbf{A}(X_1 + \alpha_1^* S_1) + B]}{2 S_2{}^T \mathbf{A} S_2} \equiv -\frac{S_2{}^T (2\mathbf{A} X_1 + B)}{2 S_2{}^T \mathbf{A} S_2} \tag{2.40}$$

as before. Thus the sequential stepping produces the same point, the minimum in the plane.

This result generalizes to the $j$th cycle in that the sequential minimization along the conjugate vectors $S_i$, $i = 1,2,\ldots,j$, produces the minimum point of the function $Q$ in the subspace spanned by the vectors $S_1,\ldots,S_j$. Thus at or before the $n$th step, the global minimum point of $Q$ will be reached.

Note that these results require each step to be a *minimizing* step in the given direction. This point is emphasized because it is the numerical difficulty of exactly computing the minimizing steps at each iteration that causes most of the practical problems with these methods.

The conjugacy relations do not define a unique set of directions, but any set of $n$ independent, mutually $\mathbf{A}$-conjugate directions will suffice. The various ways for generating such directions without knowing $\mathbf{A}$ (or $\mathbf{J}_M$ in the case of the general function) form the basis for different methods which are quadratically convergent. We now show that Powell's method generates conjugate directions.

Given two vectors $X_a$ and $X_b$ and a direction $S$. If $Y_a$ is a minimum of $Q$ from $X_a$ along $S$, and $Y_b$ is a minimum from $X_b$ along $S$, i.e., if

$$Y_a = X_a + \alpha_a^* S \,, \tag{2.41}$$

$$Y_b = X_b + \alpha_b^* S \,, \tag{2.42}$$

then $Y_a - Y_b$ and $S$ are $\mathbf{A}$-conjugate (see Fig. 2.23). This fact is easily demonstrated, starting with the definition of $\alpha^*$. By definition,

$$\frac{d}{d\alpha}\{Q(Y_a + \alpha S)\} = 0 \,, \qquad \text{at } \alpha = 0 \,, \tag{2.43}$$

$$\frac{d}{d\alpha}\{Q(Y_b + \alpha S)\} = 0 \,, \qquad \text{at } \alpha = 0 \,. \tag{2.44}$$

Therefore by substituting the above expressions into the equations of the quadratic, differentiating and then setting $\alpha = 0$, we obtain

$$S^T(2\mathbf{A}Y_a + B) = 0 \,, \tag{2.45}$$

$$S^T(2\mathbf{A}Y_b + B) = 0 \,. \tag{2.46}$$

Then subtracting Eq. (2.46) from Eq. (2.45), we find

$$2S^T\mathbf{A}(Y_a - Y_b) = 0 \,, \tag{2.47}$$

which demonstrates the conjugacy of $S$ and $(Y_a - Y_b)$.

Returning now to the flow diagram of Fig. 2.20, we see that in Block A

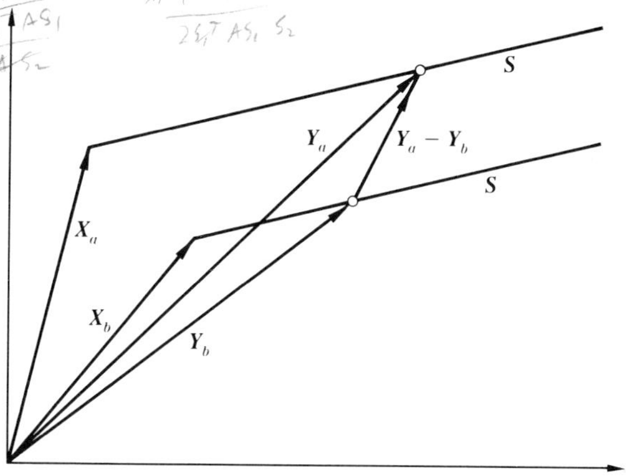


**Figure 2.23**

both $X$ and $Y$ are minima along the direction $S_n$, and therefore $S_{n+1}$ is conjugate to $S_n$. Thus after $n$ cycles, all the $S_q$ are mutually conjugate and a quadratic will theoretically be minimized in $n^2$ 1-dimensional minimizations.

As is so often the case in these matters, things are not so good as they first seem. To begin with, we do not usually minimize quadratics, and thus the number of iterations will ordinarily be greater than $n$. However, consider the least possible computational effort for $n^2$ minimized steps. Suppose it requires at least three function evaluations per step. (Table 2.3 lists $3n^2$ for several values of $n$ and an arbitrary selected unit computational time.) In practice, moreover, it develops that even with luck this can skyrocket to $n^3$ or more minimizations of 5 to 7 function evaluations each. This brings the estimated time for 50 variables to about 2 hr.

**Table 2.3. Ideal computation time for Powell's method**

| $n$ | $3n^2$ | Computation time at 0.01 sec/evaluation |
|---|---|---|
| 2 | 12 | 0.12 sec |
| 5 | 75 | 0.75 sec |
| 10 | 300 | 3.00 sec |
| 50 | 7500 | 1.25 min |
| 100 | 30000 | 5 min |

In addition to the possibility of requiring a large number of function evaluations, the version of Powell's method described above can simply come to a halt before the minimum is reached. Both this complete failure and the previously mentioned inefficiency are because the $S_j$ may become dependent or almost dependent. The original set of $S_j$ is, of course, independent, and in theory each of the succeeding directions that are generated should be linear combinations of *all* the preceding $S_j$, unless some $\alpha^* = 0$ during the cycle.

For example, consider the 3-dimensional problem in which the vectors $S_1$, $S_2$, and $S_3$ are the coordinate unit vectors. After one cycle of minimizations through the original directions starting from $X_1$,

$$X_4 = X_1 + \alpha_1^* S_1 + \alpha_2^* S_2 + \alpha_3^* S_3 , \tag{2.48}$$

and hence

$$S_4 = X_4 - X_1 = \alpha_1^* S_1 + \alpha_2^* S_2 + \alpha_3^* S_3 . \tag{2.49}$$

If $\alpha_i^* \neq 0$ for $i = 1,2,3$, then $S_4$ is independent of the two directions $S_2$ and $S_3$ that are retained, since $S_4$ clearly cannot be written as a linear combination of $S_2$ and $S_3$ alone. However, if $\alpha_1^*$ were very small or zero, then $S_1$ would be lost forever. As a result, if the vector from the starting point $X_1$ to the minimum

$X_M$ had any component of $S_1$, then the function could not be minimized by any of the succeeding directions.

The basic method has a tendency to choose nearly dependent directions in ill-conditioned problems to such an extent that, in these problems having more than 5 variables, it usually becomes hopeless. One simple remedy is to reset the directions to the original coordinate vectors periodically and/or whenever there is some indication that the directions are no longer productive. This technique is sometimes useful, but a procedure recommended by Powell, while somewhat more complicated, is also very effective. It consists of adding the following steps and logic to the basic iteration.

1. After minimizing in the directions $S_i$, find the integer $m$, $1 \leqslant m \leqslant n$, so that $[F(X_{m-1}) - F(X_m)] \equiv \Delta$ is a maximum.
2. Compute $f_3 \equiv F(2X - Y) \equiv F(X + S_{n+1})$ and define $f_1 \equiv F(Y), f_2 \equiv F(X)$.
3. If $f_3 \leqslant f_1$ and/or $(f_1 - 2f_2 + f_3)(f_1 - f_2 - \Delta)^2 \geqslant \Delta(f_1 - f_3)^2$, use the old set of directions for the next cycle of minimizations. Otherwise go on to step 4.
4. Minimize along $X - Y$ and replace $S_m$ by $X - Y$, placing the new $S_m$ last in the sequence of $S$-vectors.

Step 1 essentially determines which, if any, direction should be replaced, and steps 2 and 3 determine whether the new direction should be added.[19,20] Note the important maneuver that places the new direction last in the sequence, even though it replaces some $S_m$, $m \neq n$. This must be done to guarantee the **A**-conjugacy of the next pattern move with $S_n$ (see the fifth cycle of the illustration that follows).

In his original paper on the method, Powell applied it to the function

$$F_4 = \frac{1}{1 + (x - y)^2} + \sin\left(\frac{1}{2}\pi y_z\right) + \exp\left[-\left(\frac{x + z}{y} - 2\right)^2\right], \tag{2.50}$$

which has minima at

$$x = y = z = \sqrt{4n + 1}\,,\ n \text{ integral.} \tag{2.51}$$

His results for a particular run, starting from (0.0, 1.0, 2.0), are shown in Table 2.4. The particular solution to which the algorithm approximately converges is $x = y = z = 1$, $F_4 = 3$. (The particular code used to produce these results makes a complete preliminary sweep through the directions before beginning in earnest, instead of just minimizing along $S_n$.) The directions $S_4$

---

[19] See Powell (1964) for the reasoning behind these criteria.

[20] Zangwill (1967) has shown that if some $\alpha_j^* = 0$, then even with the above procedure the method may fail to produce independent directions. Other than correcting the deficiency, Zangwill's proposed alternative does not seem as effective computationally.

**Table 2.4.* Powell's method applied to $F_4$**

| Cycle | Direction | $x$ | $y$ | $z$ | $F_4$ |
|---|---|---|---|---|---|
| 0 | — | 0.0000 | 1.0000 | 2.0000 | 1.5000 |
| 1 | $x$ | 0.3674 | 1.0000 | 2.0000 | 1.5879 |
| 1 | $y$ | 0.3674 | 0.4799 | 2.0000 | 1.9857 |
| 1 | $z$ | 0.3674 | 0.4799 | 2.0827 | 1.9876 |
| 2 | $x$ | 0.4799 | 0.4799 | 2.0827 | 2.0000 |
| 2 | $y$ | 0.4799 | 0.4802 | 2.0827 | 2.0000 |
| 2 | $z$ | 0.4799 | 0.4802 | 2.0821 | 2.0000 |
| 2 | $S_4$ | 0.4801 | 0.4802 | 2.0821 | 2.0000 |
| 3 | $y$ | 0.4801 | 0.4803 | 2.0821 | 2.0000 |
| 3 | $z$ | 0.4801 | 0.4803 | 2.0815 | 2.0000 |
| 3 | $S_4$ | 0.4802 | 0.4803 | 2.0815 | 2.0000 |
| 3 | $S_5$ | 0.7449 | 0.7511 | 0.8648 | 2.8320 |
| 4 | $z$ | 0.7449 | 0.7511 | 0.9217 | 2.8387 |
| 4 | $S_4$ | 0.6401 | 0.7509 | 0.9222 | 2.8670 |
| 4 | $S_5$ | 0.6357 | 0.7463 | 0.9426 | 2.8683 |
| 4 | $S_6$ | 0.5505 | 0.7426 | 1.0033 | 2.8768 |
| 5 | $z$ | 0.5505 | 0.7426 | 1.0472 | 2.8813 |
| 5 | $S_5$ | 0.5581 | 0.7503 | 1.0125 | 2.8853 |
| 5 | $S_6$ | 0.5627 | 0.7505 | 1.0092 | 2.8853 |
| 5 | $S_7$ | 0.7995 | 0.9050 | 1.1236 | 2.9731 |
| 6 | $S_5$ | 0.8159 | 0.9218 | 1.0482 | 2.9870 |
| 6 | $S_6$ | 0.8656 | 0.9239 | 1.0127 | 2.9904 |
| 6 | $S_7$ | 0.9272 | 0.9641 | 1.0424 | 2.9968 |
| 6 | $S_8$ | 0.9272 | 0.9641 | 1.0424 | 2.9968 |

* Powell (1964).

and $S_5$ are inserted just as they would be in the basic method; however, $S_6$ replaces not the $z$ direction but $S_4$, and then $S_7$ replaces the $z$ direction.

Powell recommends a termination criterion for ordinary use such that when a cycle produces a change in all variables of less than one-tenth of the required accuracy, the process is stopped. A safer (i.e., less likely to stop prematurely) but much more time-consuming criterion also given by Powell is:

1. Apply the normal procedure until a cycle causes a change of less than one-tenth of the desired accuracy. Call the resultant point $A$.
2. Increase every variable by ten times the desired accuracy.
3. Apply the normal procedure until a cycle again causes a change of less than one-tenth of the desired accuracy. Call the resultant point $B$.
4. Find the minimum on the line through $A$ and $B$; call it $C$.

5. Assume ultimate convergence if the components of $(\boldsymbol{A}-\boldsymbol{C})$ and $(\boldsymbol{B}-\boldsymbol{C})$ are less than one-tenth of the desired accuracy in the corresponding variables. Otherwise go on to step 6.
6. Include the direction $(\boldsymbol{A}-\boldsymbol{C})$ in place of $\boldsymbol{S}_1$ (i.e., the $x_1$ direction), and restart the procedure from step 1.

It should be mentioned that one of the most confounding problems in minimization (indeed in most iterative procedures) is termination. The preceding is a relatively safe rule, but it is expensive (essentially the problem must be solved at least twice); in some problems, a more lax criterion may be appropriate and even other kinds of criteria may be reasonable. It is, however, difficult to set down general rules for termination with anything approaching confidence.

It may be that this is another point where the computer must touch base with the human engineer. Very often during a cursory study of the output of a computer run, it becomes clear to the engineer that it could have been terminated much sooner than it was or, conversely, that it is not yet finished in spite of having satisfied some criterion. The human ability to integrate information and perceive patterns transcends that of the most sophisticated computer program. The extent to which these human talents are used in the operation of a program depends on engineering and administrative judgment. There is on the one hand the desire to produce literally foolproof computer programs, and on the other hand there is a recognition of the impossibility of replacing human judgment in difficult situations. Between these two a balance must be struck. Human intervention in a numerical process should not become a substitute for attempts to understand the mathematics involved in a method, nor should a complete lack of belief in human judgment lead to acceptance of meaningless answers or wasted computer time.

## 2.7 GRADIENT METHODS: STEEPEST DESCENT

The previous methods of minimization have utilized only a sampling of the values of the function itself to determine the direction and extent of the individual steps of the iteration. In this and succeeding sections, we discuss a number of methods based, in a sense, on a larger amount of local information about the function.

Central to these methods is the concept of the *gradient* of the function being minimized. This vector, denoted $\nabla F$, lies in the direction of greatest rate of change of the function and has that rate of change as its magnitude. We first examine the pertinent properties of this vector and then discuss some of the methods that are based on it.

The gradient of the function $F(X)$ is defined as

$$\nabla F \equiv \boldsymbol{G} \equiv \left(\frac{\partial F}{\partial x_1}, \frac{\partial F}{\partial x_2}, \ldots, \frac{\partial F}{\partial x_n}\right). \tag{2.52}$$

Equation (2.52) actually defines a vector field in the design space, and we denote the gradient vector associated with a particular point $X_q$ as $\nabla F_q$ or $G_q$.

Recalling that the differential of any function $F$ is

$$dF = \frac{\partial F}{\partial x_1}\, dx_1 + \frac{\partial F}{\partial x_2}\, dx_2 + \cdots + \frac{\partial F}{\partial x_n}\, dx_n\,, \tag{2.53}$$

we note that it can be written as

$$dF = \nabla F^T dr\,, \tag{2.54}$$

where

$$dr \equiv (dx_1, dx_2, \ldots, dx_n)\,. \tag{2.55}$$

If the vector $dr$ is defined by

$$dr = \hat{e}\, d\beta\,, \tag{2.56}$$

where $\hat{e}$ in any unit vector and $d\beta$ is an infinitesimal scalar, then Eq. (2.54) may be rewritten as

$$\frac{dF}{d\beta} = G^T \hat{e}\,. \tag{2.57}$$

Any direction $\hat{e}$ such that $G^T\hat{e} < 0$ is called a *direction of descent,* since $F$ is decreasing locally in the positive $\hat{e}$ direction.

Some other directions $\hat{e}$ are of special interest. First suppose $\hat{e}$ has the same direction as $G$:[21]

$$\hat{e} = G/|G|\,. \tag{2.58}$$

Then

$$dF/d\beta = G^T G/|G| = |G|\,, \tag{2.59}$$

which merely means that the rate of change of the function in the direction of the gradient is $|G|$.

That this direction is the one of maximum rate of change is seen from the following. If we denote the components of $\nabla F$ as $g_i$ and those of $\hat{e}$ as $e_i$, we can write Eq. (2.57) as

$$dF/d\beta = \sum_{i=1}^{n} g_i e_i\,. \tag{2.60}$$

The direction of maximum rate of change can be determined from the condition

$$\frac{\partial}{\partial e_i}\left[\frac{dF}{d\beta}\right] = 0\,, \qquad i = 1, \ldots, n\,,$$

[21] The notation $|G|$ means

$$|G| = \left[\sum_i^n g_i^2\right]^{1/2} = \left[G^T G\right]^{1/2},$$

which is the *Euclidian norm,* or length of the vector. Note that according to Eq. (2.58), $|\hat{e}| = 1$.

except that the $e_i$ are not independent. That is, since we seek a *unit vector*, the $e_i$ must satisfy $\Sigma_{i=1}^{n} e_i^2 = 1$. The problem can be handled by the method of Lagrange multipliers[22] by introducing a new variable $\lambda$ and noting that $(dF/d\beta)_{\max}$ occurs for the direction components $e_i$ and $\lambda$ which satisfy

$$\frac{\partial}{\partial e_i}\left[\frac{dF}{d\beta} + \lambda\left(1 - \sum_{j=1}^{n} e_j^2\right)\right] = 0, \qquad i = 1,2,\ldots,n \tag{2.61a}$$

and

$$\sum_{j=1}^{n} e_j^2 = 1\,. \tag{2.61b}$$

This yields

$$g_i - 2\lambda e_i = 0, \qquad i = 1,2,\ldots,n \tag{2.62a}$$

and

$$\sum_{j=1}^{n} e_j^2 = 1\,. \tag{2.62b}$$

Or, rearranging, we have

$$e_i = g_i/2\lambda \tag{2.63a}$$

and

$$2\lambda = \left(\sum_{j=1}^{n} g_j^2\right)^{1/2} \equiv |\boldsymbol{G}|\,. \tag{2.63b}$$

Equations (2.63) are equivalent to (2.58).

Another interesting set of directions is that for which $dF/d\beta = 0$. Such directions are those in which $F$ is constant for infinitesimal "moves" $d\beta$. These directions satisfy

$$dF/d\beta = \boldsymbol{G}^T\hat{e} = 0\,, \tag{2.64}$$

which is merely a statement of the orthogonality (perpendicularity) of $\boldsymbol{\nabla} F$ and $\hat{e}$. Equation (2.64) thus defines the tangent hyperplane to the surface $F(\boldsymbol{X}) = $ const at any point $\boldsymbol{X}$.

Another result is an expression for the rate of change of a function with respect to a parameter along some direction $\boldsymbol{S}$ away from a point $\boldsymbol{X}_q$. Consider $F$ along $\boldsymbol{S}$ according to $\boldsymbol{X} = \boldsymbol{X}_q + \alpha\boldsymbol{S}$:

$$F(\alpha) = F(\boldsymbol{X}_q + \alpha\boldsymbol{S})\,, \tag{2.65}$$

where $\alpha$ is a variable as in the previously discussed methods of minimization. By the chain rule,

$$\frac{dF}{d\alpha} = \sum_{i=1}^{n} \frac{\partial F}{\partial x_i}\frac{dx_i}{d\alpha}\,, \tag{2.66}$$

but

$$\frac{dx_i}{d\alpha} = \frac{d(x_{qi} + \alpha s_i)}{d\alpha} = s_i\,. \tag{2.67}$$

[22] See Section 4.1 for a more thorough discussion of Lagrange multipliers.

Therefore

$$\frac{dF}{d\alpha} = \sum_{i=1}^{n} \frac{\partial F}{\partial x_i} s_i = \nabla F^T S \equiv G^T S\,. \tag{2.68}$$

Note that if $\alpha = \alpha^*$ (the $\alpha$ which minimizes $F$ in the direction $S$), then, at the point $X = X_q + \alpha^* S_q$,

$$\left(\frac{dF}{d\alpha}\right)_{\alpha=\alpha^*} = G^T S = 0\,, \tag{2.69}$$

and thus $S$ is in the hyperplane tangent to the function contours at $X = X_q + \alpha^* S$. Stated another way, the gradient of the function taken at the minimum point along $S$ is perpendicular to $S$ itself.

A quantity useful as a numerical test for the minimum along a line is

$$c = \frac{G^T S}{|G|\ |S|}\,. \tag{2.70}$$

Clearly $-1 \leqslant c \leqslant 1$, and it can be visualized as the cosine of the angle between $G$ and $S$. At $\alpha^*$, $c = 0$, and at points along $S$, "near" $\alpha^*$, one would expect $c \ll 1$.

Summarizing these results we arrive at the following properties:

1. The gradient is a vector that points in the direction of steepest ascent, and therefore $-\nabla F$ is the direction of *steepest descent*.
2. $|G| \equiv \left[\sum_{i=1}^{n} g_i^2\right]^{1/2}$ is the rate of decrease of the function in the direction $S = -\nabla F$.
3. Any vector $S$ which satisfies $\nabla F_q^T S = 0$ lies in the tangent hyperplane of $F$ at $X_q$.
4. The derivative $dF/d\alpha$ at any point given by $\bar{\alpha}$ along the line $X_q + \alpha S$ is
$$dF/d\alpha = \nabla F(X_q + \bar{\alpha} S)^T S \equiv G_{\bar{\alpha}}^T S. \tag{2.71}$$
5. The quantity $c$, defined by Eq. (2.70), lies between plus and minus 1 and is zero at $\alpha^*$.

Property 1 was recognized by Cauchy[23] in 1847 as making the negative of the gradient vector a good direction for minimization. Given a trial minimum point of $F$, namely $X_q$, the best direction to move to reduce the function value would seem to be the one in which the function decreases most rapidly, i.e., the step

$$X_{q+1} = X_q + \alpha^*(-G_q). \tag{2.72}$$

It develops, surprisingly, that often there *are* better directions, but the method

[23]Cauchy (1847).

defined by Eq. (2.72), called the *method of steepest descents*, can be useful in some problems.

The method requires hardly more elaboration than Eq. (2.72). It is of the form

$$X_{q+1} = X_q + \alpha^* S_q, \tag{2.73}$$

where $S_q = -\nabla F_q$. The flow diagram of Fig. 2.24 defines the algorithm when combined with the following prescription for block A:

$$\boxed{S_q \leftarrow -\nabla F_q} \quad \text{A}$$

The reason for expressing the contents of Block A in this way is that the rest of the methods discussed in this chapter also use Fig. 2.24, but with different computations in Block A. Similarly Block B contains some version of minimizing steps (e.g., Fig. 2.14).

Two-dimensional illustrations of the method of steepest descents are unsatisfactory in view of property 5. If steepest descent is started from point 2 of Fig. 2.16, it would proceed along exactly the same path as the univariate

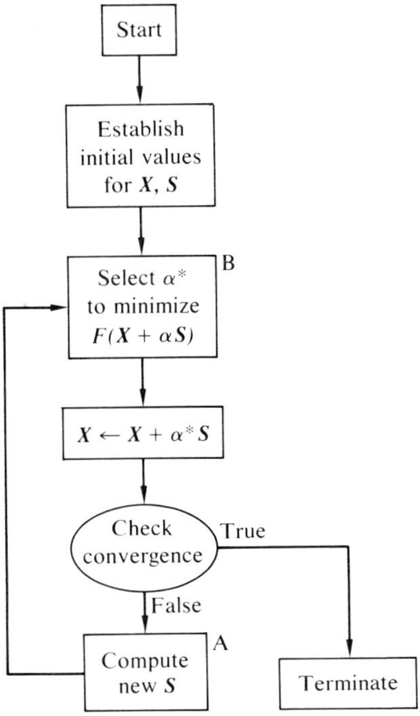


**Figure 2.24**

method. While it is true that in 2 dimensions the path is made up of parallel and perpendicular segments, this does not generalize to higher dimensions, and the method has different characteristics than the univariate method.

Steepest descents has been used with moderate success on a wide variety of problems. Through the middle 1950s, it was one of the most popular methods. It develops, however, that even in some problems of low dimensionality the process can be hopelessly slow. This is because successive moves are perpendicular and the method gradually settles into a steady $n$-dimensional zigzag for functions with significant eccentricity. If the function contours are mildly distorted hyperspheres, the method will work well for 2 dimensions as illustrated in Fig. 2.25.

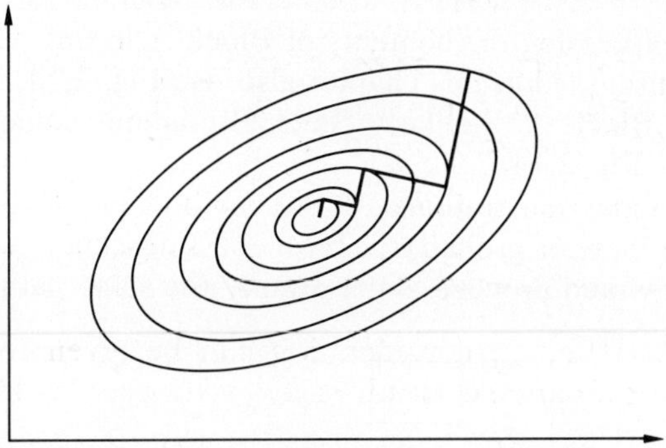

**Figure 2.25**

Numerous attempts have been made over the years[24] to strengthen the method for eccentric functions, but in the light of more recent developments, some of which are described in Sections 2.9 through 2.11, these modifications have little value. Pattern moves have been used in various ways with limited success; in other cases, moves which were longer or shorter than $\alpha^*$ have been used in order to break the zigzag pattern. One interesting idea stems from the observation that if infinitesimal "moves" $d\alpha$ are taken, the path to the optimum is the orthogonal trajectory passing through the starting point. Thought of in this way, the minimization path is the solution to the system of differential equations

$$dx_i/d\alpha = -\,\partial F/\partial x_i, \qquad i = 1,2,\ldots,n, \tag{2.74}$$

subject to the "initial conditions" at $\alpha = 0$:

$$x_i = x_{1i}, \qquad i = 1, 2, \ldots, n. \tag{2.75}$$

Numerical integration of these by Euler's method is identical with steepest descents, using small $\alpha$'s instead of $\alpha^*$'s, and is not very attractive (see Exer-

[24]For example, see Crocket and Chernoff (1955) for some interesting ideas.

cise 2.12). However, work has been done with the integration of Eqs. (2.74) on the analog computer. Some workers, noting that the equations are analogous to the equation of motion of a massless particle in a viscous medium subject to a force field of $-\nabla F$ (in $n$-dimensional space) have extended the analogy by giving the particle mass. These ideas, while interesting, are not generally useful, due to the difficulty of analog methods for complicated functions or large numbers of variables. Furthermore, the inherent inaccuracy and drift of analog computers may spoil the answers, since we are not really interested in the trajectory itself but in the critical point $\nabla F = \mathbf{0}$.

We have assumed thus far that the partial derivatives $\partial F/\partial x_i$ are readily available for use in a gradient minimization method. There are three circumstances, however, in which we must consider the situation further:

1. Expressions for $\partial F/\partial x_i$ can be derived but are extremely time-consuming to compute (for example, in excess of twice the time it takes to compute $F$ itself for each component $\partial F/\partial x_i$.
2. $\nabla F$ exists everywhere, but expressions for $\partial F/\partial x_i$ are impractical or impossible to derive.
3. $\nabla F$ is not defined everywhere (for example $F_2$ of Eq. 2.5).

In circumstances 1 and 2, consideration can be given to finite difference approximations of the partial derivatives. The difference formula

$$\frac{\partial F}{\partial x_i} \simeq \frac{F(X_q + \epsilon_i \hat{e}_i) - F(X_q)}{\epsilon_i}, \tag{2.76}$$

where $\hat{e}_i = (0,0,\ldots,0,1,0,\ldots,0)$ with the 1 in the $i$th position, and $\epsilon_i$ is a small scalar, requires one function evaluation per variable. A more accurate formula, which requires two function evaluations, is

$$\frac{\partial F}{\partial x_i} \simeq \frac{F(X_q + \epsilon_i \hat{e}_i) - F(X_q - \epsilon_i \hat{e}_i)}{2\epsilon_i}. \tag{2.77}$$

In Eq. (2.76) there are $n$ function evaluations for $\nabla F$, and in Eq. (2.77) there are $2n$ evaluations. The choice between these formulas depends partly on the ease with which a suitable value of $\epsilon_i$ can be chosen. If $\epsilon_i$ is taken too small, the result will be mostly roundoff noise; if $\epsilon_i$ is too large, the truncation error will be high. While it is not rigorously true, it usually occurs that for a given $\epsilon_i$, Eq. (2.77) is more accurate than (2.76). In fact, if $F$ is a quadratic, Eq. (2.77) is exact (see Exercise 2.10). For the method of steepest descent, the approximate gradient $\widetilde{G}$ need not be extremely accurate, since if

$$\widetilde{G}^T \nabla F > 0, \tag{2.78}$$

then $-\widetilde{G}$ is also a direction of descent, although not the steepest descent direction. The main question is: Should a gradient method be used if $\nabla F$ must be approximated by finite difference? For engineering applications, the answer can be complicated by a number of factors which will be discussed in Section 2.12 and in Chapter 5. As a general rule, if $2n$ complete function evaluations are required for an approximation to $\nabla F$, and $F$ is reasonably behaved, then a non-gradient method such as Powell's is probably preferable.

The third situation ($\nabla F$ not defined) is more difficult. The use of finite difference is to be discouraged, as are schemes which attempt to "average" two or more gradients at a point of discontinuity in the derivative (see Fig. 2.9). While such ideas occasionally work, they usually lead to a complete breakdown of the process. Finite difference taken at a point along a discontinuity will be meaningless, and averaging will not reliably produce a direction of descent. Univariate methods are applicable in these cases but, of course, even Powell's method will not converge quadratically. A method of handling this situation by constrained minimization was mentioned earlier (see footnote 6 in this chapter).

## 2.8 MINIMIZING STEPS USING SLOPE INFORMATION

If the gradient of the function being minimized is easily obtained, it is reasonable to consider a version of a minimizing step algorithm based on derivatives of the function. Two approaches will be described: one that uses 2-point cubic interpolation and another that is a more direct numerical attack on finding the root of $\alpha^*$ of $dF(\mathbf{X}+\alpha\mathbf{S})/d\alpha \equiv dF(\alpha)/d\alpha = 0$.

### Cubic Interpolation

As in Section 2.4, the first method hinges on approximating $F(\mathbf{X}+\alpha\mathbf{S}) \equiv F(\alpha)$ by a function $H(\alpha)$. However, rather than a quadratic, $H$ is taken to be the cubic:

$$H(\alpha) = a + b\alpha + c\alpha^2 + d\alpha^3. \tag{2.79}$$

We assume that values of $F(A)$, $(dF/d\alpha)_A$, $F(B)$, and $(dF/d\alpha)_B$ are available,[25] and thus the parameters of $H$ can be determined from the solution of

$$\begin{aligned} a + bA + cA^2 + dA^3 &= f_A \equiv F(A), \\ a + bB + cB^2 + dB^3 &= f_B \equiv F(B), \\ b + 2cA + 3dA^2 &= f'_A \equiv (dF/d\alpha)_A, \\ b + 2cB + 3dB^2 &= f'_B \equiv (dF/d\alpha)_B. \end{aligned} \tag{2.80}$$

The minimum would be one of the *two* points where

$$dH/d\alpha \equiv H' = 0 \tag{2.81}$$

or where

$$b + 2c\alpha + 3d\alpha^2 = 0, \tag{2.82}$$

[25] Recall from Eq. (2.68) that $dF/d\alpha = \nabla F^T \mathbf{S}$.

the roots of which are

$$\alpha^* = \frac{-2c \pm (4c^2 - 12db)^{1/2}}{6d} = \frac{-c \pm (c^2 - 3db)^{1/2}}{3d}. \tag{2.83}$$

The general solution, however, is rather complicated to obtain directly and the following trick is used: Assume $A = 0$ and $B > 0$, which lead to the equations

$$\begin{aligned} a &= f_A, \\ b &= f'_A, \\ cB^2 + dB^3 &= f_B - f_A - Bf'_A, \\ 2cB + 3dB^2 &= f'_B - f'_A. \end{aligned} \tag{2.84}$$

From these we obtain

$$c = -\frac{1}{B}\left[\frac{3(f_A - f_B)}{B} + 2f'_A + f'_B\right] \tag{2.85}$$

and

$$d = \frac{1}{B^2}\left[\frac{2(f_A - f_B)}{B} + f'_A + f'_B\right]. \tag{2.86}$$

Most references[26] define a convenient quantity at this stage:

$$\bar{Z} \equiv \frac{3(f_A - f_B)}{B} + f'_A + f'_B; \tag{2.87}$$

and thus

$$c = -\frac{1}{B}[\bar{Z} + f'_A], \tag{2.88}$$

$$d = \frac{1}{3B^2}[2\bar{Z} + f'_A + f'_B]. \tag{2.89}$$

With these definitions, the minimum, denoted $\bar{\alpha}^*$ for the special case $A = 0$, is located at

$$\bar{\alpha}^* = \frac{\dfrac{1}{B}[\bar{Z} + f'_A] \pm \dfrac{1}{B}[(\bar{Z} + f'_A)^2 - (2\bar{Z} + f'_A + f'_B)f'_A]^{1/2}}{\dfrac{1}{B^2}[2\bar{Z} + f'_A + f'_B]}. \tag{2.90}$$

This reduces to

$$\bar{\alpha}^* = B\,\frac{f'_A + \bar{Z} \pm \bar{Q}}{f'_A + f'_B + 2\bar{Z}}, \tag{2.91}$$

where

$$\bar{Q} \equiv [\bar{Z}^2 - f'_A f'_B]^{1/2}. \tag{2.92}$$

The sign alternative in Eq. (2.91) reflects the two possibilities for the vanishing of $H'(\alpha)$: at a maximum of $H(\alpha)$ and at a minimum. Furthermore, if $\bar{Z}^2 < f'_A f'_B$,

[26]See Davidon (1959).

then $\bar{Q}$ is undefined, indicating that the cubic has no extreme. These uncertainties can be avoided if the conditions that $f'_A < 0$ and $f'_B > 0$ are ensured. The first inequality is automatic; since $\mathbf{S}$ is a direction of descent, $f'_A$ will be negative by definition. Assuming that there is a minimum along $\mathbf{S}$, $f'_B$ can be made positive if $B$ is large enough. With these assumptions and the fact that the requirement for the minimum is

$$\frac{d^2H}{d\alpha^2} > 0, \tag{2.93}$$

$$2c + 6d\bar{\alpha}^* > 0, \tag{2.94}$$

we can establish the formula for $\bar{\alpha}^*$. Equations (2.83) and (2.94) yield

$$2c + 6d\left[\frac{-c \pm (c^2 - 3db)^{1/2}}{3d}\right] > 0, \tag{2.95}$$

or

$$\pm (c^2 - 3db)^{1/2} > 0, \tag{2.96}$$

which clearly indicates that the plus sign is required. Moreover, since $f'_A < 0$ and $f'_B > 0$, $f'_A f'_B < 0$ and hence $\bar{Z}^2 > f'_A f'_B$ (or $c^2 > 3db$), and the square root is defined.

The result can be generalized to the case where $A \neq 0$ by simply making a translation of the formula for $\bar{\alpha}^*$:

$$\alpha^* = A + \frac{f'_A + Z + Q}{f'_A + f'_B + 2Z}(B - A), \tag{2.97}$$

where now

$$Z = \frac{3(f_A - f_B)}{B - A} + f'_A + f'_B, \tag{2.98a}$$

$$Q = [Z^2 - f'_A f'_B]^{1/2}. \tag{2.98b}$$

Note that the convention adopted here is that $B$ in Eqs. (2.97) and (2.99) is still measured from the origin, $\alpha = 0$. Equation (2.97) can be rewritten as

$$\alpha^* = B - \frac{f'_B + Q - Z}{f'_B - f'_A + 2Q}(B - A), \tag{2.99}$$

which is said to be better from the roundoff error standpoint and is the form given in most references.[27] The conditions $f'_A < 0$ and $f'_B > 0$ ensure that the estimated minimum point $\alpha^*$ will lie between $A$ and $B$.

The flow diagram shown in Fig. 2.26 is the logic for a basic algorithm using cubic interpolation. The two things left undetermined in this flow diagram, $t_0$ and the contents of block A, are related and will be discussed together. The choice of $t_0$ is crucial to efficiency, since each traverse of the loop

[27] Davidon (1959) or Fletcher and Powell (1963).

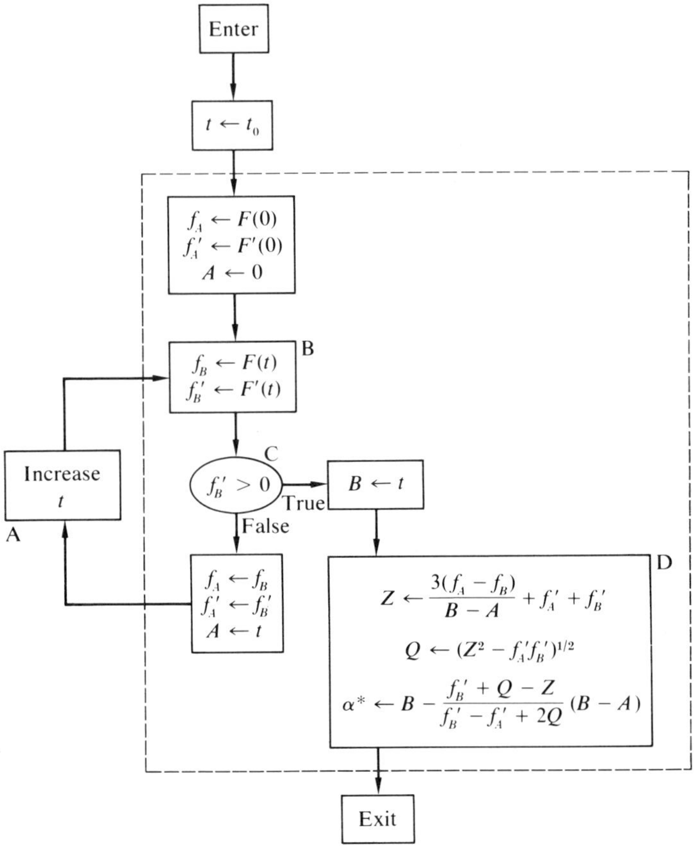


**Figure 2.26**

containing block A adds significantly to the labor involved in making the step. Indeed, in most problems the major effort of making an iteration is that expended in block B, and ideally it should be done only once. The conflict is this: if $t_0$ is chosen comfortably large so that $f'_B$ is certain to be positive in the first pass through test C, the interpolation may take place over so large an interval that it produces a poor approximation (see Fig. 2.27). On the other hand, if $t_0$ is too small, numerous increases in $t$ will be necessary before test C is satisfied.

A variety of techniques has been used to attempt to establish a proper range for $t_0$. Perhaps the most widely used *a priori* method is to assume initially that $F(\alpha)$ can be approximated by a quadratic and then use $F(0)$, $F'(0)$, and a guess at the minimum value of the function along $\boldsymbol{S}$ (designated $\widetilde{F}$) as the data for interpolation. Thus

$$F(\alpha) \simeq \bar{H}(\alpha) = \bar{a} + \bar{b}\alpha + \bar{c}\alpha^2 \tag{2.100}$$

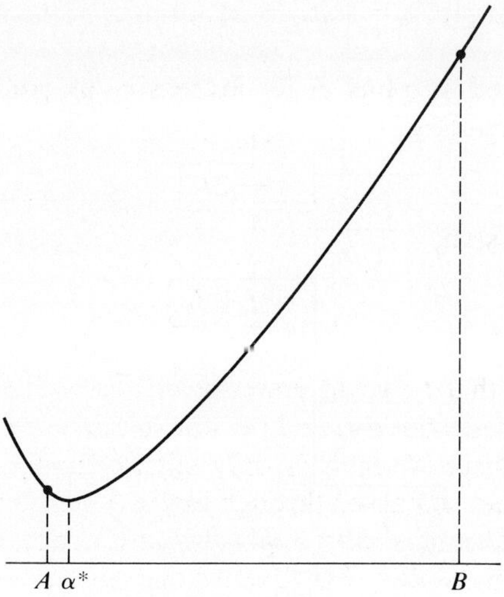


**Figure 2.27**

and immediately

$$\bar{a} = F(0) \equiv f_0 , \tag{2.101}$$

$$\bar{b} = F'(0) \equiv f'_0 . \tag{2.102}$$

For the minimum,

$$t_0 = -\frac{\bar{b}}{2\bar{c}}, \tag{2.103}$$

and hence

$$\bar{a} + \bar{b}\left(-\frac{\bar{b}}{2\bar{c}}\right) + \bar{c}\left(-\frac{\bar{b}}{2\bar{c}}\right)^2 \simeq \tilde{f}. \tag{2.104}$$

From this equation,

$$\bar{c} = \frac{\bar{b}^2}{4(\bar{a} - \tilde{f})} \tag{2.105}$$

and thus

$$t_0 = -\frac{2(f_0 - \tilde{f})}{f'_0}. \tag{2.106}$$

Of course, this still leaves $\tilde{f}$ to be determined, and strictly speaking nothing has been accomplished except that perhaps a working scale is now inherent in Eq. (2.106). In practice, however, a lower bound on $F$ may be known or can be estimated, and the use of this for $\tilde{f}$ will generally result in overestimating $t_0$, but with a certain amount of reasonableness. Another approach to picking $\tilde{f}$ is to estimate the expected reduction (or percentage reduction) in $F$ by using the results of successive iterations.

A different technique for selecting $t_0$ is to base an estimate on previous values of $\alpha^*$; for example, $t_0 = (\alpha^*_{q-1} + \alpha^*_{q-2} + \alpha^*_{q-3})/3$ is an average of the last three values.

The rationale used in block A for increasing an undersize $t_0$ can be anything from a simple doubling:

$$\boxed{t \leftarrow 2t}$$

to an additive progression:

$$\boxed{t \leftarrow t + t_0}$$

The conflict here is that $t$ should increase fast enough to accommodate efficiently a badly underestimated $t_0$ and yet not so fast as to cause the interval to grow unreasonably large when $t_0$ is only slightly undersize. One possibility is to record the number of passes through block A which were required on the previous iteration and immediatly apply this entire increase on the first cycle through A. Another possibility is to record the number of passes and use this to correct the $t_0$ for the next cycle. This is shown in Fig. 2.28 for the doubling

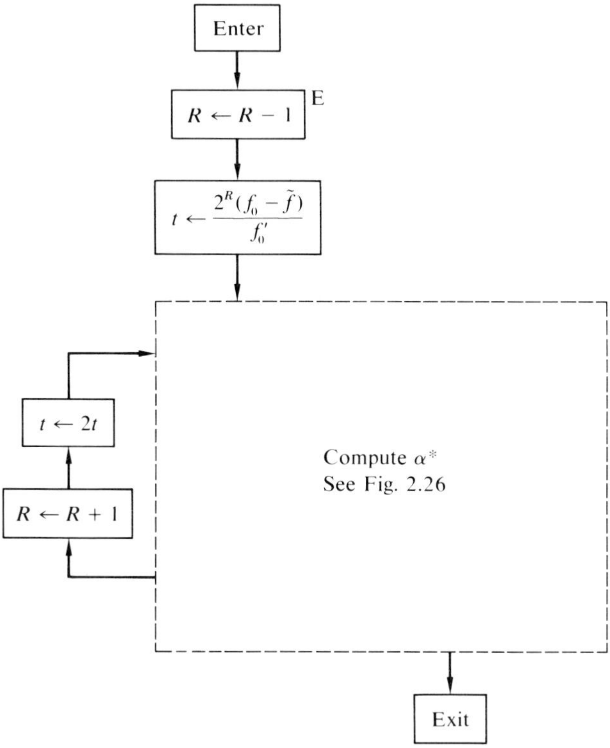


**Figure 2.28**

case. The integer $R$ is carried over from one step to the next, and block E allows the estimate to shrink gradually, should that be advantageous.

The possibilities are endless, and what is efficient in one problem or one class of problems may be inappropriate in another. It should be emphasized that in spite of the difficulties, great care should be taken in this aspect of the minimization routine since much time-consuming computation is generated here.

Once the appropriate conditions are fulfilled and an $\alpha^*$ is calculated, the "goodness of fit" can be checked by computing $f^* \equiv F(X + \alpha^* S)$ and then (see Eq. 2.70):

$$c = \frac{S^T G_*}{|S|\,|G_*|}, \tag{2.107}$$

where $G_* \equiv \nabla F(X + \alpha^* S)$. If $f^*$ is less than both $f_A$ and $f_B$, then at least $X_*$ is a candidate for a minimum point. The test $|c| < \epsilon$ may then be used as the final criterion for acceptance of $\alpha^*$. Values of $\epsilon$ from $10^{-2}$ down to $10^{-m}$, where $m$ is the number of working digits in the computer, have been used. However, these lower values can be very difficult to satisfy, especially if there are many variables in the problem. The stringency of this orthogonality requirement really should bear a relationship to the overall method in which the minimizing step routine is embedded, and even at this level it cannot be stated with certainty what the best strategy is.

If the test for a minimum fails, then block D of Fig. 2.26 may be re-entered and a new interpolation attempted. Before entering, it is merely necessary to test the sign of $S^T G_*$. If it is positive, then set

$$\boxed{\begin{aligned} B &\leftarrow \alpha^*, \\ f_B &\leftarrow f^*, \\ f'_B &\leftarrow S^T G_*. \end{aligned}} \tag{2.108}$$

Otherwise set

$$\boxed{\begin{aligned} A &\leftarrow \alpha^*, \\ f_A &\leftarrow f^*, \\ f'_A &\leftarrow S^T G_*. \end{aligned}} \tag{2.109}$$

Clearly, since the formula for $\alpha^*$ is arranged so that $A \leqslant \alpha^* \leqslant B$, each refit will narrow the gap $B$-$A$ (the size of which should also be tested as a precaution against pathological functions or overly zealous criteria for the minimum) and in principle we can locate the minimum to within the desired accuracy by successive refits.

### The Direct Root Method

Sometimes with ill-conditioned functions the computed quantities $\partial F/\partial x_i$ are not sufficiently in agreement with the numerically computed function $F$ for the cubic interpolation to produce good results. This difficulty manifests itself in actual computational work by requiring numerous iterations of the cubic interpolation, producing small corrections, and all the while remaining close to the solution before a convergence criterion $dF/d\alpha \simeq 0$ can be satisfied. In such situations it seems natural[28] to try to satisfy the convergence criterion directly by seeking that $\alpha^*$ which solves $dF(\alpha)/d\alpha = 0$.

The simplest root-finding method that is applicable is the *regula falsi* or "false position" technique. Suppose we have the slope of $F$ in the direction $S$ at two points $A$ and $B$ and we designate them $f'_A$ and $f'_B$ as before. Further suppose that $f'_A < 0$ and $f'_B > 0$. If we surmise that $dF/d\alpha$ will vary approximately linearly between $A$ and $B$, then we can interpolate it with the formula

$$dF(\alpha)/d\alpha \simeq a + b\alpha\,, \tag{2.110}$$

$$f'_A = a + bA\,, \tag{2.111}$$

$$f'_B = a + bB\,, \tag{2.112}$$

from which

$$a = \frac{f'_B A - f'_A B}{A - B}\,, \tag{2.113}$$

$$b = \frac{f'_A - f'_B}{A - B}\,. \tag{2.114}$$

Finally from $dF(\alpha^*)/d\alpha = 0$ we get

$$\tilde{\alpha}^* = -\frac{a}{b} = \frac{f'_A B - f'_B A}{f'_A - f'_B}\,. \tag{2.115}$$

The geometric interpretation of this formula is indicated in Fig. 2.29. It is significant that because this formula assumes $dF/d\alpha$ to be linear, it implies that $F$ is approximated by a quadratic. This means that for a true quadratic, the result of the first iteration will theoretically produce the exact $\alpha^*$. When the method is applied to actual highly eccentric quadratics, this formula often produces more accurate results than the cubic formula.[29]

It should be noted that Eq. (2.115) does not actually depend on $f'_A$ and $f'_B$ having different signs, but it is recommended that this condition be sought as a starting state for the process. The standard iteration can then be:

1. Given $A$, $B$, and the corresponding $f'_A$ and $f'_B$ of different signs, compute $\tilde{\alpha}^*$ as in Eq. (2.115).

---

[28] See Stanton (1968).

[29] *Ibid.*

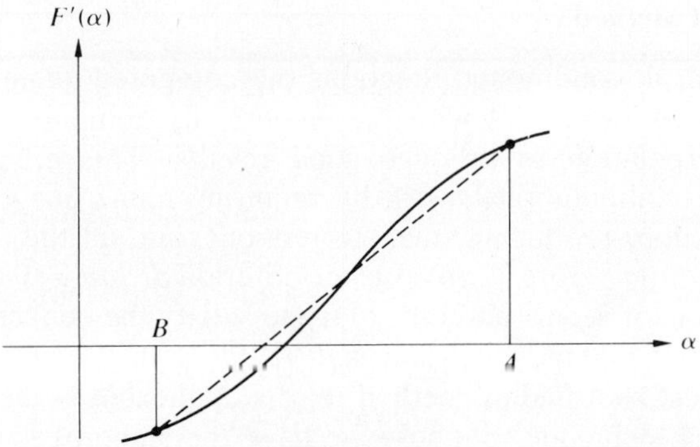


**Figure 2.29**

2. Compute $dF(\tilde{\alpha}^*)/d\alpha$ and compare with the convergence criterion. If the criterion is satisfied, terminate; otherwise go on to step 3.

3. If $dF(\tilde{\alpha}^*)/d\alpha$ agrees in sign with $f'_A$, replace $A$ by $\tilde{\alpha}^*$ and $f'_A$ by $dF(\tilde{\alpha}^*)/d\alpha$; otherwise replace $B$ by $\tilde{\alpha}^*$ and $f'_B$ by $dF(\tilde{\alpha}^*)/d\alpha$, and then repeat step 1.

Note that the third step is the same as the prescription given by Eqs. (2.108) and (2.109).

An important feature of this algorithm is that the interval $B$-$A$ is always decreasing and convergence is usually quite rapid. Occasionally, however, the situation depicted in Fig. 2.30 will arise. Here point $B$ will only slowly approach the root $\alpha^*$ after many iterations, and point $A$ will remain unchanged. A technique for avoiding this consists simply of alternating a *bisection iteration* with the *regula falsi* iteration; that is, compute $\tilde{\alpha}^*$ according to Eq. (2.115) and, if the result does not produce the root sufficiently closely, make the exchange indicated by step 3. Then compute a new $\tilde{\alpha}^*$ from

$$\tilde{\alpha}^* = \frac{A+B}{2}, \tag{2.116}$$

which simply produces the point midway between $A$ and $B$. If this does not produce the root, make the substitution indicated by step 3, repeat Eq. (2.115), and so on. This process gives very effective relief from the problem without undue algorithm complication.

Naturally, it is possible to use the quantity $c$ defined by Eq. (2.70) in place of $dF/d\alpha$ in these iterations. However, $dF/d\alpha$ appears the better choice because, among other things, $c$ is not linear even when $dF/d\alpha$ is.

The preceding discussion regarding $t_0$ and the convergence criterion applies equally to the direct root method.

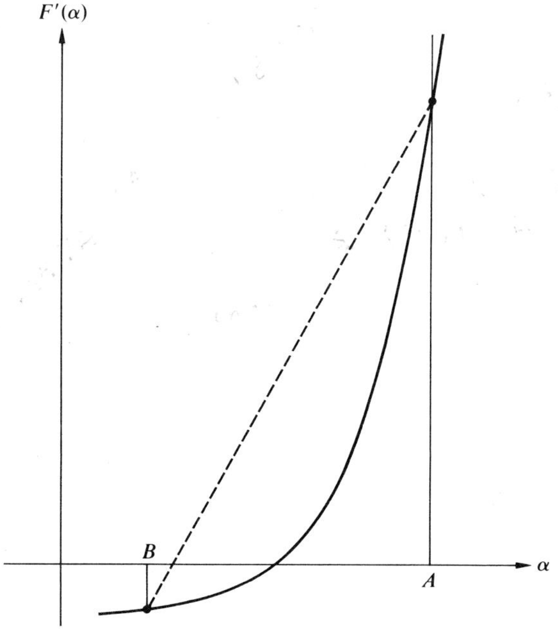


**Figure 2.30**

## 2.9 FLETCHER AND REEVES METHOD: CONJUGATE GRADIENTS

The convergence difficulties of the steepest descent (gradient) method can be greatly reduced by a very simple modification which converts it to the *conjugate gradient* method.[30] This consists of replacing block A of Fig. 2.24 by

$$\beta \leftarrow \frac{|\nabla F_{\text{new}}|^2}{|\nabla F_{\text{old}}|^2}$$

$$S \leftarrow -\nabla F_{\text{new}} + \beta S_{\text{old}}$$

A

Writing the entire algorithm out, we have

$$X_0 = \text{arbitrary}\,, \qquad (2.117\text{a})$$

$$G_0 = \nabla F(X_0)\,, \qquad (2.117\text{b})$$

$$S_0 = -G_0\,, \qquad (2.117\text{c})$$

$$X_{i+1} = X_i + \alpha_i^* S_i\,, \qquad (2.117\text{d})$$

[30] Fletcher and Reeves (1964).

$$G_{i+1} = \nabla F(X_{i+1}) , \tag{2.117e}$$

$$\beta_i = |G_{i+1}|^2/|G_i|^2 , \tag{2.117f}$$

$$S_{i+1} = -G_{i+1} + \beta_i S_i . \tag{2.117g}$$

Clearly from this definition of $S_{i+1}$, it is a linear combination of $G_{i+1}$ and $S_0, S_1, \ldots, S_i$, and hence it is a linear combination of $G_0, G_1, \ldots, G_{i+1}$. Returning to the minimization of the quadratic $X^T\mathbf{A}X + X^TB + c$, we see that if the $S_i$ are **A**-conjugate, the minimum is attained in $n$ or fewer steps. The process described by Eqs. (2.117) is so constituted that the $S_i$ do satisfy the condition $S_i^T\mathbf{A}S_j = 0$, $i \neq j$. This particular algorithm is derived from a *Gram-Schmidt orthogonalization*[31] of the $G_i$. The general problem of Gram-Schmidt orthogonalization is: Given any set of $s$ linearly independent vectors $V_i$, $i = 1,2, \ldots, s$, form a set of $s$ **A**-conjugate vectors $P_i$.

This is accomplished in the Gram-Schmidt orthogonalization procedure by selecting any $V_i$, say $V_1$, as a first vector $P_1$, and then forming $P_2$ by subtracting from $V_2$ any component not **A**-conjugate to $P_1$. The third and fourth vectors, etc., are similarly formed.

It can be shown[32] that the conjugate gradient method (applied, of course, to a quadratic function) automatically generates exactly such a set of **A**-conjugate $S_i$, using the sequence of vectors $-G_j$ as the independent vectors.

The conjugate gradient method, in fact, was originally proposed as a technique for solving any system of linear algebraic equations derived from the stationary conditions of a quadratic.[33]

Theoretically because the directions are **A**-conjugate the process should converge in $n$ or fewer cycles for a quadratic; however, for very badly conditioned quadratics (i.e., those with highly eccentric contours), it can take considerably more than $n$. This phenomenon is due fundamentally to the finite digit arithmetic in which all actual calculations must be carried out. It manifests itself as a progressive contamination of $S_i$, the only quantity carried over from iteration to iteration. All the errors resulting from inaccuracies in the determination of $\alpha_i^*$ and from the roundoff in accumulating the successive $\beta_i S_i$ terms are carried forward in this vector. This fact leads to the proposal that the process be periodically *restarted* in order to clear out the error. That is, after $m$ cycles, $S_{m+1}$ is set equal to $-G_{m+1}$ instead of the usual form. Originally it was recommended that this be done after the $n + 1$th cycle,[34] since failure to converge in this many cycles was considered evidence that the contents of the carryover term were obliterated by roundoff error. Computational experience with quadratics has shown this not to be the case.[35] In

[31] See Ayres (1962).

[32] See Kowalik (1966), or for a different view see Fletcher and Reeves (1964).

[33] Hestenes and Stiefel (1952).

[34] Fletcher and Reeves (1964).

[35] Fox and Stanton (1968).

highly eccentric quadratics, convergence may occur, for example, in $n + m$ cycles ($1 < m < n$) if no restarting is done, but it may fail to occur at all if the process is restarted periodically in $n + 1$ or less cycles. The implication is clear that in the case of a quadratic there is still useful information in the carryover term even though convergence has not occurred in the theoretical $n$ cycles.

There is, however, another side to the restart question. With functions of higher degree than quadratic (or with nonpolynomial functions), the carryover term may bear the scars of iterations performed at points distant from the minimum where the quadratics which approximate the function may be entirely different from those which approximate it near the minimum. The "error" developed in $\beta_i S_i$ from this source can be very detrimental to convergence, and the process does not readily refine it out as the iteration proceeds. The situation is best remedied by a restart, and we are then presented with a dilemma: When convergence requires significantly more than $n$ cycles, is it due to a highly eccentric but quadraticlike function, a situation that dictates saving the carryover term; or is it due to the distorted nature of the function encountered in the early stages of the iteration, and hence best restarted? No hard and fast answer can be given, but many heuristic approaches are possible. In general, if the starting point is known to be a poor approximation to the minimum of a nonquadratic function, it may pay to restart after the first $n$ or so cycles should they fail to produce a minimum, but not restart thereafter. This advice may, however, be incorrect if the function is both highly eccentric *and* twisted, like the function[36]

$$F_5 \equiv 10x_1^4 - 20x_2x_1^2 + 10x_2^2 + x_1^2 - 2x_1 + 5 \tag{2.118}$$

(see Fig. 2.31), which has a minimum of 4 at (1,1).

Several paths of the conjugate gradient method applied to $F_5$ are given in Table 2.5. Set $A$ was run with no restarts, set $B$ with restarts after every 4 cycles, and set $C$ with restarts after every 2 cycles. The rows marked $G$ were obtained from the previous row by a straight gradient step and hence are the first steps in "restarted" sequences. Table 2.6 (on page 92) presents the results of applying the pure gradient method to the same problem.

---

[36] This function and $F_1$ in Eq. (2.6) were devised in an interesting way. Consider the parabola $y = x^2$ and the straight line $x = 1$. These curves can be thought of as the loci of points satisfying the equations $y - x^2 = 0$ and $x - 1 = 0$, and they have one common point at (1,1). If we square these two functions and add them, we have $F_1$ except for an additive constant of 4, $F_1 = (y - x^2)^2 + (x - 1)^2 + 4$. The 4 was added simply to keep the example functions from having a zero minimum, and it has no bearing on the minimization problem. The present function $F_5$ is $10(y - x^2)^2 + (x - 1)^2 + 4$, and thus the parabolic valley is accentuated. A commonly used test function that is very difficult to minimize is Rosenbrock's "banana" function, which is $100(y - x^2)^2 + (x - 1)^2$. (See Rosenbrock, 1960.) Clearly this is in the same family as $F_1$ and $F_5$.

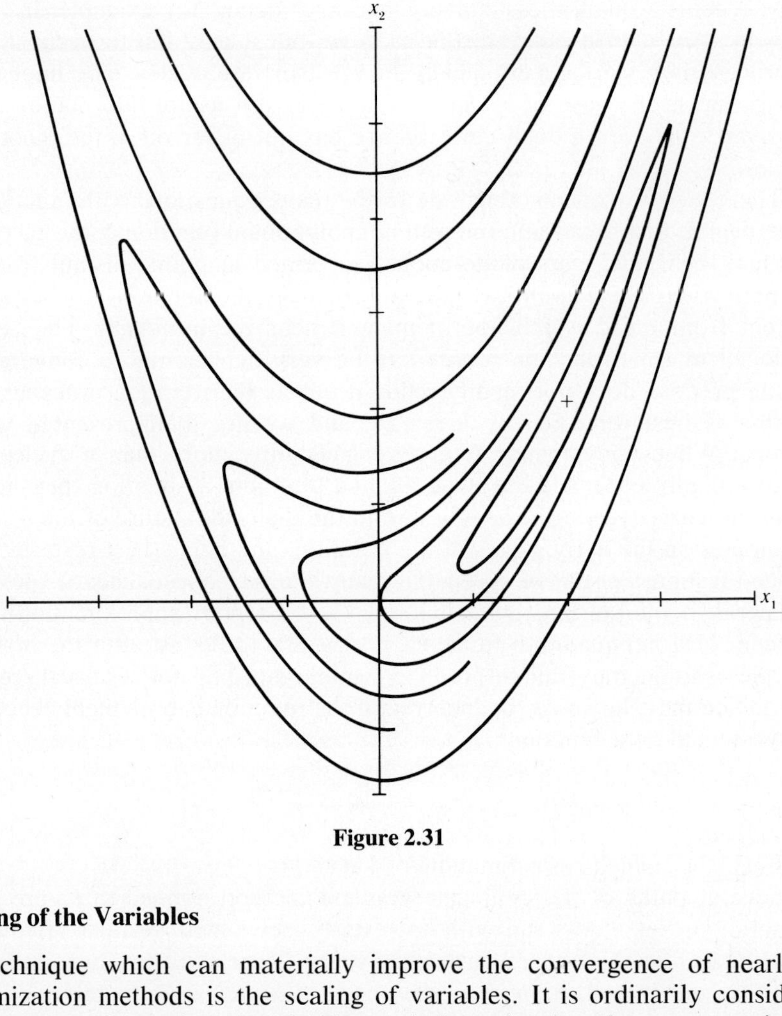


Figure 2.31

## Scaling of the Variables

A technique which can materially improve the convergence of nearly all minimization methods is the scaling of variables. It is ordinarily considered good practice in engineering to choose balanced units of measure or intelligently nondimensionalize the variables of a problem in order to improve the numerical behavior of the solution. In minimization the eccentricity, and hence the difficulty, can be greatly influenced by the scales chosen, as we see in the following functions:

$$F_6 = 144x_1^2 + 4x_2^2 - 8x_1x_2 = \begin{pmatrix} x_1 \\ x_2 \end{pmatrix}^T \begin{bmatrix} 144 & -4 \\ -4 & 4 \end{bmatrix} \begin{pmatrix} x_1 \\ x_2 \end{pmatrix} \tag{2.119}$$

versus

$$\widetilde{F}_6 = x_1^2 + x_2^2 - \tfrac{1}{3}x_1x_2 = \begin{pmatrix} x_1 \\ x_2 \end{pmatrix}^T \begin{bmatrix} 1 & -\frac{1}{6} \\ -\frac{1}{6} & 1 \end{bmatrix} \begin{pmatrix} x_1 \\ x_2 \end{pmatrix}, \tag{2.120}$$

**Table 2.5. The conjugate gradient method with various restart cycles**

| | *A* | | | | *B* | | | | *C* | | |
|---|---|---|---|---|---|---|---|---|---|---|---|
| | $x_1$ | $x_2$ | $F$ | | $x_1$ | $x_2$ | $F$ | | $x_1$ | $x_2$ | $F$ |
| | −1.200 | 1.000 | 10.776 | | −1.200 | 1.000 | 10.776 | | −1.200 | 1.000 | 10.776 |
| *G* | −0.993 | 1.071 | 8.045 | *G* | −0.993 | 1.071 | 8.045 | *G* | −0.993 | 1.071 | 8.045 |
| | −0.657 | 0.275 | 6.992 | | −0.657 | 0.275 | 6.992 | | −0.657 | 0.275 | 6.992 |
| | −0.409 | −0.073 | 6.564 | | −0.409 | 0.073 | 6.564 | *G* | −0.490 | 0.346 | 6.332 |
| | −0.241 | −0.227 | 6.355 | | −0.241 | 0.227 | 6.355 | | −0.132 | −0.098 | 5.416 |
| | −0.112 | −0.302 | 6.224 | *G* | 0.059 | 0.100 | 4.979 | *G* | 0.837 | 0.681 | 4.030 |
| | −0.003 | −0.335 | 6.129 | | 0.289 | 0.008 | 4.565 | | 0.833 | 0.688 | 4.028 |
| | 0.010 | −0.342 | 6.048 | | 0.582 | 0.235 | 4.283 | *G* | 0.842 | 0.694 | 4.027 |
| | 0.191 | −0.327 | 5.973 | | 0.767 | 0.628 | 4.070 | | 0.972 | 0.926 | 4.004 |
| | 0.287 | −0.290 | 5.893 | *G* | 0.792 | 0.616 | 4.044 | *G* | 0.965 | 0.930 | 4.001 |
| | 0.390 | −0.226 | 5.802 | | 0.928 | 0.834 | 4.013 | | 1.000 | 0.999 | 4.000 |
| | 0.504 | −0.125 | 5.689 | | 0.965 | 0.935 | 4.001 | *G* | 1.000 | 0.999 | 4.000 |
| | 0.636 | 0.029 | 5.542 | | 0.969 | 0.937 | 4.001 | | | | |
| | 0.792 | 0.267 | 5.340 | *G* | 0.969 | 0.938 | 4.001 | | | | |
| | 0.986 | 0.649 | 5.045 | | 1.000 | 0.998 | 4.000 | | | | |
| | 1.249 | 1.301 | 4.602 | | 1.000 | 0.999 | 4.000 | | | | |
| | 1.418 | 1.943 | 4.186 | | | | | | | | |
| | 1.404 | 1.979 | 4.163 | | | | | | | | |
| | . | . | . | | | | | | | | |
| | . | . | . | | | | | | | | |
| | . | . | . | | | | | | | | |

**Table 2.6. The pure gradient method applied to $F_5$**

| $x_1$ | $x_2$ | $F$ |
|---|---|---|
| − 1.200 | 1.000 | 10.776 |
| − 0.993 | 1.071 | 8.045 |
| − 0.793 | 0.493 | 7.403 |
| − 0.662 | 0.538 | 6.862 |
| − 0.552 | 0.218 | 6.483 |
| − 0.388 | 0.275 | 6.081 |
| − 0.306 | 0.037 | 5.739 |
| 0.633 | 0.361 | 4.151 |
| 0.625 | 0.382 | 4.141 |
| 0.654 | 0.392 | 4.132 |
| 0.648 | 0.411 | 4.125 |
| 0.672 | 0.420 | 4.118 |
| 0.667 | 0.437 | 4.112 |
| 0.689 | 0.444 | 4.106 |
| 0.683 | 0.460 | 4.101 |
| 0.703 | 0.466 | 4.096 |
| 0.698 | 0.481 | 4.091 |
| 0.716 | 0.487 | 4.087 |
| 0.711 | 0.500 | 4.083 |
| 0.728 | 0.505 | 4.080 |
| 0.724 | 0.517 | 4.077 |
| . | . | . |
| . | . | . |
| . | . | . |

where $\widetilde{F}_6$ has been derived from

$$\widetilde{F}_6\,(x_1, x_2) = F_6\left(\frac{x_1}{12}, \frac{x_2}{2}\right). \tag{2.121}$$

Function contours of both $F_6$ and $\widetilde{F}_6$ are shown in Fig. 2.32(a, b). Clearly, $F_6$ is much more eccentric than $\widetilde{F}_6$ and would be harder to minimize.

Further, consider the function

$$F_7 = 36x_1^2 + x_2^2 - 6x_1x_2 = \begin{pmatrix} x_1 \\ x_2 \end{pmatrix}^T \begin{bmatrix} 36 & -3 \\ -3 & 1 \end{bmatrix} \begin{pmatrix} x_1 \\ x_2 \end{pmatrix} \tag{2.122}$$

and a scaled version

$$F_7 = x_1^2 + x_2^2 - x_1x_2 = \begin{pmatrix} x_1 \\ x_2 \end{pmatrix}^T \begin{bmatrix} 1 & -\frac{1}{2} \\ -\frac{1}{2} & 1 \end{bmatrix} \begin{pmatrix} x_1 \\ x_2 \end{pmatrix}, \tag{2.123}$$

the contours of which are shown in Fig. 2.33(a, b). The function is still somewhat eccentric in scaled coordinates.

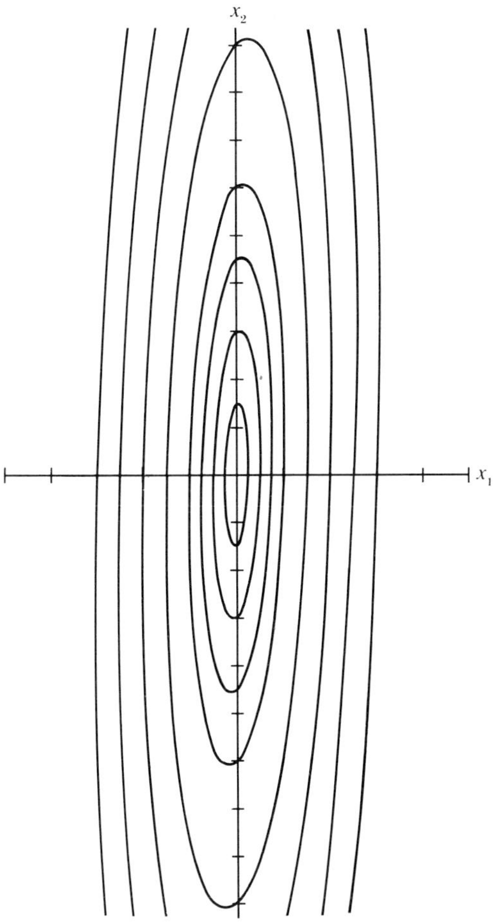


**Fig. 2.32(a).** $F_6 = 144_1{}^2 + 4x_2{}^2 - 8x_1x_2$.

The objective of scaling is to accomplish a coordinate expansion or contraction which will minimize the eccentricity. As the latter example illustrates, the coordinate transformation of simple scaling may still leave considerable eccentricity. Furthermore, the technique of making the coefficients of the squared terms equal is not, in general, *optimal* scaling even in quadratic problems, beyond the two-variable case. The theory of optimal scaling[37] is difficult and beyond the scope of this text. In practice, however, considerable benefit can often be gained by this simple diagonal equalization.

[37] See, for example, Bauer (1963).

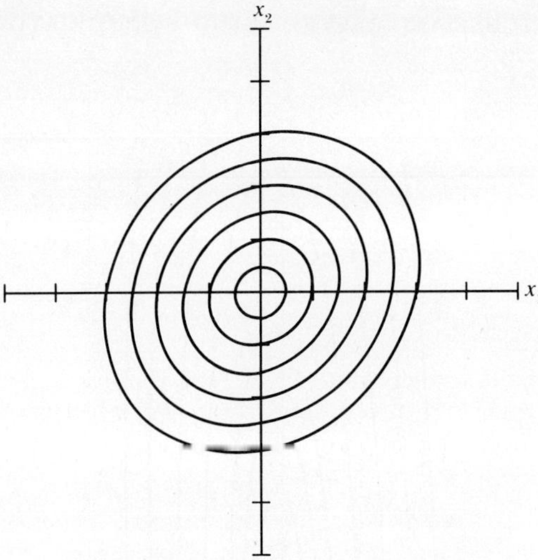


**Fig. 2.32(b).** $\widetilde{F}_6 = x_1{}^2 + x_2{}^2 - \frac{1}{3}x_1x_2$.

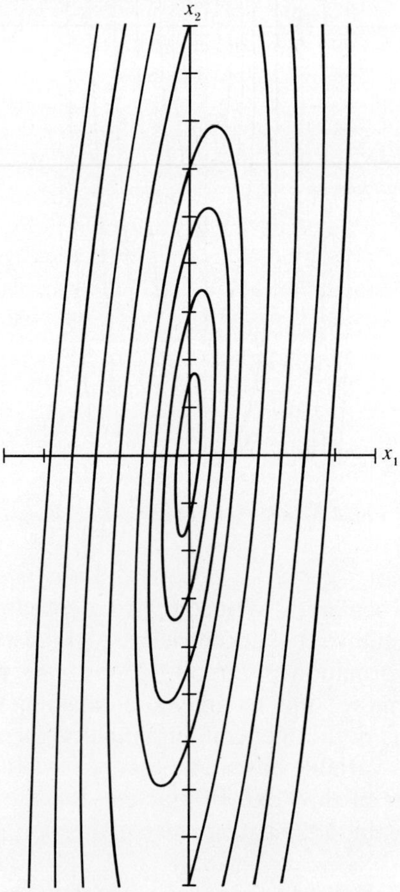


**Fig. 2.33(a).** $F_7 = 36x_1{}^2 + x_2{}^2 - 6x_1x_2$.

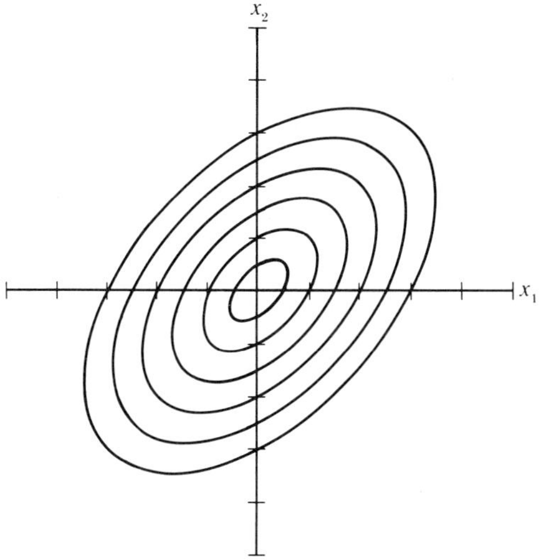


**Fig. 2.33(b).** $F_7 = x_1^2 + x_2^2 - 6x_1x_2$.

In nonquadratic problems, of course, there is no fixed matrix upon which to base the scaling. An alternative in such problems is to obtain expressions or difference approximations to the diagonal of the matrix of second partial derivatives, **J**. For such problems, the matrix is not constant throughout the space and the indicated scaling will change as the iteration proceeds. It might, however, defeat the basis of operation of the conjugate gradient method if the scaling were changed at each step, and much computational effort would be required if the second partials had to be approximated.

An approach which has met with some success is using a scaling based on the matrix of second partial derivatives at the starting point, and then revising the scaling whenever the conjugate gradient is restarted.

The mechanics of scaling are simple and require little computation once the scale factors have been determined. Given a function $F$ formulated in terms of the variable $X$, the local matrix of the second partial derivatives, $\mathbf{J} = [\partial^2 F/\partial x_i \partial x_j] \equiv [J_{ij}]$, is transformed to a matrix with diagonal elements equal to 1 by the substitution into $F$ of $\mathbf{D}X$ for $X$ where

$$\mathbf{D} = \begin{bmatrix} 1/\sqrt{J_{11}} & & & \bigcirc \\ & 1/\sqrt{J_{22}} & & \\ & & \ddots & \\ \bigcirc & & & 1/\sqrt{J_{nn}} \end{bmatrix} \tag{2.124}$$

Since

$$F(X) = F(X_0) + \nabla F_0{}^T(X - X_0) + \tfrac{1}{2}(X - X_0)^T\mathbf{J}(X_0)(X - X_0)\ldots, \tag{2.125}$$

$$\widetilde{F}(X) = \widetilde{F}(X_0) + \nabla\widetilde{F}(X_0)^T(X - X_0) + \tfrac{1}{2}(X - X_0)^T\widetilde{\mathbf{J}}(X_0)(X - X_0)\ldots, \tag{2.126}$$

we note that

$$\frac{\partial\widetilde{F}}{\partial x_i} = \frac{\partial F}{\partial x_i}\frac{\partial(d_{ii}x_i)}{\partial x_i} = d_{ii}\frac{\partial F}{\partial x_i}, \tag{2.127}$$

which implies $\nabla\widetilde{F} = \mathbf{D}\nabla F$. In addition,

$$\frac{\partial^2\widetilde{F}}{\partial x_i \partial x_j} = d_{ii}d_{jj}\frac{\partial^2 F}{\partial x_i \partial x_j}, \tag{2.128}$$

which implies $\widetilde{\mathbf{J}} = \mathbf{DJD}$. The expansion thus becomes

$$\widetilde{F}(X) = \widetilde{F}(X_0) + \mathbf{D}\nabla F(X_0)^T(X - X_0) + \tfrac{1}{2}(X - X_0)\mathbf{DJ}(X_0)\mathbf{D}(X - X_0) + \ldots. \tag{2.129}$$

Thus if we have a rule or procedure for computing $F(X)$ we can operate on $\widetilde{F}(X)$ by computing as follows:

1. $X \leftarrow \mathbf{D}X$.
2. Compute $F(X)$.
3. Compute $\nabla F(X)$ (if needed).
4. $\nabla\widetilde{F}(X) \leftarrow \mathbf{D}\nabla F(X)$.

Multiplication of $X$ by $\mathbf{D}$ is equivalent to simply replacing $x_i$ by $d_{ii}x_i$, a trivial computation. Note that if the minimum of $F$ is at $X_M$, for example, the minimum of $\widetilde{F}$ is at $\mathbf{D}X_M$, and so the final result of minimizing $\widetilde{F}$ must be transferred back to the original coordinate by the transformation $X_M = \mathbf{D}^{-1}\widetilde{X}_M$ or $x_{Mi} = \widetilde{x}_{Mi}/d_{ii}$. Furthermore, if a starting point $X_0$ is deemed good for minimizing $F$, then in the absence of other information the starting point for minimizing $\widetilde{F}$ would be $\mathbf{D}X_0$. The reader is invited to carry out the above procedure on $F_6$ or $F_7$, keeping in mind that the matrices in Eqs. (2.119) and (2.122) are $\tfrac{1}{2}\mathbf{J}$.

It is possible to view the whole process of scaling from a different point of view by imagining the coordinate system transformed rather than the function. The two are entirely equivalent, but one may be more convenient than the other for particular applications.

In summary, the conjugate gradient method is a rapidly convergent technique suitable for use when the gradient of the function is readily computed. It usually far surpasses the steepest descent method except in unusual cases. With careful application, it is one of the more effective minimization techniques. In programming the method, attention should be paid to the accuracy required in determining $\alpha^*$, to a strategy for restarting, and to a proper scaling.

The methods discussed in the following two sections are even more powerful, but may be impractical for large or complicated problems.

## 2.10 SECOND-ORDER METHODS: NEWTON'S PROCEDURE

There has been little standardization of nomenclature in the field of minimization, and the designations we are about to use are not universal. If the nongradient methods were called zeroth-order methods (no derivatives involved), and the gradient-based methods were called first-order (first derivatives involved) methods, then a technique that made explicit use of the second derivatives of a function might be called a second-order method. In this chapter, we discuss some variations of Newton's procedure (the Newton-Raphson iteration) which would, by this definition, be called a second-order method.

To develop the method, we return again to the Taylor's series expansion of $F$, this time expanding about the point $X_q$, the $q$th approximation to the minimum point. The expansion up to the quadratic terms is thus

$$F(X) \simeq F(X_q) + \nabla F_q^T(X - X_q) + \tfrac{1}{2}(X - X_q)^T \mathbf{J}_q (X - X_q)\,,$$

where $\mathbf{J}_q$ is the matrix of second partial derivatives of $F$ evaluated at $X_q$. Designating this approximation as $\bar{F}_q(X)$, with the subscript $q$ reminding us of its dependence on the choice of the point $X_q$, we may use the minimum of $\bar{F}_q(X)$ as an approximation to the minimum of $F(X)$. As we have seen, this will be where $\partial \bar{F}_q / \partial x_i = 0$, or when $X$ satisfies the vector equation

$$\nabla \bar{F}_q \equiv \nabla F_q + \mathbf{J}_q(X - X_q) = 0\,, \tag{2.130}$$

which can also be written

$$\mathbf{J}_q X = \mathbf{J}_q X_q - \nabla F_q\,. \tag{2.131}$$

Multiplying through by the inverse of $\mathbf{J}_q$, we obtain

$$X_{q+1} = X_q - \mathbf{J}_q^{-1} \nabla F_q\,, \tag{2.132}$$

having designated the left-hand side as the new iterate $X_{q+1}$.

This process can converge extremely rapidly in many problems and is one of the preferred methods of solving systems of simultaneous nonlinear equations.[38] Indeed, if $F$ is a quadratic, we obtain the solution in a single step, since the Taylor series expansion is exact (of course, for the quadratic there is no savings in effort over conventional methods). On the other hand, the method may diverge in some problems; it will converge to saddle points and maxima

---

[38] If we have a system of equations $l_j(X) = 0$ that are derivable from a potential function $F$ so that $l_j(X) \equiv \partial F / \partial x_j$, the application is clearly indicated if we take the elements of $\mathbf{J}$ to be $\partial l_j / \partial x_i$. This approach is also applicable when the system does not derive from a potential function.

(something which the methods we have discussed earlier will not do); and sometimes the matrix $\mathbf{J}_q$ can be singular or near singular in otherwise properly formed problems.

Some of these situations can be grasped by examining the results of applying the method to $F_3$ (Eq. 2.8). In Fig. 2.34, several minimization paths from different starting points are shown. The path from starting point $A$ is as expected. In some sense, $A$ is under the influence of the saddle point and the process converges to it. Point $B$ behaves similarly for the upper minimum. Point $C$ is somewhat more interesting; first, it is actually closer to the saddle than $A$, but the path converges to the minimum instead. This is because the

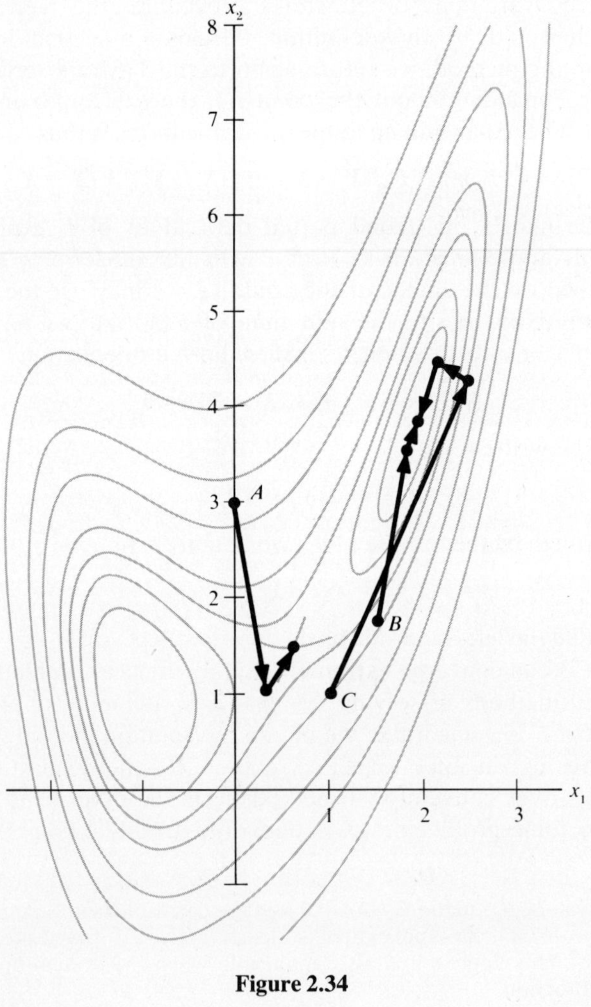


**Figure 2.34**

approximating quadratic at $C$ is just barely predominated by the minimum. In fact, at the point $C$ ($x_1 = x_2 = 1$), the matrix $\mathbf{J}$ is approaching singularity, being very near the transition point. Another feature worth noting is that on the first step from point $C$, the function value actually increases slightly.

In order to further demonstrate the iteration process, we have superimposed the contour plots of the approximating quadratics onto those of $F_3$ for the points of paths $A$ and $C$, as illustrated in Figs. 2.35(a, b) and 2.36(a, b). The ellipses or hyperbolas shown in these figures are the contours of $\bar{F}_q(X)$.

The traditional Newton-Raphson method described here can be improved

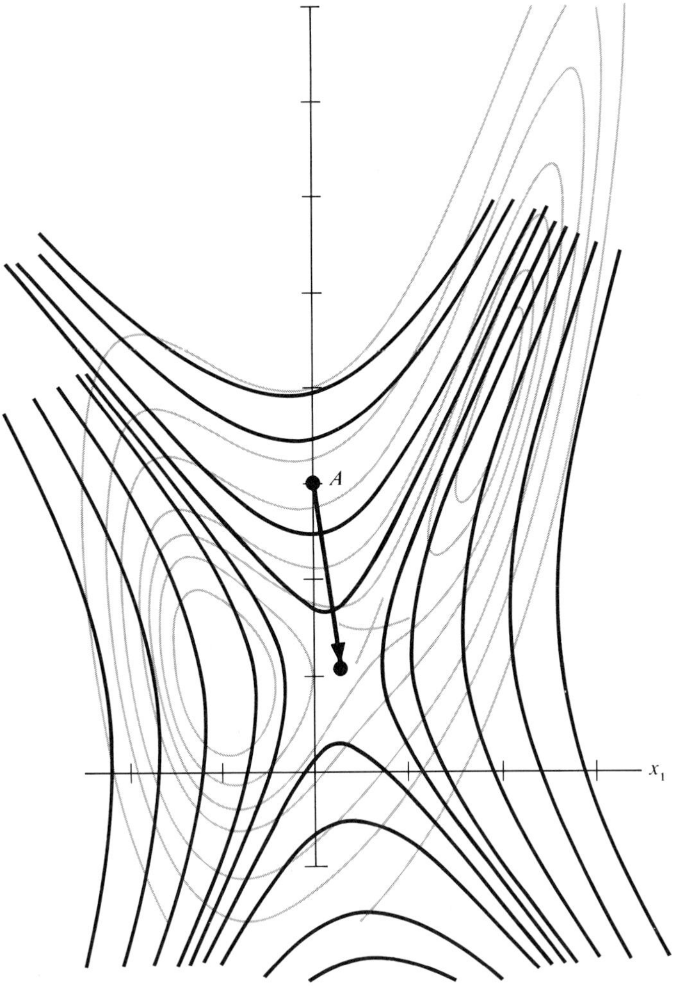


**Figure 2.35(a)**

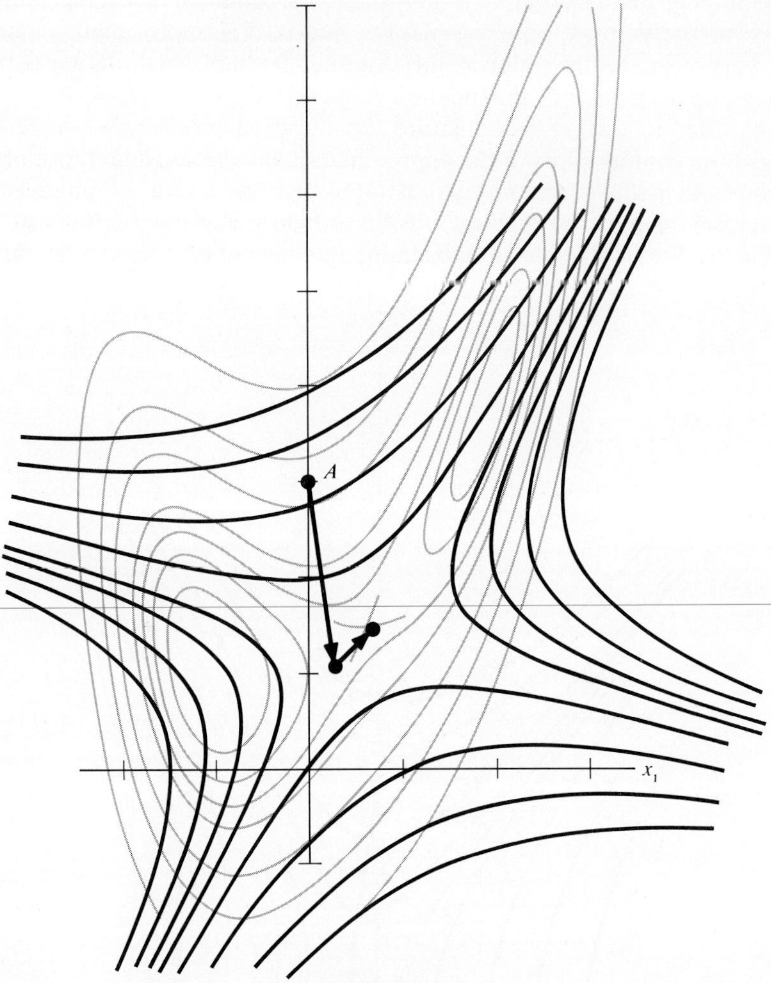


**Figure 2.35(b)**

for use in minimization work by replacing block A of Fig. 2.24 with

$$\downarrow$$
$$\boxed{S \leftarrow \mathbf{J}_q^{-1}\nabla F_q} \quad \text{A}$$
$$\downarrow$$

This has the effect of modifying the Newton-Raphson iteration to

$$X_{q+1} = X_q - \alpha_q^* \mathbf{J}_q^{-1}\nabla F_q, \tag{2.133}$$

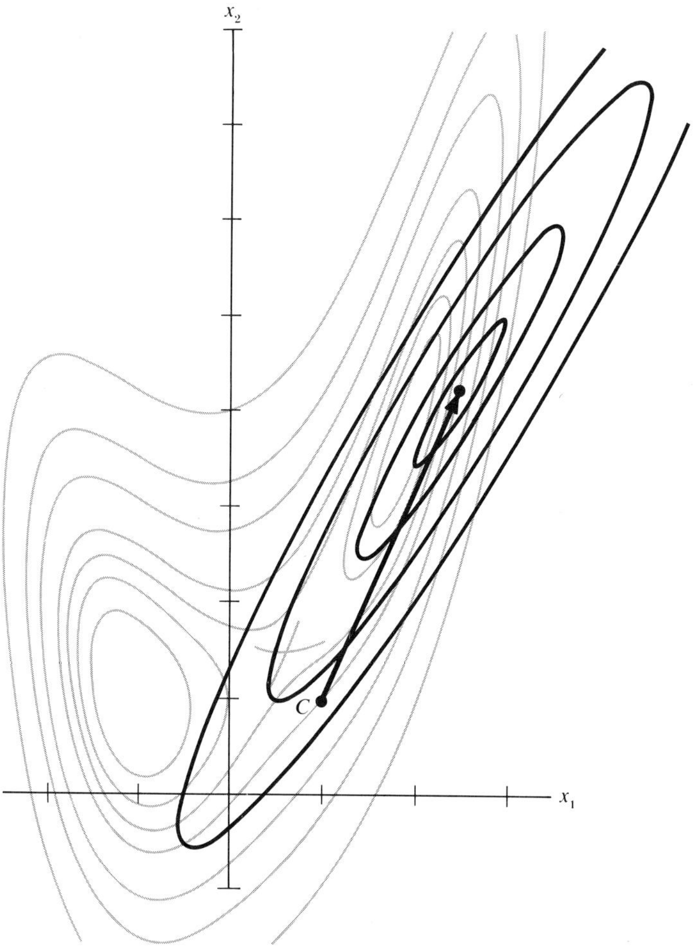


**Figure 2.36(a)**

where $\alpha_q^*$, as in the previous discussions, is the value of the scalar which minimizes $F(\boldsymbol{X}_{q+1})$.

This modification has a number of advantages which make it worth the comparatively small additional effort. First, it will usually speed convergence and can even secure convergence when the direct method diverges. Second, it will usually avoid convergence to a saddle point or a maximum. With this modification, the method is tailored to minimization problems; in fact, it is the most powerful of minimization methods.

However, the disadvantages of the method can be formidable, as the reader may have noted. First, it may be difficult or impossible to compute the elements

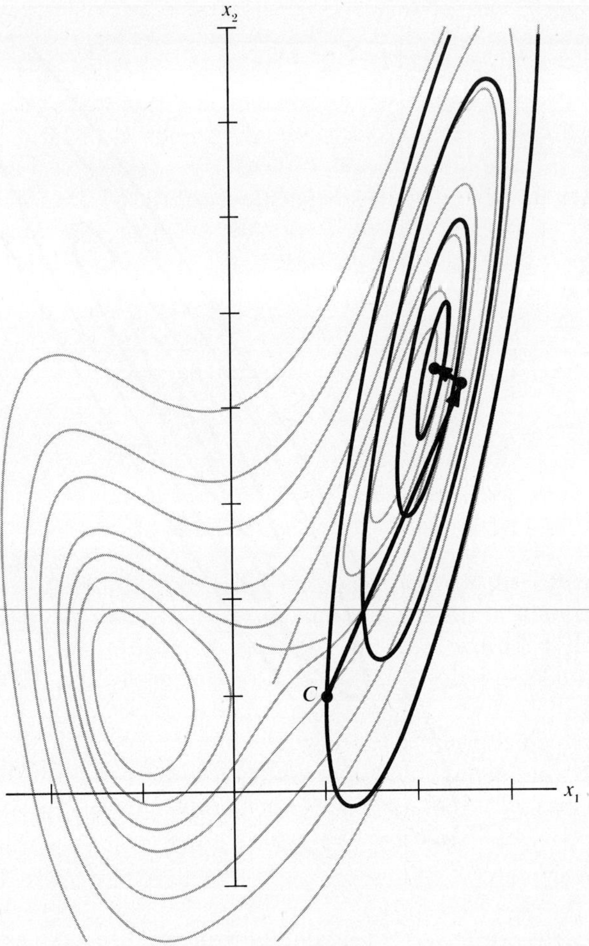


**Figure 2.36(b)**

of $\mathbf{J}_q$, and this is often the main obstacle to its use. Even for simple functions, $\partial^2 F/\partial x_i \partial x_j$ may be hopelessly complicated or too time-consuming to compute. Second, it should be obvious that the computation of the vector $-\mathbf{J}_q^{-1}\nabla F_q$ is a major undertaking in problems of significant size. These features make the method impractical for large or complicated problems.

A technique which is only slightly helpful with regard to these difficulties, but which introduces ideas to be applied in the next section, will now be described. In Section 2.9, we discussed a scaling transformation as an aid to reducing the eccentricity of a function. The *diagonal* transformation we dealt with there is a special case of the general transformation

$$X \leftarrow \mathbf{T}X\ , \tag{2.134}$$

where $\mathbf{T}$ is a full $n \times n$ matrix. If we were minimizing a quadratic $(\frac{1}{2}X^T\mathbf{A}X + X^TB + c)$, the object in picking such a transformation would still be to reduce the eccentricity of the quadratic part $\frac{1}{2}X^T\mathbf{T}^T\mathbf{AT}X$ in the new coordinate system. If the matrix $\mathbf{A}$ is positive definite, there always exist $\mathbf{T}$ such that $\mathbf{T}^T\mathbf{AT}$ is the identity matrix, with *zero* eccentricity. For example, the quadratic form $5x_1^2 + 5x_2^2 - 8x_1x_2 \equiv Q(X)$ can be written

$$Q \equiv \begin{pmatrix} x_1 \\ x_2 \end{pmatrix}^T \begin{bmatrix} 5 & -4 \\ -4 & 5 \end{bmatrix} \begin{pmatrix} x_1 \\ x_2 \end{pmatrix},$$

and the transformation

$$\begin{pmatrix} x_1 \\ x_2 \end{pmatrix} \leftarrow \frac{\sqrt{2}}{6} \begin{bmatrix} 3 & -1 \\ 3 & 1 \end{bmatrix} \begin{pmatrix} x_1 \\ x_2 \end{pmatrix}$$

converts it to

$$\tilde{Q} \equiv \begin{pmatrix} x_1 \\ x_2 \end{pmatrix}^T \begin{bmatrix} 1 & 0 \\ 0 & 1 \end{bmatrix} \begin{pmatrix} x_1 \\ x_2 \end{pmatrix} = x_1^2 + x_2^2\ ,$$

as the reader may verify. With the eccentricity removed, the gradient of the function evaluated anywhere in the space passes through the minimum [in this case (0,0)]. In other words, when the function is transformed so that its contours are spheres (or hyperspheres), the steepest descent method will work in one step.

We may now ask whether it is possible to work with the original (untransformed) function and define for it an operator similiar to the gradient operator but producing a vector that always passes through the minimum. Consider a $\mathbf{T}$ with the property given above:

$$\mathbf{T}^T\mathbf{AT} = \mathbf{I}\ .$$

Then postmultiplying by $\mathbf{T}^{-1}$,

$$\mathbf{T}^T\mathbf{A} = \mathbf{T}^{-1}\ ,$$

and premultiplying by $\mathbf{T}$, we obtain

$$\mathbf{TT}^T\mathbf{A} = \mathbf{I}\ ,$$

which demonstrates that $\mathbf{TT}^T = \mathbf{A}^{-1}$. Thus we see from the Newton-Raphson procedure that the desired vector for the quadratic function is $S = -\mathbf{A}^{-1}\nabla F \equiv -\mathbf{TT}^T\nabla F$, since the hessian of the quadratic is $\mathbf{A}$.

If we did not have available the exact $\mathbf{J}^{-1}$, but instead had some approximate $\mathbf{T}$ or $\mathbf{TT}^T$ which did a good, but not perfect, job of removing the eccentricity, we could use it in an iteration process of the form

$$X_{q+1} = X_q - \alpha_q^* \mathbf{TT}^T\nabla F_q\ . \tag{2.135}$$

Another way of thinking about the matrix $\mathbf{TT}^T$ is as a *metric* for measuring distance in the $X$ space. In other words, we generalize the concept of the length of a vector from

$$(\boldsymbol{R}^T\boldsymbol{R})^{1/2} \equiv |\boldsymbol{R}| \tag{2.136}$$

to

$$(\boldsymbol{R}^T\mathbf{H}\boldsymbol{R})^{1/2} \equiv |\boldsymbol{R}|_{\mathbf{H}}, \tag{2.137}$$

where $\mathbf{H}$ is our metric (for example $\mathbf{H} = \mathbf{TT}^T$). The symbol on the right is often read, "length with respect to $\mathbf{H}$." Such a definition of length emphasizes some directions over others in determining the scalar measure of "length." We see that in order for the metric to be useful it must be such that

$$\boldsymbol{R}^T\mathbf{H}\boldsymbol{R} > 0$$

for all $\boldsymbol{R}$ except $\boldsymbol{R} = \boldsymbol{0}$; in other words, $\mathbf{H}$ must be positive definite. The practical reason for this in the minimization problem is that if $-\boldsymbol{\nabla}F_q$ is a direction of descent, $-\mathbf{H}\boldsymbol{\nabla}F_q$ should also be a direction of descent. As we have noted, a direction $\boldsymbol{S}$ is one of descent only if

$$dF/d\alpha = \boldsymbol{S}^T\boldsymbol{\nabla}F_q < 0\,, \tag{2.138}$$

and in this case

$$\boldsymbol{S}^T\boldsymbol{\nabla}F_q = -\,\boldsymbol{\nabla}F_q{}^T\mathbf{H}^T\boldsymbol{\nabla}F_q\,, \tag{2.139}$$

which will be negative if $\mathbf{H}$ is positive definite.

Returning now to the Newton-Raphson iteration, we see that if $\boldsymbol{X}_0$ is reasonably near the solution, a viable iteration scheme is

$$\boldsymbol{X}_{q+1} = \boldsymbol{X}_q - \alpha_q^*\mathbf{J}_0{}^{-1}\boldsymbol{\nabla}F_q\,, \tag{2.140}$$

in which $\mathbf{J}_0{}^{-1}$ serves as a metric. If $\boldsymbol{X}_0$ is close enough to the minimum $\boldsymbol{X}_M$, then $\mathbf{J}_0{}^{-1}$ should serve as substitute for $\mathbf{J}_q{}^{-1}$ or $\mathbf{J}_M{}^{-1}$. It is possible, however, for $\mathbf{J}_0{}^{-1}$ as well as $\mathbf{J}_M{}^{-1}$ to be useless for these purposes, because there is no guarantee that they will be positive definite or even nonsingular (consider, for example, the function $x_1{}^4 + x_2{}^4 + 3x_1{}^2x_2{}^2$). In such cases, the Newton-Raphson method and the variants mentioned here are more or less useless and other techniques should be applied. On the other hand, the iteration given by Eq. (2.140) can be a useful compromise to the general procedure when it is applicable. There are numerous variations on the basic ideas: for example, we might periodically upgrade the matrix $\mathbf{J}$ by taking a number of iterations of Eq. (2.140) and then reevaluate the $\mathbf{J}^{-1}$, using the matrix associated with the current point.

In the next section we will see the concept of a metric utilized to produce a very powerful, quadratically convergent *first-order* method.

## 2.11 DAVIDON-FLETCHER-POWELL METHOD: THE VARIABLE METRIC

Of the disadvantages of the Newton-Raphson procedure, it is hard to say whether the formulation and computation of $\mathbf{J}_q$ or the solution to $\mathbf{J}_q\boldsymbol{S}_q = \boldsymbol{\nabla}F_q$

is the most troublesome. In this section we will describe a first-order method which replaces the local hessian $\mathbf{J}_q^{-1}$ by an approximate metric $\mathbf{H}_q$. The method of computing this metric completely eliminates the need for evaluating second derivatives and performing matrix inversions, and yet the sequence of iterates converges quadratically to the minimum point $X_M$. Furthermore, we will see that the metric, which is improved at each iteration, converges to $\mathbf{J}_M^{-1}$.

We first describe the method with minimal justification and then look at some of its theoretical aspects. The theoretical knowledge will prove useful when we attempt to remedy some of the problems that arise in applying the method to difficult functions.

Its original inventor[39] considered the method in terms of a variable metric, others[40] think of it as a "quasi-Newton" method, and still others think of it as a conjugate direction method.[41] It is actually all of these, as will be seen.

The iteration proceeds as follows:

1. Start with an initial $X_0$ and an initial positive definite symmetric matrix $\mathbf{H}_0$ (for example, the identity matrix), and set $S_0 = -\mathbf{H}_0 \nabla F_0$.
2. Compute $X_{q+1} = X_q + \alpha_q^* S_q$, where $\alpha_q^*$ minimizes $F(X_q + \alpha S_q)$.
3. Compute $\mathbf{H}_{q+1} = \mathbf{H}_q + \mathbf{M}_q + \mathbf{N}_q$, where, defining

$$Y_q \equiv G_{q+1} - G_q \equiv \nabla F(X_{q+1}) - \nabla F(X_q),$$

$$\mathbf{M}_q = \alpha_q^* \frac{S_q S_q^T}{S_q^T Y_q}$$

and

$$\mathbf{N}_q = -\frac{(\mathbf{H}_q Y_q)(\mathbf{H}_q Y_q)^T}{Y_q^T \mathbf{H}_q Y_q}.$$

4. Compute $S_{q+1} = -\mathbf{H}_{q+1} G_{q+1}$ and repeat from step 2.

We can view the algorithm in the framework of the general flow diagram of Fig. 2.24 by inserting into block A the following:

$$\downarrow$$

$$\boxed{\begin{array}{l} \mathbf{H} \leftarrow \mathbf{H} + \mathbf{M} + \mathbf{N} \\ S \leftarrow -\mathbf{H} \nabla F(X) \end{array}} \quad \text{A}$$

$$\downarrow$$

We assume, of course, that the proper computational rules for $\mathbf{M}$ and $\mathbf{N}$ have been supplied and that an initial, positive definite symmetric matrix $\mathbf{H}_0$ is available.

---

[39] The method was essentially invented by Davidon (1959) and was further described and sharpened by Fletcher and Powell (1963).

[40] See Broyden (1965 and 1967).

[41] See Pearson (1968).

The basic algorithm is extremely powerful for a first-order method, converging quadratically and possessing very good stability. By stability we mean here that even in highly distorted and eccentric functions it continues to progress and needs little of the special attention required by the conjugate gradient method. There is a plausible argument for this increase in stability in that with conjugate gradients the entire history of the path is carried to $S_{q+1}$ in the intelligence of $\beta_q S_q$, a single vector. In the variable metric method, on the other hand, we carry the data in a full matrix that we carefully upgrade at each step. Another point of view is that the carryover term $\beta_q S_q$ is good only if applied to $\nabla F(X_q)$ and produces nonsense if applied to the gradient at some other point. On the other hand, it can be shown that $\mathbf{H}_q$ is a positive definite approximation to the matrix of second partial derivatives and, to the extent that it is a good approximation, it is applicable anywhere in the space.

As will be seen, the positive definiteness is preserved in theory only if $\alpha_q^*$ is the true minimum point (i.e., if $G_{q+1}^T S_q = 0$), but roundoff error in other computations can again cause trouble. Before discussing modifications of the iteration to protect against this possible breakdown, we will state without proof some important results concerning the theory of the method.

Again we return to the quadratic

$$\tfrac{1}{2}X^T\mathbf{A}X + X^T B + c$$

and state that for the iteration given by steps 1 through 4[42] above:

$$\text{a) } S_i^T\mathbf{A}S_j = 0\,, \qquad i \neq j\,,$$

$$\text{b) } \sum_{i=0}^{n-1} \mathbf{M}_i = \mathbf{A}^{-1}\,,$$

$$\text{c) } \mathbf{H}_0 + \sum_{i=0}^{n-1} \mathbf{N}_i = \mathbf{0}\,,$$

d) $\mathbf{H}_q$ is positive definite.

Thus (a) indicates that it is a conjugate direction method and quadratically convergent, while (b) and (c) show that $\mathbf{H}_n = \mathbf{A}^{-1}$ regardless of $\mathbf{H}_0$. For the general nonquadratic problem, (a), (b), and (c) have no exact meaning because there is no single $\mathbf{A}$-matrix, but as the iteration nears the solution $X_M$, it is expected that $\mathbf{H}_q$ will tend to $\mathbf{J}_M{}^{-1}$.

We will now show that the $\mathbf{H}_q$-matrix is always positive definite even in the general problem and hence that the method is stable. Assuming that the matrix $\mathbf{H}_q$ is positive definite, we must show that $\mathbf{H}_{q+1}$ also is, and hence that $X^T\mathbf{H}_{q+1}X > 0$ for all nontrivial vectors $X$. From the definition of $\mathbf{H}_{q+1}$, we obtain

$$X^T\mathbf{H}_{q+1}X = X^T\mathbf{H}_qX + X^T\mathbf{M}_qX + X^T\mathbf{N}_qX \tag{2.141}$$

[42] For a proof of these, see Fletcher and Powell (1963).

or

$$X^T\mathbf{H}_{q+1}X = X^T\mathbf{H}_qX + \alpha_q^* \frac{X^TS_qS_q{}^TX}{S_q{}^TY_q} - \frac{X^T\mathbf{H}_qY_qY_q{}^T\mathbf{H}_qX}{Y_q{}^T\mathbf{H}_qY_q}\,. \tag{2.142}$$

Let us now define two vectors:

$$P \equiv \mathbf{H}_q{}^{1/2}X\,, \tag{2.143}$$

$$Q \equiv \mathbf{H}_q{}^{1/2}Y_q\,, \tag{2.144}$$

where $\mathbf{H}_q{}^{1/2}$ is a matrix such that $\mathbf{H}_q{}^{1/2}\mathbf{H}_q{}^{1/2} = \mathbf{H}_q$; it exists because $\mathbf{H}_q$ is positive definite.[43] Equation (2.142) now becomes

$$X^T\mathbf{H}_{q+1}X = P^TP - \frac{(P^TQ)(Q^TP)}{Q^TQ} + \frac{\alpha_q^*}{S_q{}^TY_q}X^TS_qS_q{}^TX\,. \tag{2.145}$$

The first two terms on the right combine to

$$\frac{(P^TP)(Q^TQ) - (P^TQ)^2}{Q^TQ}\,,$$

which is always nonnegative.[44] Thus

$$X^T\mathbf{H}_{q+1}X \geqslant \frac{\alpha_q^*}{S_q{}^TY_q}(X^TS_q)^2\,, \tag{2.146}$$

which is positive if $S_q{}^TY_q$ is positive. Since $Y_q \equiv G_{q+1} - G_q$, we have

$$S_q{}^TY_q = S_q{}^TG_{q+1} - S_q{}^TG_q\,, \tag{2.147}$$

but $S_q{}^TG_{q+1} = 0$ since the point $X_{q+1}$ is the minimum along $S_q$. Therefore since

$$-S_q{}^TG_q = G_q{}^T\mathbf{H}_qG_q > 0\,, \tag{2.148}$$

$\mathbf{H}_{q+1}$ is positive definite *provided* $\alpha_q^*$ is such that $S_q{}^TG_{q+1} = 0$. Thus the positive definiteness of $\mathbf{H}_{q+1}$ depends only on the accuracy with which $\alpha_q^*$ is determined and not at all on the form of $F$.

In applying the method, therefore, care must be exercised to ensure that the **H**-matrix is not updated with data arising from poor approximations to $\alpha_q^*$. There are many approaches to this problem: first, the algorithm used for

---

[43] A procedure called the Cholesky decomposition would accomplish this if one actually had to perform such computation. See Isaacson and Keller (1966).

[44] The denominator is positive because it is merely $|Q|^2$. The numerator is positive by Schwartz's inequality or, in a form which may be more familiar in three dimensions, it is

$$|P|^2|Q|^2 - (P\cdot Q)^2 = |P|^2|Q|^2 - |P|^2|Q|^2\cos^2\alpha$$
$$= |P|^2|Q|^2(1-\cos^2\alpha) \geqslant 0\,,$$

where $\alpha$ is the "angle" between $P$ and $Q$.

computing $\alpha_q^*$ may be reapplied until $S_q^T G_{q+1}$ is sufficiently small;[45] another alternative is simply to skip the "update" cycle (step 3) when $S_q^T G_{q+1}$ is too large. In other words, if $\alpha_q^*$ is not close enough to the minimum along $S_q$, set $\mathbf{H}_{q+1} = \mathbf{H}_q$ and $\mathbf{S}_{q+1} = \mathbf{H}_{q+1} G_{q+1}$, and continue as before. As long as $F_{q+1} < F_q$, the method will continue to progress towards the minimum.

It is difficult to choose between these approaches; the first may require excessive computation to refine $\alpha^*$ at points far from $X_M$, but the second approach may pass up valuable opportunities to improve the **H**-matrix. A reasonable compromise is to set a moderate criterion for $S_q^T G_{q+1}$, limit the number of refits, and then skip the update if the criterion is not met after a few tries.

Another area of numerical difficulty with the method has been identified.[46] This is a classical roundoff error problem. Suppose that $\mathbf{H}_0 = \mathbf{I}$ and that the elements of $\mathbf{N}_0$ are on the order of 1. However, the elements of $\mathbf{M}_0$ will be on the order of $|\alpha_0^* S_0| / |Y_0|$, which may be anything, depending on the scale factors of $F$ and $X$. Consider minimizing $bF$, where $b$ is some positive scalar; $\mathbf{M}_0$ will be scaled by $b$, but $\mathbf{N}_0$ will be unchanged. On the other hand, if we are working in the space $aX$ where $a$ is a positive scalar, $\mathbf{M}_0$ will be scaled by $a^2$. The numerical significance of this is that if the scaling turns out to be bad, depending upon the scale factor we may have, in finite digit arithmetic, either

$$\mathbf{H}_1 \simeq \mathbf{H}_0 + \mathbf{N}_0$$

or

$$\mathbf{H}_1 \simeq \mathbf{M}_0 ,$$

and the latter form is *singular*. Once some $\mathbf{H}_q$ is singular, there is little hope of recovery. Bard[47] recommends overcoming the problem in one of two ways:

1. Increase the precision of the arithmetic.
2. Scale the variables appropriately.

The initial scaling should (for these purposes) be such that the diagonal elements of $\mathbf{M}_0$ are approximately 1. The scaling should be rechecked and revised as necessary either if the method bogs down or if it is observed that the magnitudes of **H**, **M**, and **N** are consistently disparate.

In practice the method is so powerful that difficulties seldom arise except on very badly distorted or eccentric functions. In such problems, however, the **H**-matrix will occasionally become indisposed in spite of all precautions, and $G_{q+1}^T S_{q+1}$ will be positive, indicating that $S_{q+1}$ is not a direction of descent. In this case, the most efficacious remedy seems to be to set **H** back to $\mathbf{H}_0$ (or

[45] Equation (2.147) indicated that $S_q^T G_{q+1}$ must be small compared to $S_q^T G_q$, so perhaps a better indicator than $c$ (Eq. 2.70) would be $S_q^T G_{q+1} / S_q^T G_q$.

[46] See Bard (1968).

[47] *Ibid.*

some other predetermined positive definite matrix) and proceed as if starting over. The previously mentioned rescaling would have to be done in conjunction with a resetting of $\mathbf{H}$. Of course, if this has to be done repeatedly and in many fewer cycles than $n$, the method could not be expected to work well.

It is possible to alter the update equations (step 3) so that the positive definiteness is theoretically preserved regardless of the accuracy of $\alpha_q^*$. Such a technique may be of value, but in the case of an inaccurate $\alpha_q^*$, since the data are really not correct, it may do more harm than good to update $\mathbf{H}$.

For termination of the method, we may use any of the previously discussed ideas. Also, because $\mathbf{H}_q$ is approaching $\mathbf{J}_M^{-1}$, we have at least one additional option. Assume that $\mathbf{H}_q$ is a good approximation to $\mathbf{J}_M^{-1}$; then in the iteration

$$X_{q+1} = X_q + \alpha_q^* S_q \equiv X_q - \alpha_q^* \mathbf{H}_q \nabla F_q$$

the step $\alpha_q^*$ would be approximately of unit length. Thus

$$X_{q+1} - X_q \simeq - \mathbf{H}_q \nabla F_q .$$

The Taylor series about $X_q$ produces

$$F(X_{q+1}) = F(X_q) + (X_{q+1} - X_q)^T \nabla F_q + \cdots$$

and we have

$$F(X_{q+1}) - F(X_q) \simeq - \nabla F_q^T \mathbf{H}_q \nabla F_q .$$

Thus a reasonable stop criterion is available by testing the expected function difference between the current point and the minimum. In a fractional form the criterion becomes

$$\frac{\nabla F_q^T \mathbf{H}_q \nabla F_q}{|F(X_q)|} < \epsilon .$$

It would be wise to use other checks in conjunction with this test to safeguard against premature termination or prolonged iteration in pathological situations.

Finally we note that, as with any gradient method, the computation of $\nabla F$ by finite difference (see Section 2.7) can be considered for the variable metric method. A paper by Stewart (1967) develops some special techniques for the variable metric method. Briefly, these involve the fact that since $\mathbf{H}_q$ is an approximation to $[\partial^2 F/\partial x_i \partial x_j]^{-1}$, we can extract an approximation to $\partial^2 F/\partial x_i^2$ from it. With this and an *a priori* estimate of the accuracy with which $F(X)$ itself can be computed, Stewart develops a solid estimate of the increment size ($\epsilon_i$ in Eq. 2.76) that will produce maximum accuracy. With Stewart's modifications, this method becomes competitive with Powell's method for situations in which formulas for the gradient components are not available or are impractical to derive or compute.

## 2.12 CHOOSING A METHOD

We have discussed a wide variety of unconstrained minimization methods in this chapter. In order to give the reader some guidance in choosing among them, we will briefly present our experience in their application. Some of these points were made as we discussed the methods, but a general drawing together of pertinent material may be useful.

This aspect of optimization (picking a method) is largely an art, although, to be sure, the better one's knowledge of the theory the better he is at the art. We will limit the discussion to three methods: Powell's (POW), conjugate gradient (CG), and variable metric (VM). These are the only ones which the author would consider using except in special situations. We will consider two problem classes: those for which the gradient is not available and those for which it is.

### Nongradient Problems

Taking the nongradient problems first, we would recommend that CG (with finite difference derivatives) not be considered except perhaps for very large, well-conditioned problems. Its stability is usually too weak to compensate for the use of approximate gradients. The possible exception is that in very large problems (200 variables and up) both POW and VM require excessive storage capacity and hence become impractical.

In small problems (2 to 10 variables) without gradients, it is probably a toss-up between POW and VM (with finite difference derivatives); any differences in efficiency for this size problem are strongly dependent on the problem. For the medium-size problem (10 to 50 variables), VM with finite difference derivatives is probably preferred for ill-conditioned problems, but otherwise it is still a draw. For large problems (50 to 200 variables), VM is usually more dependable. For very large, ill-conditioned problems (200 variables or more) with no gradients available, one is likely to need divine assistance, but VM is probably the best bet, the storage problem notwithstanding.

If, in the nongradient situation, the function is known *not* to possess a continuous gradient, POW is the preferred method across the board, with extra care being exercised in the minimizing step section of the code.

### Gradient Problems

As a general rule, if the exact gradient of the function is available at negligible computational cost (e.g., if $\nabla F$ requires less time than $n$ computations of $F$), it should be used in conjunction with a gradient method. If the function is ill-behaved, the compulsion to use the exact gradient is increased, and one might be well advised to use it in order to obtain the increased accuracy, even if the computational cost *exceeds* that of finite difference.

Beyond this, VM is preferred for small- and medium-sized problems. At somewhere between 50 and 150 variables, the computational effort required in the steps of the VM algorithm itself becomes appreciably greater than for the CG method. When the computation becomes a significant portion of the total, the CG method is preferred. In any event, beyond 200 to 300 variables, most computers run out of core storage for **H**, and backing store[48] is usually prohibitively slow. Thus, in spite of its weaker stability, the CG method eventually becomes the most efficient as problem size increases.

With regard to the 1-dimensional minimization required in all three methods, the cubic interpolation is usually the best of those discussed if the gradient or slope is readily computed.

Finally, we note that there are many other methods besides those discussed here. Some of these are ineffective, and others fill more or less the same needs as those presented here. New methods seem to be devised almost daily; occasionally one of these turns out to represent a real advance. References are given at the end of this chapter for those interested in learning about other methods or in obtaining more detail about the methods given here.

## EXERCISES

**2.1** Given a real symmetric matrix **K**, we define its $m$th discriminant $\Delta_m$ as the determinant of the matrix obtained by deleting all elements that do not simultaneously lie in the first $m$ rows and columns of **K**. It can be shown that **K** is positive definite if and only if all $\Delta_m$ are positive, $m = 1, \ldots, n$. Apply this test to the matrix of second derivatives of $F_1$ (Eq. 2.6) at the following points:

$$1{,}1 \qquad 2{,}2 \qquad 1{,}2 \qquad 0{,}1\,.$$

Relate your results to the shape of the contours at the corresponding points in Fig. 2.1.

**2.2** The Taylor series expansion of a function of two variables about the point $(\bar{x}_1, \bar{x}_2)$ is

$$\begin{aligned} F(x_1, x_2) = \bar{F} &+ (x_1 - \bar{x}_1)\overline{\frac{\partial F}{\partial x_1}} + (x_2 - \bar{x}_2)\overline{\frac{\partial F}{\partial x_2}} \\ &+ \frac{1}{2}(x_1 - \bar{x}_1)^2\overline{\frac{\partial^2 F}{\partial x_1{}^2}} + \frac{1}{2}(x_2 - \bar{x}_2)^2\overline{\frac{\partial^2 F}{\partial x_2{}^2}} \\ &+ (x_1 - \bar{x}_1)(x_2 - \bar{x}_2)\overline{\frac{\partial^2 F}{\partial x_1 \partial x_2}} + \cdots \end{aligned}$$

where the overbar denotes "evaluated at $(\bar{x}_1, \bar{x}_2)$." Verify that the vector-matrix form up to the quadratic terms

$$F(X) \simeq Q(X) = \bar{F} + (X - \bar{X})^T\overline{\nabla F} + \tfrac{1}{2}(X - \bar{X})^T\bar{\mathbf{J}}(X - \bar{X})$$

is justified.

**2.3** Verify that **J** at (0.61173, 1.4929) for $F_3$ (Eq. 2.8) is not positive definite.

---

[48] Tape, drum, or disc.

**2.4** Write a computer program to apply the extended random walk (Fig. 2.6) to $F_1$, $F_2$, and $F_3$. Print out sufficient data to allow the progress of the algorithm to be followed, using several different starting points.

**2.5** Given the function

$$F = \frac{10x^2 - 4xy + 2y^2}{5x^2 - 4xy + 5y^2}.$$

Substitute $X = X_q + \alpha S_q$ into the function in the form of $x = x_q + \alpha s_{q,1}$ and $y = y_q + \alpha s_{q,2}$ (i.e., $x_1 \equiv x$, $x_2 \equiv y$), and derive an exact formula for $\alpha^*$. What is the significance of the two values of $\alpha^*$?

**2.6** The function of Exercise 2.5 is a special case of the ratio of two quadratic forms which can be written in matrix form as

$$F = X^T \mathbf{K} X / X^T \mathbf{M} X.$$

Derive a formula for $\alpha^*$ in terms of the matrices **K** and **M** and the vectors $X_q$ and $S_q$.

**2.7** Derive an approximate formula for $\alpha^*$ (analogous to Eq. 2.19) for an arbitrary choice of points $\alpha_1$, $\alpha_2$, and $\alpha_3$. In other words, solve Eqs. (2.16) for $b$ and $c$, and substitute into Eq. (2.15).

**2.8** Verify that Eq. (2.25) gives the correct value for $H(\tilde{\alpha}^*)$.

**2.9** Program the quadratic interpolation scheme of Fig. 2.14 as a subroutine (FORTRAN) or as a procedure (ALGOL). It should have no common or global variables except the function subroutine or procedure; i.e., all input and output for the routine should be in the formal arguments. The arguments should be the current point $X$, the direction vector $S$, an estimate of the step size $t_0$, the value $F_1$ of $F$ at $X$, the new point $Y$, the minimizing step length $\alpha^*$, and a signal or flag $B$ to be used in case something goes awry in the process (e.g., looping in A). Assume that the convergence test for $\alpha^*$ is outside the routine. Test your routine on $F_1$, $F_2$, and $F_3$ by picking several different $X$'s and directions and then comparing the computer answer with either a graphical or an exact hand calculation.

**2.10** Show by direct substitution that if $F = \frac{1}{2}X^T A X + X^T B + c$, then the two-point central formula Eq. (2.77) is exact.

**2.11** Write a computer program for the basic version of Powell's method, given in Fig 2.20. Use the subprogram of Exercise 2.9 in the minimization blocks. Add a convergence check at an appropriate spot. Apply the program to $F_1$, $F_2$, and $F_3$. Apply the program to $F_4$, starting from the point (0.3674, 0.4799, 2.0000). The results should be approximately the same as in Table 2.4, through step 4 of cycle 4. Differences that develop will be due to the buildup of minor differences in the accuracy in finding $\alpha^*$.

**2.12** Euler integration is a numerical technique for approximating a solution to $dy/d\alpha = f(y,\alpha)$, given the initial condition $y = y_0$ at $\alpha = 0$. As numerical schemes go, it is fairly primitive but very simple to apply: Denote the approximation to $y$ at some point $\alpha_j$ as $y_j$; then, taking $\Delta\alpha_j$ as a small step, compute an approximation at $\alpha_{j+1} = \alpha_j + \Delta\alpha_j$ as $y_{j+1} = y_j + \Delta\alpha_j f(y_j, \alpha_j)$. For the vector differential equation $dY/d\alpha = F(Y, \alpha)$, the simplest version of the method is

$$Y_{j+1} = Y_j + \Delta\alpha_j F(Y_j, \alpha_j).$$

Apply the method to finding the minimum of $F_1$ (Eq. 2.6) by integrating the system of differential equations

$$dX/d\alpha = \nabla F_1 .$$

In component form, these would be

$$dx_1/d\alpha = -(4x_1^3 - 4x_2x_1 + 2x_1 - 2) ,$$
$$dx_2/d\alpha = -(-2x_1^2 + 2x_2) .$$

Take the initial conditions to be the point (0,1), and initially use $\Delta\alpha = 0.1$. Take about 10 steps, changing $\Delta\alpha$ as necessary [e.g., if $\nabla F_1(X_j)$ differs greatly from $\nabla F_1(X_{j+1})$, or if it gets too small].

**2.13** A shipping carton is sometimes made with top and bottom formed by flaps extending from each side as shown in Fig. 2.37. Assume that a box enclosing 2 ft³ is required; find dimensions $a$, $b$, and $c$ such that a minimum amount of material is used. Do this by formulating a function of two variables (using the volume equality constraint to eliminate a variable) and minimizing it with one of the methods in this chapter. The problem can be solved analytically, so compare the computer answer with an exact answer.

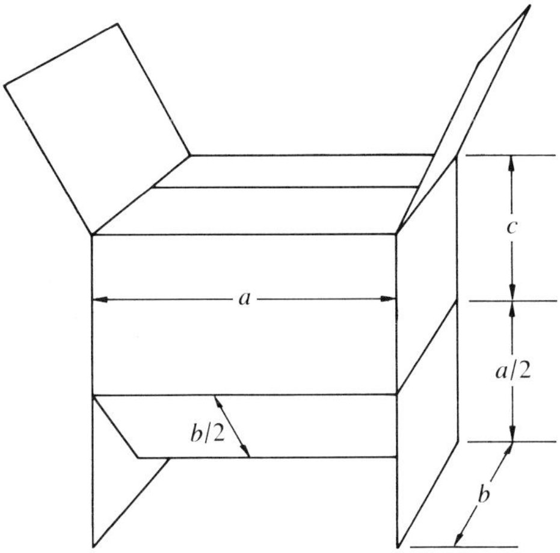


**Figure 2.37**

**2.14**(a) Repeat Exercise 2.9 for cubic interpolation, as in Fig. 2.26. Add an argument to the list which gives the number of times block A is traversed. Also, add arguments to pass the values of the gradient and the function value at the interpolated point out of the routine. Include a convergence test (e.g., $c$ of Eq. 2.70) and arrange the logic so that the approximation will be refined until the test is satisfied, but include an upper limit on the number of such refits.

b) Include a convergence check, but alternate the cubic interpolation with a bisection.

c) Substitute the regula falsi for cubic interpolation, and arrange as in part (b) above.

**2.15** Write a program for the conjugate gradient method. Utilize one of the subprograms of Exercise 2.14 to accomplish the minimization along the directions. Include a restart option and an overall termination criterion and compare the results with Table 2.5.

**2.16** Write a program for the variable metric method. Utilize one of the subprograms of Exercise 2.14 to accomplish the minimization along the directions. Include restart logic to be activated if $S_q^T \nabla F$ becomes nonnegative, and include a 1-dimensional minimization test criterion to determine whether the $\mathbf{H}$-matrix should be updated or not. Compare the results with those in Table 2.5.

## REFERENCES


Ayres, F., Jr., *Theory and Problems of Matrices*, Schaums Outline Series, Schaum Pub. Co., New York (1962)

Bard, Y., "On a Numerical Instability of Davidon-like Methods," *Math. Comp.* **22** (103), 665–666 (July 1968)

Bauer, F. L., "Optimally Scaled Matrices," *Num. Math.* **5**, 73–87 (1963)

Bradbury, W. W., and R. Fletcher, "New Iterative Methods for Solution of the Eigenproblem," *Num. Math.* **9**, 259–267 (1966)

Brooks, S. H., "A Discussion of Random Methods for Seeking Maxima," *Operations Res.* **6** (2), 244–251 (1958)

Brooks, S. H., "A Comparison of Maximum-Seeking Methods," *J. Operations Res. Soc. Am.* **7** (4), 430–457 (1959)

Broyden, C. G., "A Class of Methods for Solving Nonlinear Simultaneous Equations," *Math. Comp.*, **19** (92), 577–593 (1965)

Broyden, C. G., "Quasi-Newton Methods and Their Application to Function Minimization," *Math. Comp.* **21** (99), 368–380 (1967)

Buehler, R. J., B. V. Shah, and O. Kempthorne, "Some Further Properties of the Method of Parallel Tangents and Conjugate Gradients," Iowa State Univ. Stat. Lab. Tech. Rep. No. 3 (1961a)

Buehler, R. J., B. V. Shah and O. Kempthorne, "Some Properties of Steepest Ascent and Related Procedures for Finding Optimum Conditions," Iowa State Univ. Stat. Lab. (April 1961b)

Case Western Reserve University, Division of SMSMD, "Developments in Discrete Element Finite Deflection Structural Analysis by Function Minimization," Tech. Rep. AFFDL-TR-68-126, Air Force Structural Dynamics Laboratory (Sept. 1968)

Cauchy, A., "Méthode générale pour la résolution des systèmes d'équations simultanées," Compt. Rend. l'Academie des Sciences **25**, 536–538 (1847)

Crocket, J. B., and R. Chernoff, "Gradient Methods of Maximization," *Pacific J. Math.* **5**, 33–50 (1955)

Curry, H. B., "The Method of Steepest Descent for Nonlinear Minimization Problems," *Quart. Appl. Math.* **2** (3), 258–261 (1944)

Daniel, J. W., "The Conjugate Gradient Method for Linear and Nonlinear Operator Equations," *SIAM J. Numer. Anal.* **4** (1), 10–26 (1967a)

Daniel, J. W., "Convergence of the Conjugate Gradient Method with Computationally Convenient Modifications," *Numer. Math.* **10**, 125–131 (1967b)

Davidon, W. C., "Variable Metric Method for Minimization," Argonne Natl. Lab. ANL-5990 Rev., University of Chicago (1959)

Fletcher, R., "Function Minimization without Evaluating Derivatives—A Review," *Computer J.* **8** (1), 33–41 (1965)

Fletcher, R., and M. J. D. Powell, "A Rapidly Convergent Descent Method for Minimization," *Computer J.* **6** (2), 163–168 (1963)

Fletcher, R., and C. M. Reeves, "Function Minimization by Conjugate Gradients," *Computer J.* **7** (2), 149–154 (1964)

Forsythe, G., and T. S. Motzkin, "Acceleration of the Optimum Gradient Method, Preliminary Report," *Bull. Am. Math. Soc.* **57**, 304–305 (1951)

Fox, R. L., and M. P. Kapoor, "A Minimization Method for the Solution of the Eigenproblem Arising in Structural Dynamics," presented at the Second Air Force Conference on Matrix Methods in Structural Mechanics, Wright-Patterson AFB, Ohio (1968)

Fox, R. L., and E. L. Stanton, "Developments in Structural Analysis by Direct Energy Minimization," *AIAA J.* **6** (6), 1036–1042 (1968)

Hestenes, M. R., "The Conjugate Gradient Methods for Solving Linear Systems," *Proc. of Symp. in Appl. Math.*, vol. 6, McGraw-Hill, New York (1956)

Hestenes, M. R., and E. Stiefel, "Methods of Conjugate Gradients for Solving Linear Systems," *J. Res. Natl. Bur. Standards* **B49**, 409–436 (1952)

Hoerl, A. E., "Optimum Solution of Many Variables Equations," *Chem. Eng. Progr.* **55**, 69–78 (1959)

Hooke, R., and T. A. Jeeves, "'Direct Search' Solution of Numerical and Statistical Problems," *J. Assoc. Comp. Mach.* **8** (2), 212–229 (1961)

Hotelling, H., "Experimental Determination of the Maximum of a Function," *Am. Math. Stat.* **12**, 20–45 (1941)

Isaacson, E., and H. B. Keller, *Analysis of Numerical Methods*, Wiley, New York (1966)

Kelly, H. J., "Method of Gradients," Ch. 6 of *Optimization Techniques with Applications to Aerospace Systems*, ed. G. Leitmann, Academic Press, New York (1962)

Kowalik, J., "Iterative Methods for Large Systems of Linear Equations in Matrix Structural Analysis," *Inter. Shipbuilding Progress* **13** (138), 59–68 (1966)

Levenberg, K., "A Method for the Solution of Certain Nonlinear Problems in Least Squares," *Quart. Appl. Math.* **2**, 164–168 (1944)

Mugele, R. A., "A Nonlinear Digital Optimizing Program for Process Control Systems," *Proc. of Western Joint Computer Conference* (1962)

Pearson, J. D., "On Variable Metric Methods of Minimization," Research Analysis Corporation Technical Paper RAC-TP-302, McLean, Virginia (1968)

Powell, M. J. D., "An Iterative Method for Finding Stationary Values of a Function of Several Variables," *Computer J.* **5** (2), 147–151 (1962)

Powell, M. J. D., "An Efficient Method for Finding the Minimum of a Function of Several Variables without Calculating Derivatives," *Computer J.* **7** (4), 155–162 (1964)

Rosenbrock, H. H., "Automatic Method for Finding the Greatest or Least Value of a Function," *Computer J.* **3** (3), 175–184 (1960)

Schmit, L. A., and R. L. Fox, "Synthesis of a Simple Shock Isolator," NASA CR-55 (1964)

Shah, B. V., R. J. Buehler, and O. Kempthorne, "The Method of Parallel Tangents (PARTAN) for Finding an Optimum," O.N.R. Res. Rept. NR-042-207 (No. 2), 1961

Shah, B. V., R. J. Buehler, and O. Kempthorne, "Some Algorithms for Minimizing a Function of Several Variables," *J. SIAM* **12** (1), 74–92 (1964)

Southwell, R. V., *Relaxation Methods in Engineering Science*, Oxford University Press, New York (1940)

Spang, H. A., "A Review of Minimization Techniques for Nonlinear Functions," *SIAM Review* **4**, 373–405 (1962)

Stanton, E. L., "A Discrete Element Analysis of Elastoplastic Plates by Energy Minimization," Case Western Reserve University, SMSMD Div. Rep. No. 27 (October 1968)

Stewart, G. W., "A Modification of Davidon's Minimization Method to Accept Difference Approximations of Derivatives," *J. ACM* **14** (1), 72–83 (1967)

Wilde, D. J., "Objective Function Indistinguishability in Unimodal Optimization," *Proc. Sym. on Recent Advances in Optimization Techniques*, A. Lavi and T. Vogl, eds., Wiley, New York (1965)

Wilde, D. J., and C. S. Beightler, *Foundations of Optimization*, Prentice-Hall, Englewood Cliffs, N. J. (1967)

Zangwill, W. I., "Minimizing a Function without Calculating Derivatives," *Computer J.* **10** (3), 293–296 (1967)

CHAPTER 3

# CONSTRAINED PROBLEMS BY UNCONSTRAINED MINIMIZATION

In the previous chapter we discussed a number of methods for finding the minimum of a function $F(X)$ when there are no restrictions on the choice of values of $X$. In Chapter 1, however, we saw that, in many engineering problems, practical considerations place constraints or limitations on the range of permissible values for $X$. The unconstrained methods cannot cope directly with these limitations, and in this chapter we describe a number of reformulations that take the constraints into account with unconstrained minimization. Such methods are referred to here as *indirect methods*.

For problems of moderate complexity, the unconstrained formulations for constrained problems are usually simple to apply, provided an adequate minimization algorithm is available. Because of this, these approaches have attained widespread use for "every-day" problems. On the other hand, they may not be as efficient for some problems as the *direct methods* that will be described in Chapter 4.

The formulations to be discussed include direct transformation methods and a variety of so-called *penalty function techniques*. Before taking up these topics, however, we briefly discuss the nature of the optimization problem in the presence of constraints. The discussion will be taken up again in Chapter 4. The following remarks should set the stage for the present chapter.

## 3.1 SOME CONCEPTS IN THE CONSTRAINED PROBLEM

In the previous chapter we noted that our basic definition of a minimum as the point of least function value is not particularly useful from an operational point of view. That is to say, it is not useful in determining whether a given point is optimal. Furthermore, even if we restrict our attention to functions with continuous derivatives, we find that the vanishing of the gradient and positive definiteness of the matrix of second partial derivatives are only necessary and not sufficient conditions for a minimum because there can be relative minima. We asserted that we could reasonably consider the point to which one of our better algorithms converges as at least a relative minimum. Moreover, we contended that when an engineering design problem possesses relative minima, we are not seriously handicapped because we, as designers, know roughly where to start to secure the best of the relative minima. The reason for these assertions is, of course, that at the present time the general theory for nonlinear minimization does not provide enough guidance, and hence we must resort to our insight and intuition.

If anything, the situation is even less secure in constrained problems: relative minima occur in constrained problems for a wider variety of reasons than in unconstrained problems, and the operational tests are more complex.

Consider the following inequality constrained problem: Find $\boldsymbol{X}$ such that $F(\boldsymbol{X}) \to \min$, subject to

$$g_j(\boldsymbol{X}) \leqslant 0\,, \qquad j=1,\ldots,m\,.$$

It is evident that the minimum may be a point where the constraints have no influence, as pictured in Fig. 3.1. If $F$ has continuous derivatives, the minimum is characterized as before:

$$\boldsymbol{\nabla} F = \boldsymbol{0}\,,$$
$$\mathbf{J} \equiv [\partial^2 F/\partial x_i \partial x_j] \text{ positive definite.}$$

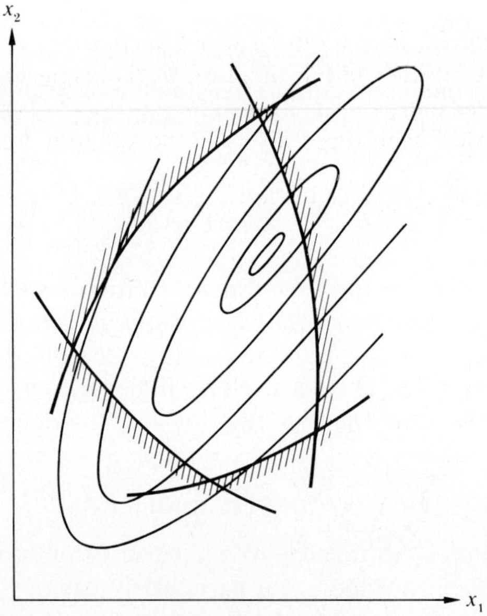


**Figure 3.1**

It is possible, however, for the situation depicted in Fig. 3.2 to obtain in constrained problems. Here the minimum *admissible* design occurs at point $P$, where $\boldsymbol{\nabla} F \neq \boldsymbol{0}$ but where one of the $g_j(X)=0$. If both $g_j$ and $F$ are differentiable, it is geometrically reasonable that a necessary condition for a minimum in this case is

$$\boldsymbol{\nabla} F = \lambda \boldsymbol{\nabla} g_j\,, \qquad \lambda < 0\,, \tag{3.1}$$

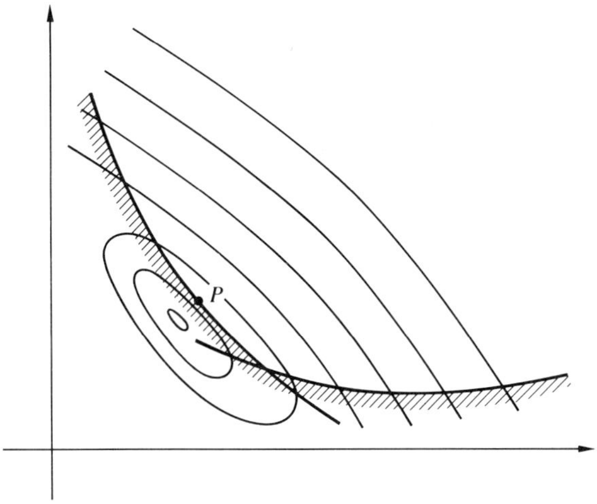


**Figure 3.2**

where $\lambda$ is some scalar. This requires that the contours of $F$ be tangent to the constraint and that both $F$ and $g_j$ increase in the same direction. That this is not a sufficient condition is seen by examining point $Q$ in Fig. 3.3. Here $\nabla F$ and $\nabla g_j$ point in the same direction, but the contour bends away from the constraint.

In this particular illustration the minimum may lie at points $P$ or $P'$.

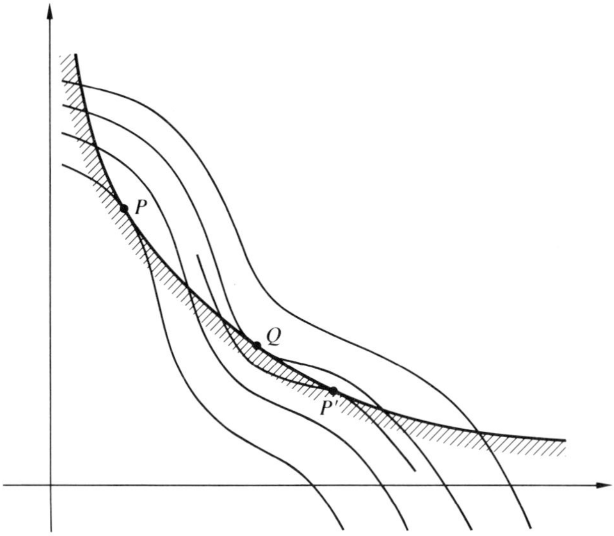


**Figure 3.3**

These two points are relative minima, in the sense that no admissible design in some small neighborhood has a lower value of the objective function.

Figure 3.4 shows another possibility. Here there are relative minima that are due to the form of the constraints, while those in Fig. 3.3 are due to the objective function. These distinctions are rather weak and defy rigorous definition, but their physical implications in design problems are interesting to consider.

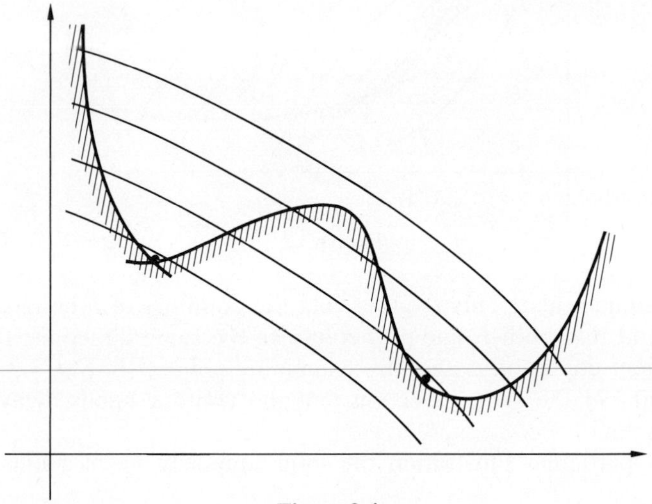

**Figure 3.4**

We can sharpen the idea of necessary conditions for a relative minimum by stating an operational test which a proposed minimum must pass. This is called the *Kuhn-Tucker condition.* Roughly it consists of defining a cone expressed by the normals to all the active constraints at the point in question and then testing to see whether the gradient to the objective function is contained in the cone. This test will be discussed in detail in Chapter 4.

## 3.2 ELIMINATION OF CONSTRAINTS: TRANSFORMATIONS

The minimization of a function subject to inequality constraints is orders of magnitude more difficult than unconstrained minimization. Occasionally, however, it is possible to eliminate some or all of the constraints from a problem. In some cases, if the $g_j(X)$ are explicit functions of the $x_i$ and have certain simple forms, it is possible to make a *change of variable* such that the constraints are automatically satisfied. In other problems, it is possible to determine in advance which constraints will be active at the solution and use the particular equation $g_j(X) = 0$ to *eliminate variables* from the problem. These two approaches are discussed briefly in this section.

As an example of the technique of transformations,[1] consider minimizing some function $F(x_1, x_2, x_3)$ with the three independent variables $x_1, x_2, x_3$ constrained by

$$0 \leqslant x_1 \leqslant x_2 \leqslant x_3 \,, \tag{3.2}$$

or, in terms of constraint functions,

$$\begin{aligned} g_1 &\equiv -x_1 \leqslant 0 \,, \\ g_2 &\equiv x_1 - x_2 \leqslant 0 \,, \\ g_3 &\equiv x_2 - x_3 \leqslant 0 \,. \end{aligned} \tag{3.3}$$

Then consider the transformations

$$\begin{aligned} x_1 &= y_1^2 \,, \\ x_2 &= y_1^2 + y_2^2 \,, \end{aligned} \tag{3.4}$$

$$x_3 = y_1^2 + y_2^2 + y_3^2 \,. \tag{3.5}$$

We note that $F(y_1, y_2, y_3)$ can be minimized without regard to the constraints. Other examples of transformations are:

$$\begin{aligned} &\text{a)}\ x_i = y_i^2 \,, \\ &\text{b)}\ x_i = e^{y_i} \,, \\ &\text{c)}\ x_i = \frac{y_i^2}{1 + y_i^2} \,, \\ &\text{d)}\ x_i = \sin^2 y_i \,, \\ &\text{e)}\ x_i = \frac{e^{y_i}}{e^{y_i} + e^{-y_i}} \,, \\ &\text{f)}\ x_i = \sin y_i \text{ or } \cos y_i \,, \\ &\text{g)}\ x_i = \frac{2y_i}{1 + y_i^2} \,. \end{aligned} \tag{3.6}$$

Transformations (a) and (b) constrain $x_i$ to be positive, (c), (d), and (e) ensure $0 \leqslant x_1 \leqslant 1$, and (f) and (g) keep $x_i$ between plus and minus 1. A common pair of constraints which can be handled with these transformations is

$$\alpha_i \leqslant x_i \leqslant \beta_i \,, \tag{3.7}$$

[1] See Box (1965).

which is satisfied by any $x_i$ satisfying

$$x_i = \alpha_i + (\beta_i - \alpha_i) \sin^2 y_i \,. \tag{3.8}$$

To provide a more complete example of the use of transformations, let us apply the method to a problem known as the post office parcel problem. The post office requires that a parcel be no longer than 42 in. and be proportioned such that its length plus its girth is less than 72 in. The problem posed is: What is the parcel of largest volume (assuming a rectangular parallelepiped) which satisfies the regulation?

Taking $L$, $W$, and $D$ as the dimensions of the package, the regulations translate to

$$\begin{aligned} &\text{i)}\ \ L \leqslant 42\,, \\ &\text{ii)}\ \ L + 2W + 2D \leqslant 72\,; \end{aligned} \tag{3.9a}$$

the objective function is the negative of the volume

$$F(L,W,D) = -V = -LWD\,; \tag{3.10}$$

and finally, for obvious reasons,

$$\begin{aligned} &\text{iii)}\ \ 0 \leqslant L\,, \\ &\text{iv)}\ \ 0 \leqslant W\,, \\ &\text{v)}\ \ 0 \leqslant D\,. \end{aligned} \tag{3.9b}$$

Note that (ii), (iii), (iv), and (v), taken together, automatically ensure $W \leqslant 42$ and $D \leqslant 42$.

We first make a transformation which converts all inequalities to the form $\alpha_i \leqslant y_i \leqslant \beta_i$. Take $L = y_1$, $W = y_2$, $y_3 = (L + 2W + 2D)$, which leads to $D = \frac{1}{2}(y_3 - y_1 - 2y_2)$. The constraints

$$\begin{aligned} 0 \leqslant y_1 \leqslant 42\,, \\ 0 \leqslant y_2 \leqslant 42\,, \\ 0 \leqslant y_3 \leqslant 72\,, \end{aligned} \tag{3.11}$$

ensure all the original constraints except $0 \leqslant D$; but clearly, since $L$ and $W$ are constrained to be positive, $D < 0$ implies $V < 0$, which cannot possibly be a maximum. Finally, we transform

$$\begin{aligned} y_1 = 42 \sin^2 \gamma_1\,, \\ y_2 = 42 \sin^2 \gamma_2\,, \\ y_3 = 72 \sin^2 \gamma_3\,, \end{aligned} \tag{3.12}$$

giving

$$F = -(42)^2 \sin^2 \gamma_1 \sin^2 \gamma_2 (72 \sin^2 \gamma_3 - 42 \sin^2 \gamma_1 - 84 \sin^2 \gamma_2)/2, \tag{3.13}$$

which has a minimum at $\gamma_1 = 0.857$, $\gamma_2 = 0.564$, $\gamma_3 = 1.571$, or $L = 24$, $W = 12$, $D = 12$, and $V = 3456$.

Hindsight being better than foresight, we can now say that we should have noted that the optimum would be a place where $W = D$ (see Exercise 3.2).

The technique of using transformations to eliminate constraints obviously requires that the $g_j$ be explicit; the technique also needs, hopefully, simple functions of the $x_i$. Beyond this the major limitations of the method lie in the user's ability to invent the necessary transformations. At least a cursory quest for such transformations should be part of the formulation stage of any engineering optimization problem.

If only some of the constraints can be eliminated, it may be better to treat them by the same method as the remaining constraints, i.e., not transform them. The transformations may possibly produce a function with poor conditioning or considerably increase the computational effort required to determine $F$ or $\nabla F$.

### Elimination of Variables

The idea of using the inequality constraints to *eliminate* variables from a problem depends on our ability to determine which constraints will be active at the optimum. Take the post office parcel problem as an example: Suppose we recognize that $W = D$ and then minimize $F = -LW^2$, subject to

$$\text{i)}\quad 0 \leqslant L \leqslant 42\,,$$

$$\text{ii)}\quad L + 4W \leqslant 72\,.$$

If we surmise that at the optimum $L = 42$, then $F = -42W^2$, which has a minimum of $-\infty$ at $W = \infty$; obviously this is an unacceptable solution. On the other hand, if we assume that (ii) is active, we get, for example, $L = 72 - 4W$ or $F = -(72 - 4W)W^2$. This has a minimum at $dF/dW = 0$ that gives $-144W + 12W^2 = 0$, or $W = 12$, etc.

In a general problem with $m$ constraints, we would have to check (1) the minimum of $F$ with no constraints, (2) the minimum of $F$ taking one constraint at a time as an equality, (3) the minimum of $F$ taking each of all possible pairs of constraints as equalities, etc. Any solution of these that is feasible and at which the Kuhn-Tucker conditions[2] are satisfied is likely to be at least a local solution to the original problem. However, in the absence of foreknowledge about which constraints are most likely to be active, the number of possibilities is enormous, namely,

$$1 + m + \frac{m(m-1)}{2} + \frac{m(m-1)(m-2)}{6} + \cdots + \frac{m!}{n!(m-n)!} = \sum_{i=0}^{n} \frac{m!}{i!(m-i)!}\,,$$

[2] See Chapter 4.

where $n$ is the number of variables in the original problem.[3] For example, with 5 variables and 8 constraints, we arrive at 219 different problems; with 9 constraints, we arrive at 382 problems.

In some problems, it may be known that *exactly n* constraints are active at the optimum.[4] Since, in general, $n$ equations in $n$ unknowns define a unique point, there are discrete points at which the minimum can occur. In such cases, a possible algorithm for solution might involve a systematic search among all these *vertices* for the point of least value $F$. The number of such points is $m!/[n!(m-n)!]$ which, for example, in the case of $n=5$, $m=9$ is 126, but for $n=10$, $m=25$, it is approximately $3 \times 10^4$. Thus the approach is not very attractive as a general method unless we can devise a scheme that involves some considerably smaller subset of the points (for example, the feasible points). Some methods which are based in part upon these ideas are discussed in Chapter 4.

### 3.3 MOTIVATION FOR THE PENALTY FUNCTIONS

In the latter part of Section 2.7, we mentioned the idea of a *differential gradient method* for minimizing a function $F(X)$ by solving the system of differential equations

$$\frac{dX(\alpha)}{d\alpha} = -\nabla F(X)\,, \tag{3.14}$$

subject to the initial condition $X(0) = X_0$. The solution $X(\alpha)$ is the so-called "orthogonal trajectory" from the point $X_0$, and it approaches a point $\nabla F = \mathbf{0}$ as $\alpha \to \infty$ in regular problems. The *long step methods* of Chapter 2 did not really make use of these differential equations, but in a sense they imitated the action of a solution procedure.

It is instructive to consider ways that we can modify Eq. (3.14) to incorporate the influence of constraints. One approach is to add something to Eq. (3.14) which would "bend" the trajectories into the feasible region. In this regard, consider

$$\frac{dX}{d\alpha} = -\nabla F(X) - \sum_j M_j \nabla g_j(X)\,, \tag{3.15}$$

where

$$M_j = M_j(X) \equiv \begin{cases} 0, & g_j(X) \leq 0\,, \\ r, & g_j(X) > 0\,, \end{cases} \tag{3.16}$$

---

[3] We assume that $m \geqslant n$, which is usually the case; otherwise the summation is taken to $m$.

[4] In particular, problems for which both the $g_j$ and $F$ are *linear functions* of the $x_i$ have solutions at points where exactly $n$ constraints are active. These problems are called *linear programming problems*, and special, efficient algorithms have been devised for them. They are discussed briefly in Chapter 4 and at length in the literature (see, for example, Hadley, 1962).

in which $r$ is some large positive constant. If $r$ is chosen sufficiently large, it causes the terms $-r\nabla g_j(X)$ to dominate in the infeasible region and hence to deflect all trajectories toward the feasible domain (see Fig. 3.5).

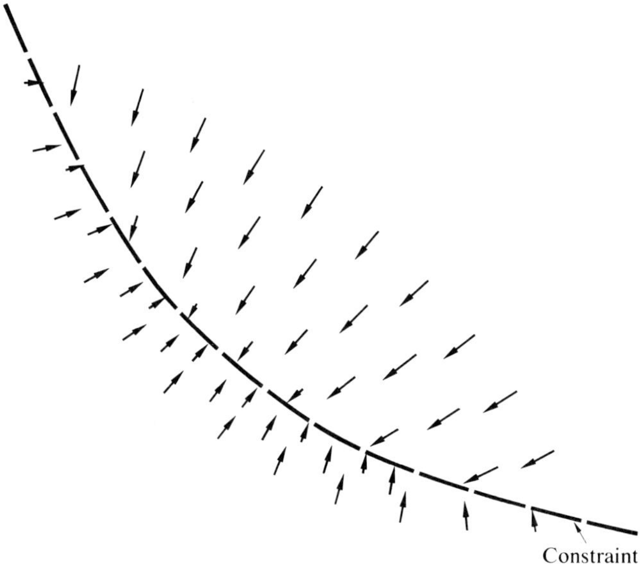


**Figure 3.5**

Since the $M_j(X)$ are discontinuous, the system Eq. (3.15) may not have a solution; hence the idea would not yield a practical method even for the analog computer. On the other hand, it is interesting to note that Eq. (3.15) does correspond to a certain unconstrained minimization problem. Consider the function

$$\phi = F + r \sum_j \langle g_j \rangle , \tag{3.17}$$

where the *bracket function* (or bracket operator) $\langle \cdot \rangle$ means[5]

$$\langle g \rangle = \begin{cases} g, & g \geq 0 , \\ 0, & g < 0 . \end{cases} \tag{3.18}$$

The derivative of $\langle g \rangle$ with respect to a scalar $x$ is

$$\frac{\partial \langle g \rangle}{\partial x} = \frac{\partial \langle g \rangle}{\partial g} \frac{\partial g}{\partial x} = H(g) \frac{\partial g}{\partial x} \tag{3.19}$$

[5] Another simple way of defining $\langle \cdot \rangle$ is $\langle g \rangle = \max[g,0]$, which is particularly useful in computer coding, as most languages contain some form of the max[. , .] function.

where $H(y)$ is the *step function,*

$$H(y) = \begin{cases} 1, & y > 0\,, \\ 0, & y \leq 0\,. \end{cases} \tag{3.20}$$

The gradient of $\langle g_j \rangle$ is thus

$$\nabla \langle g_j \rangle = H(g_j) \nabla g_j\,, \tag{3.21}$$

and we see that

$$\nabla \phi = \nabla F + r \sum_j H(g_j) \nabla g_j\,. \tag{3.22}$$

Returning to Eq. (3.17), we see that the effect of the added term $r \sum_j \langle g_j \rangle$ is to increase $\phi(X)$ in proportion to the amount by which the constraints are violated. The contours of a $\phi$-function such as this are depicted in Fig. 3.6. We see that if $r$ is chosen large enough, the minimum point of $\phi$ corresponds to a constrained minimum of $F$, subject to $g_j(X) \leq 0$.

The function described above is one of an almost endless variety of so-called penalty functions.[6] The object of these formulations is to convert the original constrained problem into one of unconstrained minimization. In Chapter 4, we will discuss a number of direct approaches to constrained

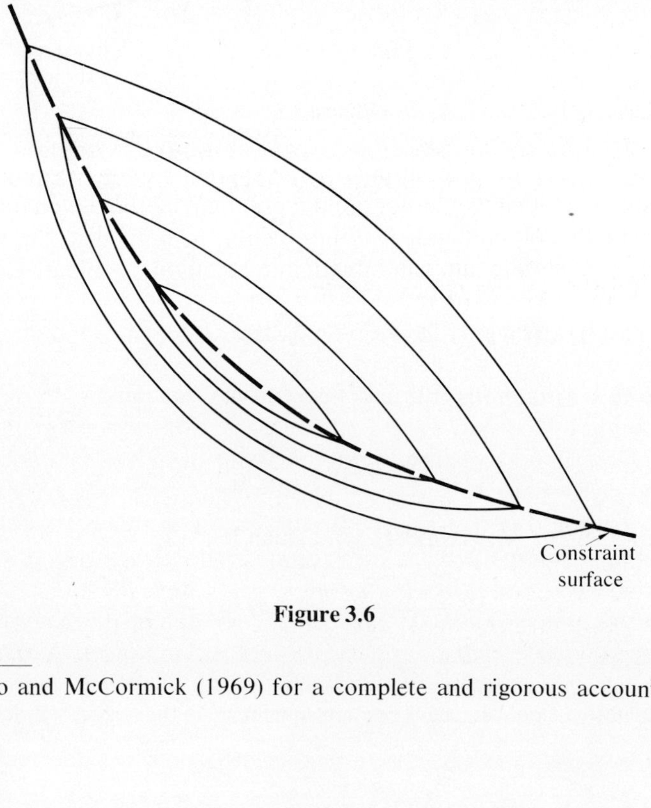


**Figure 3.6**

[6] See Fiacco and McCormick (1969) for a complete and rigorous account of penalty functions.

minimization in which we consider the constraints as limiting hypersurfaces and work at *directly* minimizing $F$ in their presence. In contrast, the penalty functions blend the constraints into a composite function and essentially make it possible to ignore them at the minimization stage. For this reason, the penalty function methods are sometimes referred to as *indirect methods*. In some cases, the penalty function approach is the most efficient means of solving a particular problem; in a number of instances, however, it is preferred mainly because of its convenience rather than its efficiency.

The penalty function formulations for inequality constrained problems which are in current use can be divided into two categories: interior and exterior. In the interior formulations, the unconstrained minima all lie in the feasible region and converge to the solution as a special parameter is varied. In the exterior formulations, they lie in the infeasible region and converge to the solution from the outside. For example, the method implied by Eq. (3.17) is an exterior formulation since, for some values of $r$, the minimum lies outside the acceptable region, and yet as $r$ is increased, the minimum of $\phi(X,r)$ is forced toward the acceptable domain. Clearly, unless $F$ has a minimum in the interior, $\phi(X,r)$ can never have a minimum which is strictly in the interior.

If there are equality constraints in the problem, there are penalty functions that can be used to provide an approach to a solution. Some of these techniques are as well justified theoretically as those for inequality constraints, but practically they turn out to be less effective. The problem of equality constraints is considered an underdeveloped area.

The remainder of this chapter will concentrate on the application of an exterior penalty function for inequalities, an interior penalty function, a penalty function for the parametric constraint $g_j(\boldsymbol{D},\theta) \leq 0$, $\theta_0 \leq \theta \leq \theta_1$, and several mixed equality/inequality penalty functions.

## 3.4 AN EXTERIOR, INEQUALITY PENALTY FUNCTION

The penalty function of Eq. (3.17) can be generalized to

$$\phi(X,r) = F + r \sum_{j}^{m} \langle g_j \rangle^z , \tag{3.23}$$

where the exponent $z$ is a nonnegative constant. Usually, if the parameter $r$ is positive, $\phi$ possesses a minimum as a function of $X$ in the unacceptable region. This formulation is perhaps one of the most natural approaches to penalty functions, and for this reason members of this class have been repeatedly reinvented by various workers over the years. Investigations of the theoretical properties of these methods, however, have been made only recently.[7]

In this section we will discuss only the application aspects of the methods

[7] See Zangwill (1967).

and will concentrate mainly on the case in which $z = 2$. First, however, consider $z = 0$. If we define $\langle g \rangle^0$ as the step function, then

$$\phi(X) = \begin{cases} F(X) + r\,, & X \text{ in the unacceptable region,} \\ F(X)\,, & X \text{ in the acceptable region.} \end{cases} \tag{3.24}$$

The function is discontinuous on the boundary of the acceptable region, and it would be difficult to search for a minimum. The function also has rather nasty properties in the vicinity of the minimum, being, as it were, at the foot of a cliff (see Fig. 3.7).

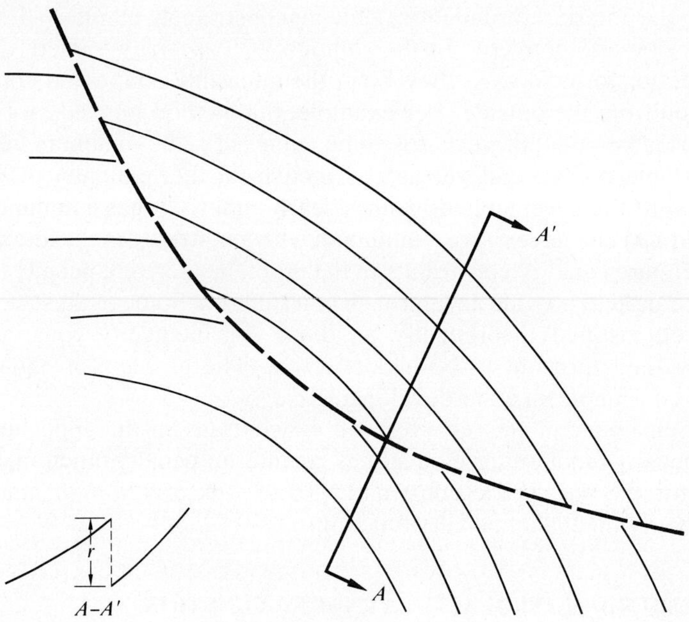


**Figure 3.7**

For $0 < z < 1$, the $\phi$-function will be continuous but may fail to penalize strongly enough in the unacceptable region to ensure the desired behavior (see Fig. 3.8). Moreover, even if $r$ is large enough to force a minimum to occur at the desired spot, the function possesses discontinuous first derivatives along the boundary and hence would also be difficult to minimize.

For $z = 1$, the function achieves one desirable characteristic: it has its minimum in the right place. In fact, it has been shown[8] that under certain restrictions there exists an $\bar{r}$ large enough that the minimum of $\phi$ is exactly the constrained minimum of the original problem for all $r \geqslant \bar{r}$. Zangwill, who

[8] Zangwill (1967).

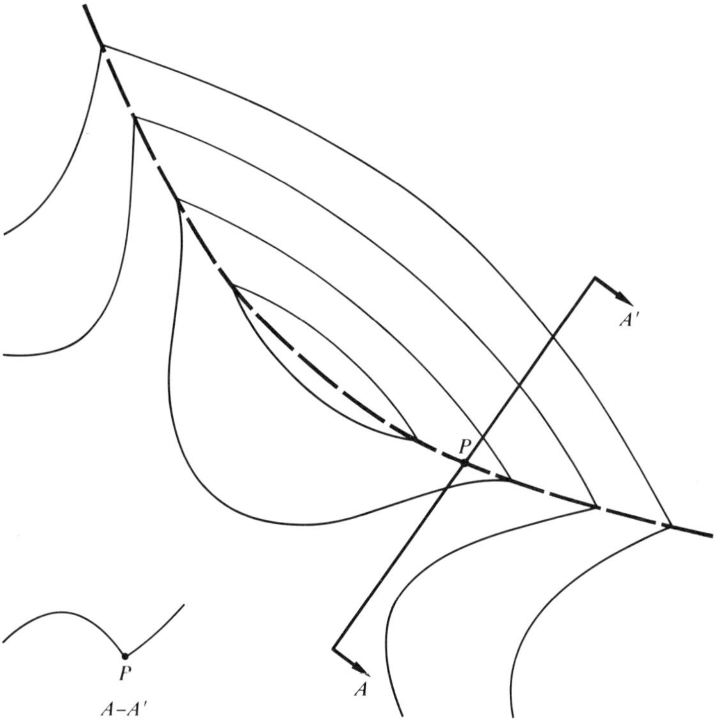


Figure 3.8

demonstrated this, also describes a technique for determining a suitable value of $\bar{r}$. In spite of the convenience of picking a single $r$ that yields the constrained minimum in one unconstrained minimization, the formulation is not particularly useful. This is principally because the function has discontinuous first derivatives along the boundary.

For $z > 1$, the $\phi$-function will have continuous first derivatives, provided that both $F$ and the $g_j$ are differentiable. This is clear if we note that

$$\frac{\partial \phi}{\partial x_i} = \frac{\partial F}{\partial x_i} + r \sum_{j=1}^{m} z\langle g_j \rangle^{z-1} \frac{\partial g_j}{\partial x_i} . \tag{3.25}$$

The choice of $z = 2$ is quite popular and will be used in the subsequent discussion, although the operation of the algorithm is essentially independent of $z$.

The framework of a method for finding the solution to the inequality constrained problem is as follows.

1. Starting from any initial design $\boldsymbol{X}$ with a "moderate" value of $r$, find a vector $\boldsymbol{X}_M$ that minimizes

$$\phi = F + r \sum_j \langle g_j \rangle^z .$$

2. Investigate the constraints to determine whether the point $X_M$ is in the feasible domain.
3. If the result of step 2 is true, terminate; otherwise, pick an $r' > r$ and, starting from $X_M$, return to step 1, minimizing $\phi(X, r')$.

The logic diagram in Fig. 3.9 contains a simple scheme for increasing $r$ by multiplying it by a constant $c > 1$.

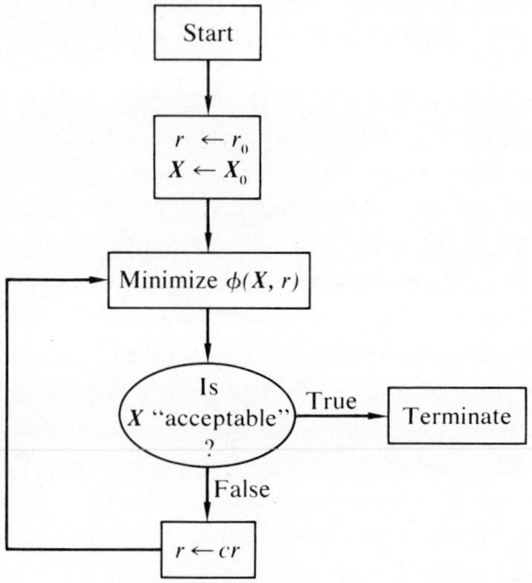


**Figure 3.9**

Several practical points should be discussed. They include the initial choice of $r$ and $X$, the rate of reduction of $r$, testing the constraints for admissibility, the details of the minimization method, and the overall convergence properties of the method.

### Picking a Value of *r*

Our first impulse might be to pick the initial $r$ quite large, so as to avoid an excessive number of minimizations of $\phi$. In other words, we might hope to force the minimum of $\phi$ toward the feasible region by choosing a large $r$ at the outset. In order to see why this is usually not a good policy, let us examine the contours of the $\phi$-function for the 2-bar truss problem (E.1). To simplify the notation, we will redefine the objective function as the volume of the structure rather than the weight. This does not change the problem; it only changes the function by a multiplicative constant. Recalling the definitions of the yield and buckling constraints (Eqs. 1.32 and 1.33) and ignoring any other explicit constraints, we have

$$F \equiv 2\pi t d (B^2 + H^2)^{1/2}, \tag{3.26}$$

$$g_1 \equiv \frac{P}{\pi t}\,\frac{(B^2+H^2)^{1/2}}{Hd} - 100{,}000, \tag{3.27}$$

$$g_2 \equiv \frac{P}{\pi t}\,\frac{(B^2+H^2)^{1/2}}{Hd} - \frac{\pi^2 E}{8}\,\frac{(d^2+t^2)}{(B^2+H^2)}. \tag{3.28}$$

The solution to the problem is $d = 1.88$ in., $H = 20.2$ in., and $F = 42.7$ in$^3$. The penalty function for the problem is simply

$$\phi(\boldsymbol{D},r) = F + r[\langle g_1\rangle^2 + \langle g_2\rangle^2]\,.$$

Figure 3.10 shows contours of this penalty function for $r = 10^{-10}$. The dashed lines in the figure indicate the constraint boundaries for reference. We see that the function has nicely rounded corners and possesses a well-defined minimum (indicated by the "+" in the figure). This function will always have a minimum inside the region $H > 0$, $d > 0$, since both $g_1$ and $g_2$ go to infinity along the axes. This figure should be compared to Fig. 3.11, which is a plot of $\phi$ for $r = 10^{-9}$, to Fig. 3.12 for $r = 10^{-8}$, and to Fig. 3.13 for $r = 10^{-7}$. In the last figure, the minimum is close to the feasible region, but the function exhibits considerably more distortion or eccentricity than before. As $r$ is increased further, the function becomes increasingly less manageable until it becomes a practical impossibility to minimize it from an arbitrary starting point. The

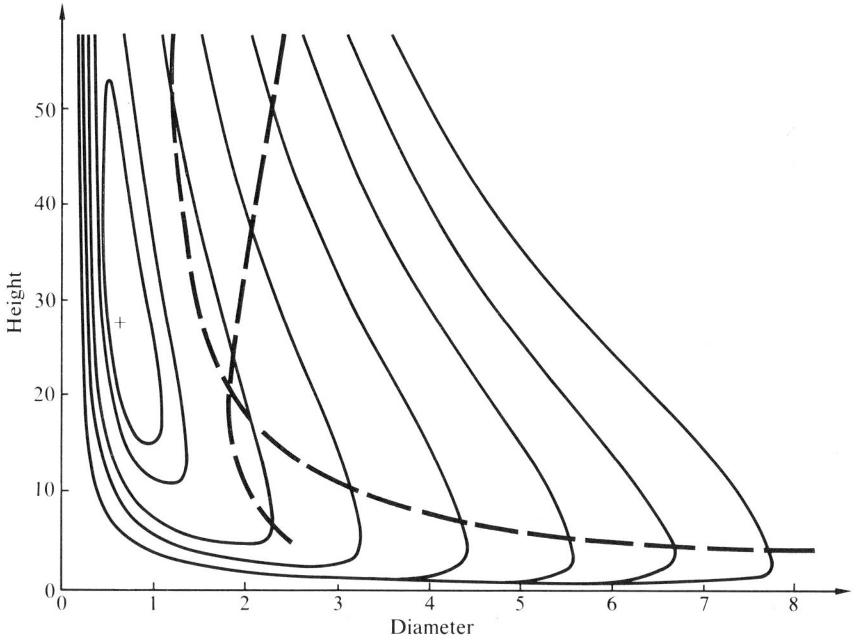


**Fig. 3.10.** $r = 10^{-10}$.

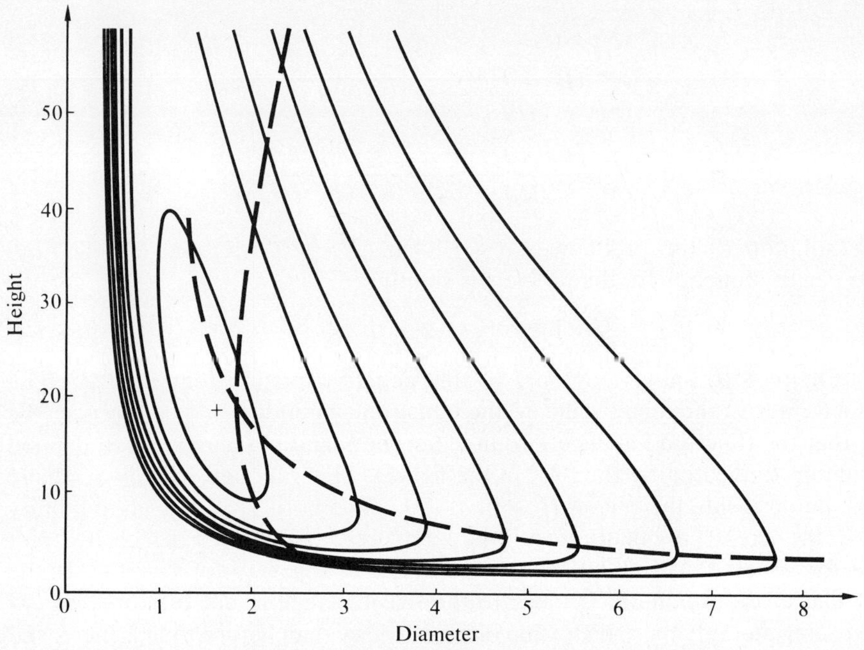


**Fig. 3.11.** $r = 10^{-9}$.

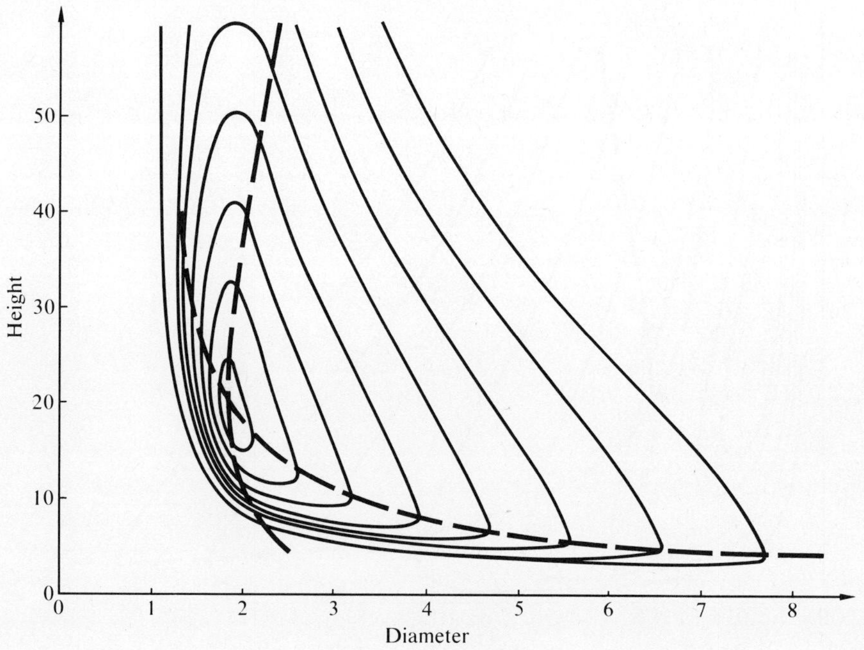


**Fig. 3.12.** $r = 10^{-8}$.

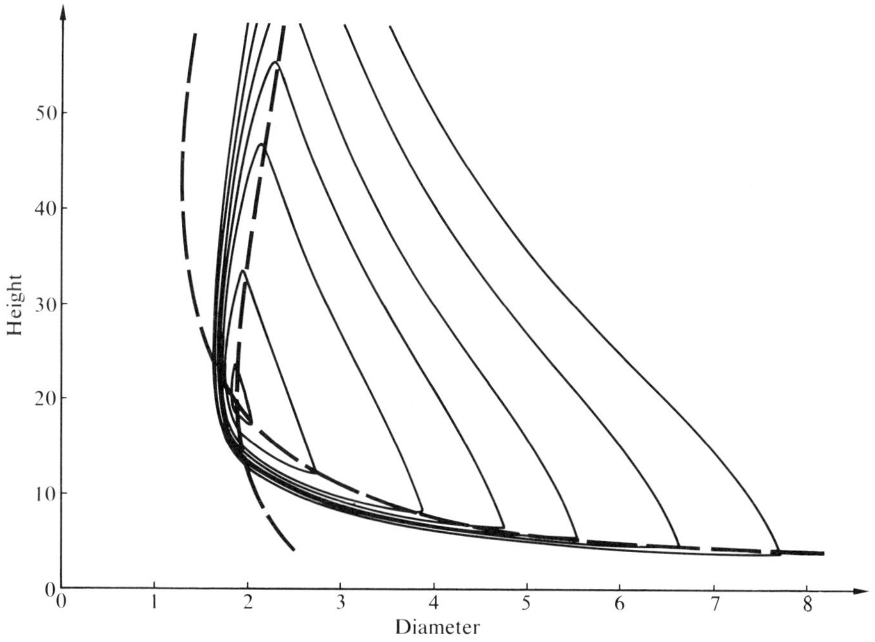


**Fig. 3.13.** $r = 10^{-7}$.

conflict is thus clear: $r$ must ultimately be "large" in order to force the minimum to approach the feasible region, but "small" to enable $\phi$ to be minimized without excessive difficulty.

This problem is the reason why, in the algorithms just presented, $r$ is sequentially increased from a "moderate" starting value. Assuming that the increase factor $c$ is not excessive, the use of $X_M$ as a starting point for the next minimization greatly improves the likelihood that the minimum will be found. This is particularly helpful when we use a quadratically convergent minimization scheme, because we find that the nearer the starting point is to the minimum, the stronger the convergence will be.

On the other hand, it is distressing to note that the matrix $\mathbf{J} = [\partial^2 F/\partial x_i \partial x_j]$ is discontinuous for the case $z = 2$. Since this is so, we cannot really speak of a quadratic approximation to $F$ along the boundary of the feasible region, and we would expect some weakening of the quadratic convergence.

The discontinuities in $\mathbf{J}$ notwithstanding, the use of a sequence of increasing values of $r$ and the associated sequence of starting values of $X_M$ form a reasonable approach to the problem. This is illustrated in Table 3.1, which presents a solution sequence for the 2-bar truss example (E.1).

The variable metric minimization method was used for this case, and the number of iteration cycles required per minimization is given in the columns

**Table 3.1**

| $r$ | $d$ | $h$ | $\phi_{\min}$ | $N_s$ | $N_r$ |
|---|---|---|---|---|---|
| Starting point | 6.0 | 30.0 | 159.9 | — | — |
| $10^{-10}$ | 0.66 | 28.6 | 23.8 | 7 | 7 |
| $10^{-9}$ | 1.57 | 18.7 | 38.4 | 8 | 12 |
| $10^{-8}$ | 1.86 | 18.8 | 41.9 | 5 | 10 |
| $10^{-7}$ | 1.88 | 20.0 | 42.6 | 8 | 12 |
| $10^{-6}$ | 1.88 | 20.2 | 42.7 | 7 | 13 |
| $10^{-5}$ | 1.88 | 20.2 | 42.7 | 7 | 19 |
| $10^{-4}$ | 1.88 | 20.2 | 42.7 | 5 | 31 |

labeled $N_s$ and $N_r$. The column $N_s$ is for the sequential starting points, and $N_r$ is for the repeated starting point of (6.0,30.0). The numbers given in these two columns do not tell the whole story, since the iterations in $N_r$ were much more arduous and time-consuming than those in $N_s$. On the whole, the process of successive minimizations for $r$ from $10^{-10}$ to $10^{-4}$ took less time than the one step starting from (6.0,30.0) with $r = 10^{-4}$. It is also worth reporting that for $r$ greater than $10^{-4}$, the function is nearly impossible to minimize even for this two-variable case. In higher dimensions, these difficulties get out of hand much more quickly.

### Termination

One of the perennial problems in optimization is the termination of the process. Looking at Table 3.1 and imagining that we do not know the answer, we can still see rather clearly that we could have stopped at $r$ equals $10^{-7}$ or $10^{-6}$. First of all, the process seems to be settling out, and second, a check on the constraints reveals that they are approaching satisfaction. These criteria are in general adequate for termination of the process.

### Constraint Margin or Tolerance

Sometimes the nature of the engineering problem is such that the inequality constraints must be strictly observed, a condition that is difficult or impossible by this approach. A ruse for accomplishing this is to add a "margin" to those constraints that must be strictly satisfied. In other words, define

$$g_j' = g_j + \epsilon_j \,.$$

Minimization of the new penalty function made up from the $g_j'$ will eventually produce a *strict* satisfaction of $g_j < 0$. However, we must carefully avoid picking $\epsilon_j$ too large, or the result may be off-optimal.

## Alterations to the Minimization Method

Some alterations to the minimization technique are in order when the function being minimized is a penalty function. To start with, the search process must be kept out of certain zones, and precautions to ensure this must be taken in the logic. Also, on the plus side, we can make certain improvements because of the sequential nature of the process.

The above example illustrates the first point. The whole problem breaks down if $d$ or $H$ becomes negative. But if the starting values are positive, the process theoretically should converge to the minimum in the first quadrant (see Fig. 3.10). On the other hand, the "long step" nature of, for example, the variable metric or conjugate gradient methods is such that the path could become diverted into regions where $\phi$ is not properly defined. We can guard against this eventuality by placing a test in the function evaluation section of the code. This test would, in the event of an overstep, signal to the minimization section that the step was too long, and the minimizer would respond by cutting the step. In the example in Section 2.6 (the 4-link mechanism), a form of this technique was used in which $F$ (in the present case $\phi$) was assigned a very large value if the step was beyond the admissible zone, and the minimization algorithm was left to correct the situation on its own. In general, it is more efficient to provide direct logic to accommodate this situation.

The potentialities that exist for improving the minimization algorithms mostly center about the idea that, since the process is one of sequential minimization, the shape of the function contours and the location of the minimum should change only incrementally from minimization to minimization. Ignoring the fact that no real quadratic approximations exist, we can conceive, for example, of carrying over the **H**-matrix of the variable metric method from one minimization to the next. If $r$ is changed modestly, then the final **H** from one minimization should be a good starting metric for the next minimization. The idea is weak theoretically, since the matrix of second derivatives is really undefined, but in practice it often produces useful acceleration of convergence.

The same technique can be applied to Powell's method by preserving the final set of directions for the next $r$-cycle. On the other hand, there is no clear way to extend the approach to the conjugate gradient method.

## Scaling and Weighing Problems

A frequent source of trouble in the penalty function methods lies in disparities of weight between the various $g_j$. For example, if $g_j$ is a constraint function such that $g_j \leq 0$, then $g_j' \equiv 1000\, g_j$ will also serve as the constraint function for the same problem. From the standpoint of penalty functions, however, there is considerable difference between $g_j$ and $g_j'$. The trouble arises when one $g_j$ changes much more rapidly than another and hence overpowers it over most of the unacceptable region.

An example of the difficulty will occur in the 2-bar truss problem (E.1) if the very natural step of dividing $g_1$ through by the constant $\sigma_y$ is taken:

$$g_1' \equiv \frac{\sigma}{\sigma_y} - 1 \equiv \frac{g_1}{\sigma_y}.$$

If $g_2$ is unaltered, then it is boosted relative to $g_1$ by a factor of $10^5$ ($\sigma_y =$ 100,000 psi).

The minimization results for various $r$'s are given in Table 3.2. The process settles down to the infeasible point $d = 1.96$, $h = 13.4$, through 7 orders of magnitude of $r$, before it begins to move toward the answer. Furthermore, as $r$ becomes large, the function becomes highly distorted and difficult to minimize.

**Table 3.2**

| $r$ | $d$ | $h$ | $\phi_{min}$ |
|---|---|---|---|
| $10^{-10}$ | 0.507 | 29.5 | 21.6 |
| $10^{-9}$ | 1.59 | 16.5 | 40.1 |
| $10^{-8}$ | 1.93 | 13.6 | 40.4 |
| $10^{-7}$ | 1.96 | 13.4 | 40.4 |
| $10^{-6}$ | 1.96 | 13.4 | 40.4 |
| $10^{-5}$ | 1.96 | 13.4 | 40.4 |
| $10^{-4}$ | 1.96 | 13.4 | 40.4 |
| $10^{-3}$ | 1.96 | 13.4 | 40.4 |
| $10^{-2}$ | 1.96 | 13.4 | 40.4 |
| $10^{-1}$ | 1.96 | 13.4 | 40.4 |
| $10^{-0}$ | 1.96 | 13.5 | 40.5 |
| $10^{+1}$ | 1.96 | 13.5 | 41.4 |
| $10^{+2}$ | 1.91 | 16.1 | 43.5 |
| $10^{+3}$ | 1.88 | 19.6 | 42.7 |
| Exact | 1.88 | 20.2 | 42.7 |

While this example is somewhat contrived, the difficulty tends to occur naturally in many engineering problems. The physical implication of the phenomenon is merely that one type of failure criterion is more sensitive to changes in design than others are. The best cure for the problem is prevention; the constraint functions should be carefully scrutinized for sensitivity. For example, displacement limits in a structure should be weighted in the presence of stress limits; side constraints on angles and lengths may compare badly, as may forces vs. dimensions, etc.

A *post facto* cure which suggests itself is to use individual $r$'s for the $g_j$. In this scheme, the penalty function might be defined

$$\phi = F + R\left\{\sum_{j=1}^{m} r_j \langle g_j \rangle^2\right\}, \tag{3.29}$$

and the operation would proceed as follows: minimize $\phi$ for several increasing values of $R$, and if some constraint, say $g_k$, is chronically unsatisfied while the others have become nearly satisfied, then increase $r_k$ and minimize again. An inherent drawback to this approach is that the logic can become quite complex.

## 3.5 AN INTERIOR PENALTY FUNCTION

The penalty function of the previous section sought an optimum feasible point by minimizing a penalty function for an increasing sequence of values of the penalty parameter. This technique forces the minimum point of $\phi(X,r)$ toward the feasible region from the outside. In this section, we also discuss a penalty function for inequality constraints which always has its minimum *inside* the feasible region. For a decreasing sequence of values of the penalty parameter $r_i$, $i = 1,2,\ldots$, the minimum point $X_M(r_i)$ is forced toward the constrained optimum from the *interior*. This approach has a number of computational and engineering advantages.

Like the penalty function in the previous section, the idea here is relatively simple. In this approach we augment the objective function with a penalty term which is small at points away from the constraints in the feasible region, but which "blows up" as the constraints are approached. The most commonly used function of this sort is[9]

$$\phi(X,r) = F(X) - r \sum_{j=1}^{m} \frac{1}{g_j(X)}, \tag{3.30}$$

where $F$ is to be minimized over all $X$ satisfying $g_j(X) \leq 0$, $j = 1,2,\ldots,m$. Note that if $r$ is positive the effect is to add a positive penalty to $F(X)$. This is because at an interior point, all the terms in the sum are negative. As a boundary is approached, some $g_j$ will approach zero and the penalty will "explode." The penalty parameter $r$ will be made successively smaller in order to obtain the constrained minimum of $F$.

To see how such a function looks, we have shown plots of its contours for the 2-bar truss problem (E.1) in Figs. 3.14, 3.15, and 3.16 for various values of $r$. The function plotted is

$$\phi = F - r\left[\frac{1}{g_1} + \frac{1}{g_2}\right], \tag{3.31}$$

where $F$, $g_1$, and $g_2$ are defined by Eqs. (3.26), (3.27), and (3.28) respectively. The interior minima (indicated by "+" in the figures) for successively smaller values of $r$ tend toward the constrained optimum of the original problem. We also observe that, as with the exterior penalty function method, the closer to the constrained optimum the minimum of $\phi$ is forced to lie, the more eccentric

[9] Another popular form is $-r\Sigma \log(-g_j)$.

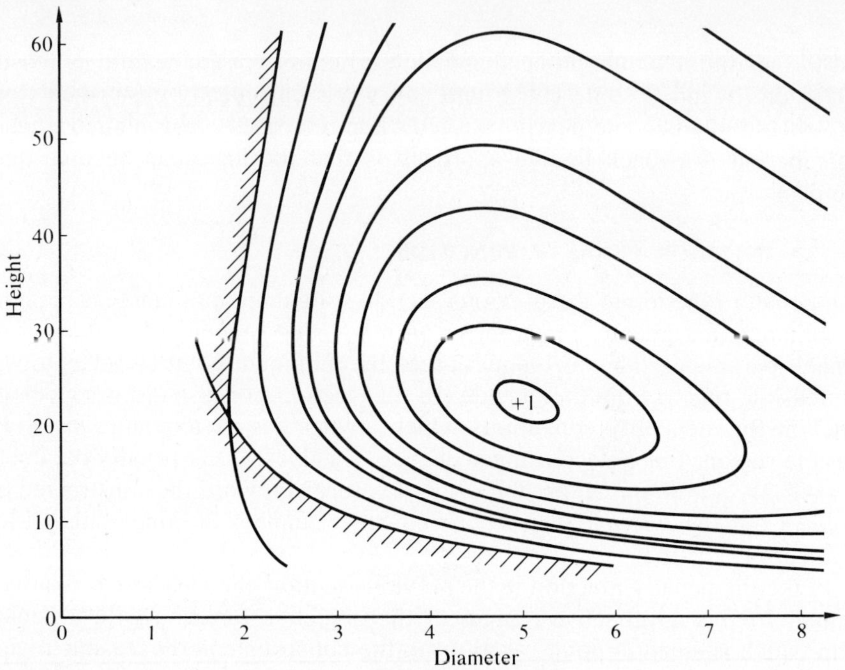


**Fig. 3.14.** $r = 10^7$.

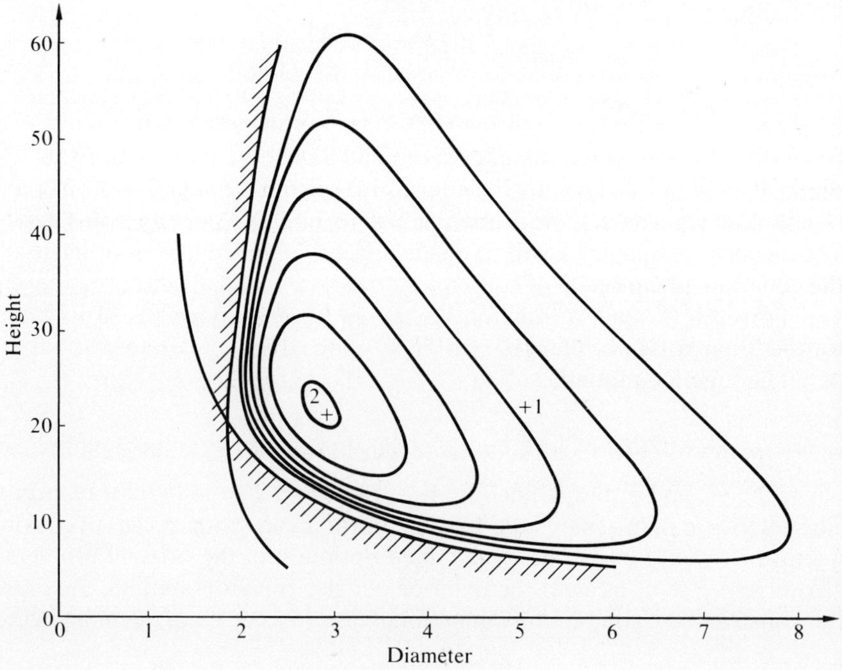


**Fig. 3.15.** $r = 10^6$.

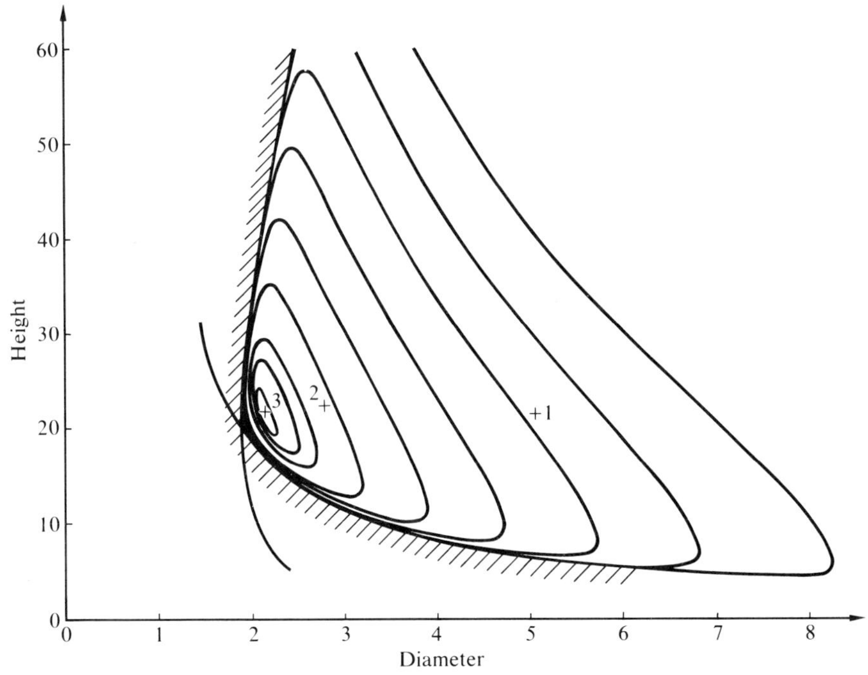


**Fig. 3.16.** $r = 10^5$.

the function becomes. This again leads to the necessity for sequential minimization of $\phi$.

**The Algorithm**

An algorithm which comprises the steps most commonly used is as follows:

1. Given a starting point $X_0$ satisfying all $g_j(X) < 0$ and an initial value for $r$, minimize $\phi$ to obtain $X_M$.
2. Check for convergence of $X_M$ to the optimum.
3. If the convergence criterion is not satisfied, reduce $r$ by $r \leftarrow rc$, where $c < 1$.
4. Compute a new starting point for the minimization, initialize the minimization algorithm, and repeat from step 1.

The logic diagram for this algorithm is shown in Fig. 3.17. There are a number of points to consider in applying the method:

a) The starting design $X_0$ required by step 1 is usually available in engineering problems, but sometimes finding such a point is difficult.
b) A proper initial value for $r$ must be selected.

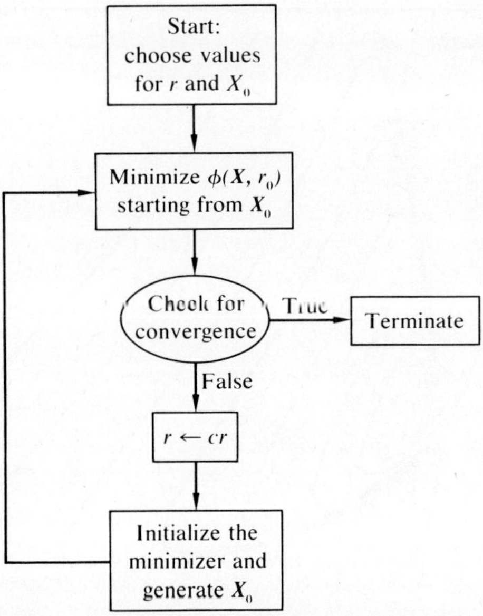


**Figure 3.17**

c) The possibilities for the convergence criteria of step 2 are numerous and there are choices to be made.

d) Because of the sequential nature of the process, it is possible to improve the starting points for the third and subsequent minimizations.

e) In some cases, considerable improvement in efficiency of the minimization method itself is possible by taking advantage of the special nature of the process.

**Starting Point**

We note that in many engineering situations, particularly in the structural and mechanical design areas, it is easy to find a point satisfying $g_j(X) \leqslant 0$ at the expense of large values of $F$. For example, in structural design, if cost or weight of the structure is ignored, it is usually easy to propose many designs which fulfill the basic requirements of strength and rigidity for the particular application. In other design situations, however, the acceptable designs may not be at all obvious. In these situations, the initial acceptable design required by the interior penalty function method can be obtained as follows.

Suppose an engineering assessment of the situation has produced the design $X_0$ which satisfies $g_j(X_0) < 0, j = 1,2, \ldots, p$, but which has $g_j(X_0) > 0$, $j = p + 1, \ldots, m$.[10] Take the $k$ for which $g_k(X_0)$ is a maximum where $k = p +$

[10] This statement assumes that the equations have been renumbered so that the last $m - r$ inequalities are the unsatisfied ones.

$1, \ldots, m$, and temporarily define it as the objective function for the following problem; Find $X$ such that

$$\begin{aligned} &g_k(X) \to \min, \\ &g_j(X) \leqslant 0\,, \qquad j = 1,2,\ldots,p\,, \\ &g_j(X) - g_j(X_0) \leqslant 0\,, \qquad j = p+1, p+2, \ldots, m\,. \end{aligned}$$

Whenever during the process of solving this problem by the penalty function method the value of $g_k(X)$ drops below zero, the procedure is halted. The point so obtained then satisfies at least one more constraint than did the original $X_0$. The procedure can be repeated until all the constraints have been satisfied and an $X_0$ is obtained for which $g_j(X_0) < 0$, $j = 1,2,\ldots, m$. Ordinarily this approach should yield such a point $X_0$ if one exists, although there are circumstances in which it will converge to a constrained or unconstrained local minimum of some $g_k(X)$ that is positive. Such situations require ingenuity in selecting new starting points from which to try another sequence.

**Trade-off Studies**

The algorithm idea involved in the above has some interesting implications in engineering applications. Sometimes when the design problem is very complicated and appears to have many conflicting requirements and no clear candidate for an objective function, a design aid known as a *trade-off study* is utilized. Suppose, as an example, that there are several conflicting qualities, expressed by $F_1(X), F_2(X), \ldots, F_r(X)$, that the designer would like to have as small as possible. One approach is to construct a trade-off chart by solving the following problem: Find $X$ such that

$$\begin{aligned} &F_l(X) \to \min \\ &g_j(X) \leqslant 0\,, \qquad j = 1,2,\ldots, m\,, \\ &F_i(X) - \bar{F}_i \leqslant 0\,, \qquad i = 1,2,\ldots, r;\ i \neq l\,, \end{aligned}$$

for different values of the $\bar{F}_i$ and for different indices $l$. The information from a well-chosen set of such experiments can be useful in making design decisions. The term "trade-off," of course, comes from the fact that the study allows the designer to determine how much of the minimum of $F_l$ he can profitably trade for a lower value of some $\bar{F}_i$.

An example of such a trade-off study is given by the 4-bar mechanism problem (E.2). You will recall that the problem was to proportion the mechanism to generate the desired output as closely as possible while satisfying certain constraints. In an example solution to this problem in Section 2.6, all constraints were ignored, but an impractical design resulted. One of the constraints was that the deviation of the transmission angle from 90° was to be limited by prescribed bounds. When this constraint is set at different levels, the resulting optimum designs have different error values, and some of the mechanisms may not be sufficiently accurate. The results of a trade-off study for this problem are given in Table 3.3. Figure 3.18 depicts the optimum output function for

**Table 3.3. Trade-off study for the 4-bar mechanism**

| $a$ | $b$ | $c$ | $\alpha$ | $\beta$ | Error ($F_{opt}$) | $T^u$ |
|---|---|---|---|---|---|---|
| 0.3102 | 0.9663 | 0.5989 | −2.39° | −50.7° | 30409 | 45° |
| 0.4579 | 1.0845 | 0.9730 | −20.0° | −52.2° | 19525 | 60° |
| 0.5734 | 1.5192 | 1.6301 | −40.0° | −53.4° | 7332 | 75° |
| 0.5658 | 2.3595 | 2.7932 | −95.4° | −74.1° | 447 | 90° |

two values of the deviation-angle constraint. These results were obtained by using the interior penalty function method in conjunction with Powell's method. The result for $T^u = 90°$, given in Table 3.3, represents the case in which the mechanism locks up and is not a usable design if the crank-rocker property is necessary or if any force must be transmitted. It does, however, provide a point of reference for comparing other designs.

After examining these results, the engineer might decide to relax his original idea of the proper values for deviation-angle constraint in order to gain accuracy, or he might even be forced to revise the whole design concept.

**An Initial Value for *r***

The matter of selecting an initial value for the penalty parameter $r$ has been discussed in the literature,[11] but while some theory is available, the task is

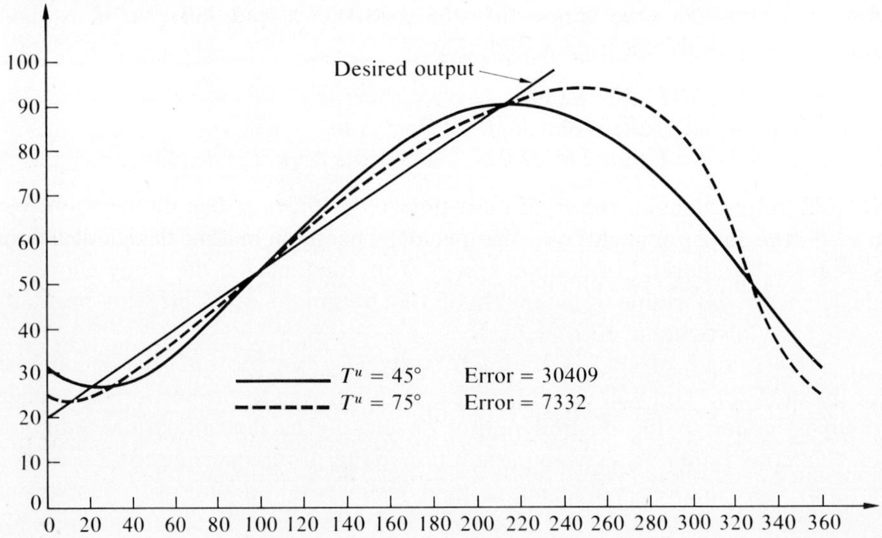


**Fig. 3.18.** Trade-off study of 4-bar linkage.

[11] Fiacco and McCormick (1963).

still mainly an art. The problem is similar to that encountered with exterior penalty functions: if $r$ is large, the function is easy to minimize, but the minimum may lie far from the desired solution to the original constrained minimization problem. On the other hand, if $r$ is small, the function will be hard to minimize.

A feeling for the problem can be developed by considering a few simple ideas. If the initial design is conservative (i.e., not near any constraints), one should pick the initial $r = r_0$ so that $F_{\min}(r_0)$ does not increase drastically over the original design. In other words, $r$ ought to be chosen small enough that in the neighborhood of the initial design the $-r\Sigma\, 1/g_j$ terms do not completely dominate $\phi$. A rule which might follow from this observation is that if $\boldsymbol{X}_0$ is a conservative design, pick $r_0$ so that $-r_0 \Sigma\, 1/g_j(\boldsymbol{X}_0)$ approximately equals $F(\boldsymbol{X}_0)$. In practice, this approach usually yields reasonable initial values for $r$.

If $\boldsymbol{X}_0$ happens to be a near-critical (i.e., such that one or more of the $g_j$ are small but negative quantities) but nonoptimal design, the situation becomes more complicated because the $r$ value dictated by the above rule might be too small to allow the first minimization to be carried out. In this case, a proper value of $r_0$ will probably be large enough that, in minimizing $\phi(\boldsymbol{X},r_0)$, $F$ will increase from its value at $\boldsymbol{X}_0$. While this is unfortunate, no other course is usually possible with this form of penalty function unless we use a good deal of complex logic. However, unless something really drastic happens, very little is lost since $r$ can be reduced quite quickly in this method.

Another approach to this latter problem is to pick a relatively large value of $r$ but temporarily add a new constraint to the problem in the form of

$$g_{m+1} = F(\boldsymbol{X}) - F(\boldsymbol{X}_0) \leq 0\,, \tag{3.32}$$

or, to make it easier to get a starting point,

$$g_{m+1} = F(\boldsymbol{X}) - [F(\boldsymbol{X}_0) + \epsilon] \leq 0\,, \tag{3.33}$$

where $\epsilon$ is some small amount of increase which will theoretically be permitted in $F$ on the first minimization. The penalty function for this revised problem is then

$$\phi(\boldsymbol{X},r) = F(\boldsymbol{X}) - r\left\{\sum_{j=1}^{m}\frac{1}{g_j} + \frac{1}{F(\boldsymbol{X}) - [F(\boldsymbol{X}_0) + \epsilon]}\right\}. \tag{3.34}$$

The minimum for large values of $r$ is approximately the point where the term in brackets alone is a minimum. As $r$ is decreased, the fictitious constraint term can be removed or left in as desired, since it will ultimately vanish.

### Convergence Criteria

As the $\phi$-function is minimized for various decreasing values of $r$, the sequence of minima $\boldsymbol{X}_M(r_i)$, $i = 1,2,\ldots$, should converge to the solution of the constrained minimization problem. A means is needed to ascertain this convergence without an unnecessarily large number of minimizations. One simple criterion is to compute the relative difference

$$\delta \equiv \frac{|F_{\min}(r_{i-1}) - F_{\min}(r_i)|}{|F_{\min}(r_i)|} \tag{3.35}$$

and stop when this value drops below a certain fraction. Clever logic is needed to prevent premature termination in situations where the process temporarily bogs down. Furthermore, the magnitude of $\delta$ must bear some relation to $c$, the fraction by which $r$ is reduced in each cycle. In general, however, this concept can form the basis for a useful convergence criterion.

An equally appealing group of convergence test numbers is contained in various norms of the vector

$$\boldsymbol{\Delta} \equiv X_M(r_{i-1}) - X_M(r_i)\,, \tag{3.36}$$

the components of which will be denoted by $\Delta_j$. For example, we could impose as a test for convergence

$$|\Delta_j| \leqslant \epsilon_j\,, \qquad j = 1,2,\ldots,n\,, \tag{3.37a}$$

or

$$\max(|\Delta_j|) \leqslant \epsilon \tag{3.37b}$$

or

$$|\boldsymbol{\Delta}| = \left[\sum_{j=1}^{m} \Delta_j^2\right]^{1/2} \leqslant \epsilon\,. \tag{3.37c}$$

All of these have been used to advantage in various problems. The choice of norm and the proper value for $\epsilon$ depend to some extent on the problem.

Another level of sophistication in methods of termination follows from the observation that $F_{\min}(r_i)$ is merely a point on what one would expect to be a continuous function of $r$, namely, $F_{\min}(r)$. This function can be approximated by a function $H(r)$ from data accumulated in two or more minimizations, and then $H(0)$ will serve as an approximation to the true solution $F_{\min}(0) \equiv F_{\text{opt}}$. If this approximation appears to be reliable and the latest solution $F_{\min}(r_i)$ is acceptably close to the latest approximation $H_i(0)$, then the process can be terminated.

Computational experience and some theoretical support[12] indicate the use of an approximation function in the form of a polynomial in $r^{1/2}$. In particular, the most commonly used form[13] is the linear polynomial in $r^{1/2}$:

$$F_{\min}(r) \simeq a + br^{1/2} \equiv H(r)\,, \tag{3.38}$$

[12] Fiacco and McCormick (1963).

[13] In Fiacco and McCormick (1963), the extrapolation as a polynomial in $r^{1/2}$ is generalized to $H_p(r) = a_0 + a_1 r^{1/2} + a_2 r + a_3 r^{3/2} + \ldots + a_p r^{p/2}$, and recursion formulas are given for the $a_i$. However as a practical matter the simplest extrapolation given by Eq. (3.38) is usually the best, all things considered.

where the $i$th approximation is determined from interpolating

$$H_i(r_{i-1}) = a_i + b_i r_{i-1}^{1/2} = F_{\min}(r_{i-1}) \,, \tag{3.39a}$$

$$H_i(r_i) = a_i + b_i(cr_{i-1})^{1/2} = F_{\min}(r_i) \,, \tag{3.39b}$$

which leads to

$$a_i = [c^{1/2}F_{\min}(r_{i-1}) - F_{\min}(r_i)]/(c^{1/2} - 1) \,, \tag{3.40a}$$

$$b_i = [F_{\min}(r_{i-1}) - a_i]/r_{i-1}^{1/2} \,. \tag{3.40b}$$

This approximation scheme fits a parabola to the data as shown in Fig. 3.19.

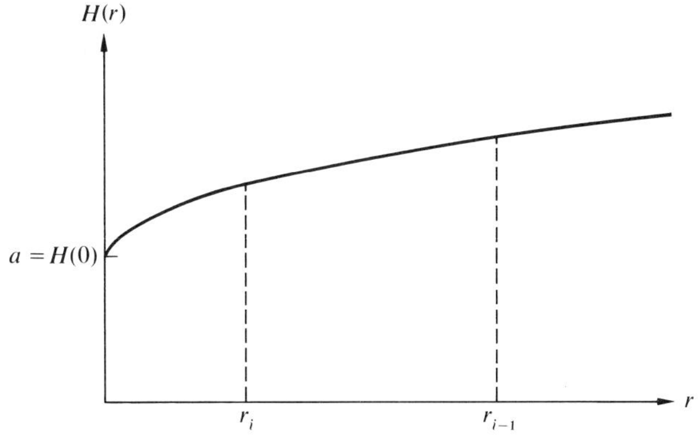


**Figure 3.19**

In order to illustrate this approach, the data for the 2-bar truss (E.1) are given in Table 3.4. These are the minima for the function given by Eq. (3.31) and partially shown in Figs. 3.14 to 3.16.

The first approximation using $r = 10^7$ and $r = 10^6$ (note $c = 0.1$) is $a_1 = 42.3$, $b_1 = 0.0239$, which implies, since $H_1(0) = a_1$, that $F_{\min}(0) \simeq 42.3$ and further that $F_{\min}(10^5) \simeq 49.9$. For most purposes the difference between the current value of $F_{\min} = 66.2$ and $H(0) = 42.3$ is too big a spread to accept, and hence the next minimization would be run to obtain $F_{\min}(10^5) = 50.0$.

**Table 3.4. Extrapolations for the 2-bar truss penalty function**

| | | $X_M(r_i)$ | | | | |
|---|---|---|---|---|---|---|
| $i$ | $r_i$ | $d$ | $H$ | $\phi_{\min}(r_i)$ | $F_{\min}(r_i)$ | $H_i(0)$ |
| 0 | $10^7$ | 5.01 | 22.4 | 287.8 | 117.8 | — |
| 1 | $10^6$ | 2.82 | 22.3 | 99.6 | 66.2 | 42.3 |
| 2 | $10^5$ | 2.14 | 21.9 | 58.4 | 50.0 | 42.5 |
| 3 | $10^4$ | 1.95 | 21.1 | 47.4 | 45.0 | 42.7 |
| | Exact | 1.88 | 20.2 | — | 42.7 | |

Since this agrees well with the estimated value of 49.9, we can assume that the approximations are reliable.

As the subsequent minimizations are carried out, the extrapolated values hold steady, adding further to their credibility. For the numbers shown in Table 3.4, the process was arbitrarily stopped at $r = 10^4$ because 45.0 was considered sufficiently close to the optimum of 42.7 (a difference of less than 5%) for practical purposes. Later in this section we discuss some interesting and practical ramifications of this conservative decision.

As a final point on the topic of convergence, we can derive a termination criterion for the sequence of minimizations on $r$ from the difference between $\phi_{\min}(r_i)$ and $F_{\min}(r_i)$. In particular, we can show that under certain rather special conditions,[14] the optimum value of $F$ lies in the range

$$2F_{\min}(r_i) - \phi_{\min}(r_i) \leq F_{\text{opt}} < F_{\min}(r_i) . \tag{3.41}$$

If we write $\phi_{\min}(r_i) = F_{\min}(r_i) + P_{\min}(r_i)$, where

$$P_{\min}(r_i) \equiv -r_i \sum_{j=1}^{m} \frac{1}{g_j} , \tag{3.42}$$

the summation $\Sigma\, 1/g_j$ being evaluated at $X_M(r_i)$, then Eq. (3.41) becomes

$$F_{\min}(r_i) - P_{\min}(r_i) \leq F_{\text{opt}} < F_{\min}(r_i) . \tag{3.43}$$

Checking Table 3.4, we see that for $r = 10^7$ the limits are: $-52.2 \leq F_{\text{opt}} \leq 117.8$; for $r = 10^6$, $32.8 \leq F_{\text{opt}} \leq 66.2$; for $r = 10^5$, $41.6 \leq F_{\text{opt}} \leq 50.0$; and for $r = 10^4$, $42.6 \leq F_{\text{opt}} \leq 45.0$. The limits hold for this problem and would provide a good guide for termination of the process. On the other hand, there are cases (and they occur frequently enough to cause concern) in which the limits fail to hold up even close to the solution. In view of this, the criterion should be used with caution unless the problem is known to possess the conditions for its strict validity.

### Improving the Starting Points: Extrapolation

The sequential process which converges the point $X_M(r_i)$ toward the solution $X_{\text{opt}}$ helps locate a sequence of good starting points for an ever more difficult sequence of minimization problems. We can improve these further by using an extrapolation scheme similar to that given in Eq. (3.38) for extrapolating $F_{\min}(r_i)$.

Writing a vector extrapolation for $X_M(r)$ as

$$X_M(r) \simeq A + r^{1/2}B \equiv H(r) , \tag{3.44}$$

[14] Fiacco and McCormick (1963) show that these bounds are true for convex programming problems (see Section 4.1).

we can interpolate two known points $\boldsymbol{X}_M(r_{i-1})$ and $\boldsymbol{X}_M(r_i)$ from

$$\boldsymbol{H}_i(r_{i-1}) = \boldsymbol{A}_i + r_{i-1}^{1/2}\boldsymbol{B}_i = \boldsymbol{X}_M(r_{i-1}) \,, \tag{3.45a}$$

$$\boldsymbol{H}_i(r_i) = \boldsymbol{A}_i + (cr_{i-1})^{1/2}\boldsymbol{B}_i = \boldsymbol{X}_M(r_i) \,. \tag{3.45b}$$

These lead to

$$\boldsymbol{A}_i = \frac{c^{1/2}\boldsymbol{X}_M(r_{i-1}) - \boldsymbol{X}_M(r_i)}{(c^{1/2} - 1)} \,, \tag{3.46a}$$

$$\boldsymbol{B}_i = \frac{\boldsymbol{X}_M(r_{i-1}) - \boldsymbol{A}_i}{r_{i-1}^{1/2}} \,. \tag{3.46b}$$

From these, an improved starting point for the next value of $r$ can be estimated:

$$\boldsymbol{H}_i(r_{i+1}) = \boldsymbol{A}_i + c(r_{i-1})^{1/2}\boldsymbol{B}_i \tag{3.47a}$$

or

$$\boldsymbol{H}_i(r_{i+1}) = (c^{1/2} + 1)\boldsymbol{X}_M(r_i) - c^{1/2}\boldsymbol{X}_M(r_{i-1}) \,. \tag{3.47b}$$

Table 3.5 gives $\boldsymbol{A}_i$, $\boldsymbol{H}_i(r_{i+1})$, and $\boldsymbol{X}_M(r_{i+1})$ for the values of $r$ given in Table 3.4. The arrows indicate the pair of $\boldsymbol{X}_M$ values used in the extrapolations.

**Table 3.5. Extrapolations on the 2-bar truss problem**

| | Predicted optimum $\boldsymbol{A}_i$ | | Predicted $\boldsymbol{X}_M$ $\boldsymbol{H}_i(r_{i+1})$ | | Actual $\boldsymbol{X}_M$ | |
|---|---|---|---|---|---|---|
| $i$ | $d$ | $H$ | $d$ | $H$ | $d$ | $H$ |
| 0 | — | — | — | — | 5.01 | 22.4 |
| 1 | 1.81 | 22.3 | 2.13 | 22.3 | 2.82 | 22.3 |
| 2 | 1.83 | 21.7 | 1.92 | 21.8 | 2.14 | 21.9 |
| 3 | 1.86 | 20.7 | 1.89 | 20.8 | 1.95 | 21.1 |
| Exact optimum | 1.88 | 20.2 | | | | |

The predictions are relatively good and would greatly speed convergence of the minimization. One thing that must be done, of course, is to check the extrapolated point $\boldsymbol{H}_i(r_{i+1})$ against the constraints. If the constraints are satisfied, the vector may be used as a starting point. If not, and there is no guarantee that they will be, it must be abandoned. We can, however, attempt to salvage something of the extrapolation in these cases by taking a *minimizing* step in the direction $\boldsymbol{S} \equiv \boldsymbol{X}_M(r_i) - \boldsymbol{X}_M(r_{i-1})$ or $\boldsymbol{S} \equiv \boldsymbol{X}_M(r_i) - \boldsymbol{H}_i(r_{i+1})$ from $\boldsymbol{X}_M(r_i)$. This will certainly produce a feasible point and will usually yield a good starting point for minimizing $\phi(\boldsymbol{X}, r_{i+1})$.

A similar idea can be used to squeeze the last full measure out of the process once a convergence criterion has been satisfied: step in small increments from $\boldsymbol{X}_M(r_i)$ along $\boldsymbol{S} \equiv \boldsymbol{X}_M(r_i) - \boldsymbol{X}_M(r_{i-1})$ until either $F$ begins to increase or the point becomes infeasible. We then take the resulting point as the ultimate approximation to $\boldsymbol{X}_{\text{opt}}$.

A final observation from Table 3.5 is that the values of $\boldsymbol{A}_i$ (recall that $\boldsymbol{A}_i = \boldsymbol{H}_i(0)$) are a good sequence of approximations to $\boldsymbol{X}_{\text{opt}}$ and could be used, if feasible, for the final answer to the problem.

**Accelerating the Minimization Process**

The remarks of the previous section regarding improvement of the minimization process apply here. Aside from the acceleration inherent in having good starting points, some of the unconstrained minimization methods can carry forward a portion of the intelligence gained in the minimization for the previous $r$ value. In interior penalty function cases, however, the function has continuous first derivatives, and the metric in the variable metric method (the **H**-matrix) as well as the conjugate directions in Powell's method can be useful for starting the next minimization.

We will have to treat Powell's method with some care, since it is inherently less self-correcting than the variable metric algorithm. In all cases, the actual computer programs should have the capability to detect a breakdown in convergence and correct for it by resetting to a standard initialization state. For example, we could set the metric in the variable metric method to the identity matrix or some other appropriate diagonal matrix.

**Minimizing-step Difficulties**

The function defined by Eq. (3.30) cannot be strictly minimized over the whole $X$-space, but only in the interior of the feasible region $g_j < 0$. The $\phi$-function is actually unbounded in both the positive and negative directions on the boundary of the feasible region, and as with the exterior penalty function in its regions of nondefinition (see Section 3.4), we must take special steps to keep the minimizer in the proper portion of the space. An effective strategy for accomplishing this requires some ingenuity, and it is not always clear what the best approach may be.

As before, the problem centers about finding the minimum in taking the step $\boldsymbol{X}_{q+1} = \boldsymbol{X}_q + \alpha \boldsymbol{S}_q$. When we apply interpolation methods, the sample points should all be in the domain of definition and preferably bracket the minimum. Figure 3.20 illustrates a hypothetical plot of $\phi$ vs. $\alpha$ along some $\boldsymbol{S}_q$. From this figure we can see that the task involves two difficulties: (1) finding at least one sample point in zone $A$, and (2) getting a reasonable interpolation of this perverse function.

In approaching the first part of the problem, we must take into account the nature of the search problem at hand: we seek a point in the narrow region $A$, which is bordered on one side by the unacceptable region $C$ and on the other by the "too near" region $B$ (see Fig. 3.20). Simple interval-splitting schemes may be appropriate for this problem. Suppose we are given a point in $B$ and

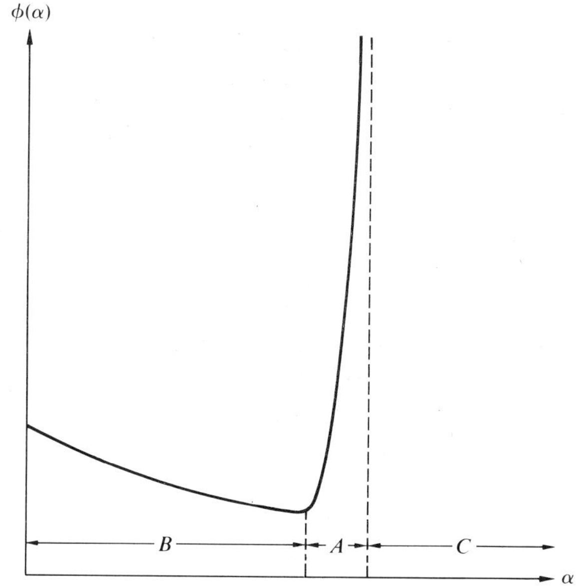


**Figure 3.20**

a point in $C$; take a point midway between them. If this point is in $B$, replace the current $B$ point by it and repeat. Do the same if the point falls in $C$. This technique is hampered by the fact that zone $B$ is distinguished from zone $A$ by a difference in the sign of the slope of $\phi$. When the derivatives of $\phi$ are too difficult to compute, we may need to use a crude finite difference scheme to locate the point.

Getting a good interpolation also requires that we give special consideration to the nature of the problem. Ordinary polynomials simply do not have the right character to do a good job of fitting the penalty function except very close to its minimum. One approach that we could use is to try an interpolation function of the form:

$$H(\alpha) = a + b\alpha + \frac{c}{\alpha - d}, \tag{3.48}$$

and then use function values and slopes at two points, or function values at four points, to perform the fit. Note that this is exactly the form that $\phi$ would have if both $F$ and $g$ were linear functions and if there were only one constraint.

### Engineering Implications of the Interior Penalty Functions

An appealing feature of the interior penalty function method is that, given an initial acceptable design, it produces an improving sequence of acceptable designs.

Moreover, we approach the constraints in this sequence in such a way that they become critical only near the end. This is a desirable feature in an engineering design process because, instead of taking the optimum design, we can choose a suboptimal but less critical design if we like. Such designs have "reserve capacity" to absorb overload or abuse and are prepared for the performance upgrading processes that are a standard part of some industries. The interior penalty function method is sometimes said to "funnel" the optimum design process "down the middle," keeping the designs away from the constraint surfaces until final convergence. Referring to Figs. 3.14, 3.15, and 3.16, we see a succession of increasingly critical designs. Point 2 in Fig. 3.15 is overweight by about 17%, but might be judged a "safer" design than the true optimum.

In spite of its appealing simplicity, this approach to true design reliability is not endorsed here. The more direct methods of reliability-based optimum design[15] should be used if these probabalistic considerations are a factor. On the other hand, these ideas can sometimes be useful if applied with a proper recognition of their true nature.

## 3.6 A PENALTY FUNCTION FOR PARAMETRIC CONSTRAINTS

The example optimization problem (E.4), the 3-bar truss with a loading envelope, has as parametric constraints

$$g_j(\mathbf{D},\theta) \leqslant 0\,, \qquad 0 \leqslant \theta \leqslant \theta^{(u)}\,. \tag{3.49}$$

As in Chapter 1, we can replace such constraints with a large number of ordinary constraints:

$$g_j(\mathbf{D},\theta_i) \leqslant 0\,, \qquad i = 1,2,\ldots,p\,, \tag{3.50}$$

but this approach, even when it works, tends to be inefficient because so many constraints are necessary. Moreover, the actual constraint (Eq. 3.49) may not be satisfied even though all the constraints given by Eq. (3.50) are satisfied, because violations may occur for some $\theta$, $\theta_i < \theta < \theta_{i+1}$.

A form of interior penalty function can be applied directly to the parametric constraint without modifying the problem. This penalty term[16] is sometimes called the "integrated penalty function":

$$\phi(\mathbf{X},r) = F - r\sum_{j=1}^{m}\int_{\theta_0}^{\theta_1}\frac{1}{g_j}\,d\theta \equiv F - r\sum_{j=1}^{m}P_j\,,$$

where, of course, the $g_j$ are functions of the parameter $\theta$. The principle of the method is the same as for the previous interior penalty function: $\phi$ is mini-

[15] Moses and Kinser (1967). See also Moses (1968).

[16] See Zoutendijk (1966).

mized for a sequence of decreasing values of $r$, and the minimum approaches the constrained minimum.

As to the integrals in the penalty function, if the $g_j(\theta)$ become small at one or more points in the interval $(\theta_0,\theta_1)$, the value of the integral grows. In the limit, as $g_j \to 0$ at a point in the interval, the integral becomes unbounded. Thus the concept is analogous to that of the ordinary constraint, in which $1/g_j$ becomes unbounded as the constraint is approached. As we mentioned in Chapter 1, the constraint surface defined by $g_j(\boldsymbol{D},\theta) \leqslant 0$ is the bounding envelope for an infinite number of ordinary constraints $g_j(\boldsymbol{D},\theta_i)$. The integrated form of penalty function is merely a means of adding up all these penalties in a unified manner.

Two of the most immediate problems inherent in the method are the evaluation of the integrals and the detection of constraint violation, which must be done for the minimization algorithm. In most practical applications, the integrals must be evaluated numerically because the $g_j$ are too complicated to integrate or simply are not known explicitly.[17] Consequently, first-order (gradient) methods as applied to the minimization of the $\phi$-function must be given special attention; in many cases, they are unusable except in finite difference form.

### Evaluation of the Integrals

The numerical evaluation of the integral can be accomplished by most of the common quadrature schemes. We will briefly describe the trapezoidal rule method because of its simplicity.[18] The trapezoidal rule for evaluating the general definite integral,

$$I = \int_{x_a}^{x_b} F(x)dx\,, \tag{3.51}$$

begins with a division of the interval from $x_a$ to $x_b$ into a number of subintervals by placing points $x_i$ between $x_a$ and $x_b$ (see Fig. 3.21). Next, the integral is approximated by summing the trapezoidal "areas":

$$A_i \equiv [F(x_i) + F(x_{i+1})](x_{i+1} - x_i)/2\,. \tag{3.52}$$

If the distances $\Delta \equiv x_{i+1} - x_i$ are all equal and $F(x_i)$ is denoted as $f_i$, then

$$A_i = \frac{\Delta}{2}(f_i + f_{i+1})\,. \tag{3.53}$$

---

[17] Thornton and Schmit (1968), apply the method to the design of an ablating thermal barrier. The constraints here are on quantities which vary through the thickness of the barrier and with time. They are derived from finite-difference thermal and stress analyses. These quantities are obviously not available as known functions of the time and space parameters.

[18] A much more accurate method but one that can be used in all respects like the trapezoidal rule described here is Romberg's integration; see Rutishauser, Bauer, and Stiefel (1962).

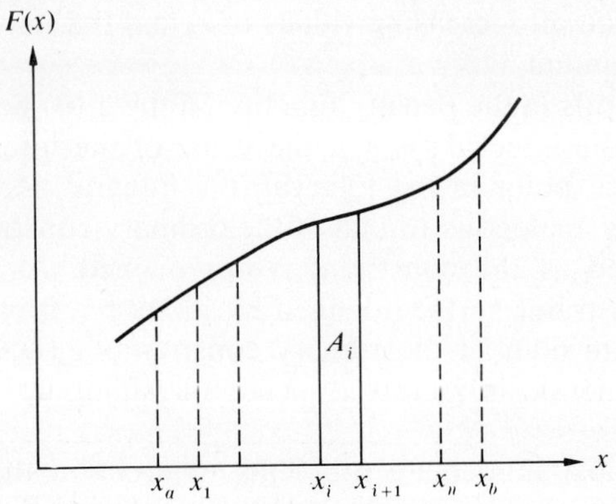


**Figure 3.21**

The integral can be approximated as

$$I \simeq \sum_{i=0}^{n} A_i = \sum_{i=0}^{n} \frac{\Delta}{2}(f_i + f_{i+1}) \,, \tag{3.54}$$

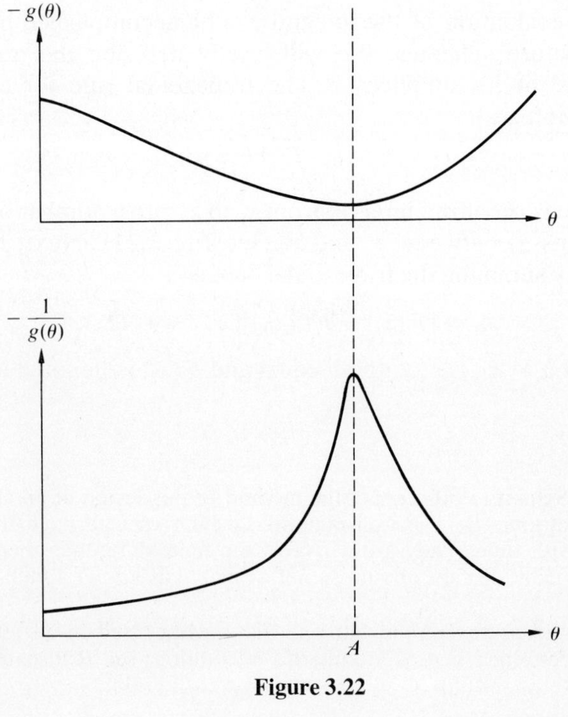


**Figure 3.22**

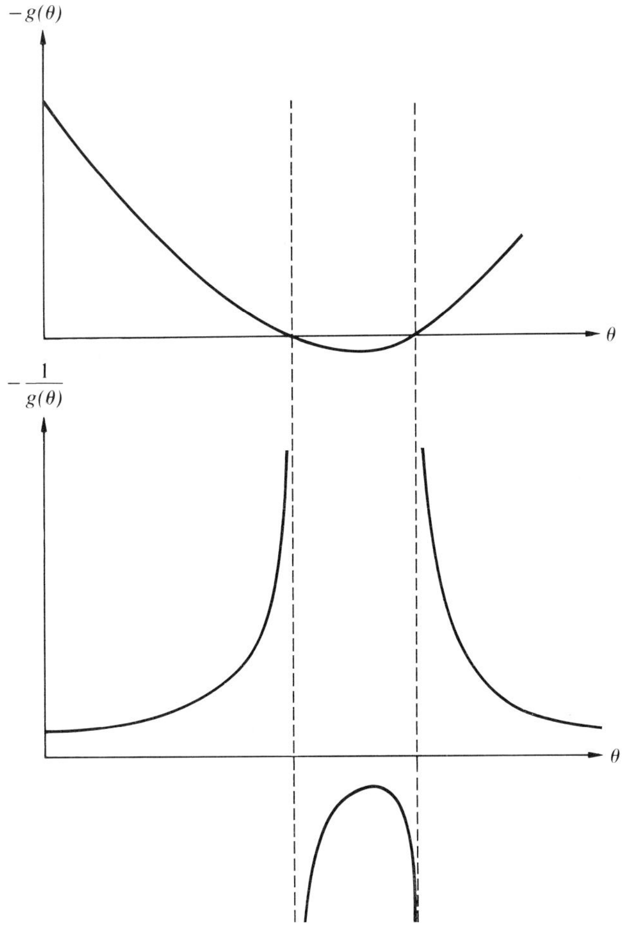


**Figure 3.23**

which reduces to

$$I \simeq \Delta\left[(f_a + f_b)/2 + \sum_{i=1}^{n} f_i\right]. \tag{3.55}$$

The difficult question with the trapezoidal rule is how large $\Delta$ must be to produce a sufficiently accurate approximation to $I$. This aspect of the method is particularly important in the penalty function application because each evaluation of $F$ (i.e., $1/g_j$) may require a complete analysis of the system under design. Furthermore, the function $1/g_j$ may be ill-behaved and hence difficult to integrate. Figures 3.22 and 3.23 illustrate the nature of this behavior; Fig. 3.22 shows the effect of $g_j$ approaching the constraint boundary at one value of $\theta$. The "spike" in $1/g_j$ makes it difficult to get a good approximation except with a large number of subdivisions. When the constraint is actually violated for some values of $\theta$, the value of the integral is undefined or "infinite" (see Fig. 3.23).

When the constraint is merely approached closely, we can handle the case by integrating with a decreasing succession of step sizes until two successive meshes yield essentially the same value for the integral. Eventually this technique should converge, even at the expense of many function evaluations. We can approach the case somewhat more efficiently by breaking up the total interval $(x_a, x_b)$ into several zones and performing the convergence on each zone separately. Since there is usually only one spike, this zonal technique is a simple way to avoid unnecessary function evaluations in zones where the function is well-behaved.

This method of performing the numerical evaluation of the integrals has another advantage in the present application: constraint violations (see Fig. 3.24) are easily detected by observing the following rules. Consider the constraint violated

1. If, for any $\theta$ where $1/g_j(\theta)$ is to evaluated, $g_j(\theta)$ is zero or positive, or
2. If after a predetermined number of mesh-size reductions, the trapezoidal rule has failed to converge.

Rule 1 is, of course, obvious from the definition of the constraint function; rule 2 is simply based on the idea that if the integral is a proper one, the error will reduce to an acceptable level if enough intervals are used, and that otherwise the integral is unbounded. In practice, the process of successive refinement often uncovers a point that violates rule 1, and this is the mode of termination in most cases.

Even with these refinements, the method requires evaluations of $g_j$ for numerous values of $\theta$ as the constraints are approached, and very little can be done to alleviate this.

**Getting a Derivative of the Penalty Function**

In order to apply any of the gradient methods, we need to compute the partial derivative

$$\frac{\partial P_j}{\partial d_k} = \frac{\partial}{\partial d_k}\int_{\theta_0}^{\theta_1} \frac{1}{g_j}\, d\theta \tag{3.56}$$

as part of the computation of $\partial\phi/\partial d_i$. Taking the derivative formally yields

$$\frac{\partial P_j}{\partial d_k} = -\int_{\theta_0}^{\theta_1} \frac{1}{g_j^2}\frac{\partial g_j}{\partial d_k}\, d\theta\,, \tag{3.57}$$

if we assume that the limits of integration are independent of the design variables $d_i$. If the quantities $(\partial g_j/\partial d_k)_{\theta_i}$ are readily computed or, better still, available in the course of computing $g_j(\theta_i)$, then we can approximate $\partial P_j/\partial d_k$

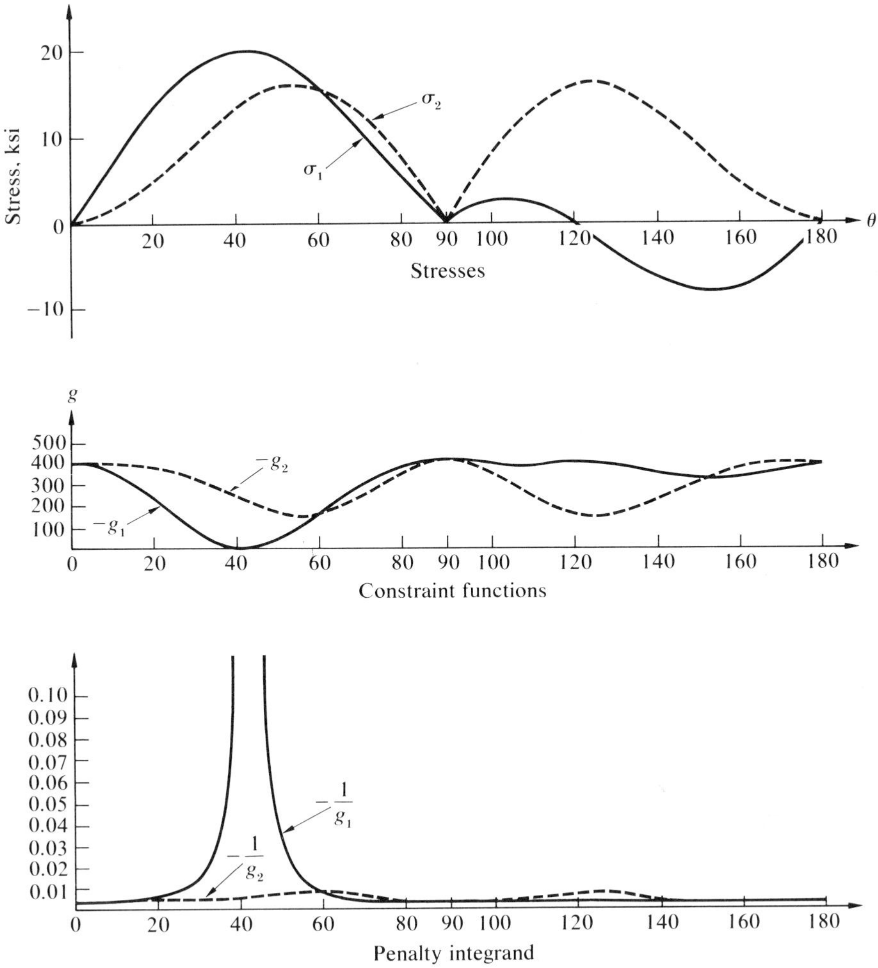


**Fig. 3.24.** Three-bar truss information in 2-lobed load case.

by the same trapezoidal rule and mesh-size that we used to compute $P_j$. Ordinarily, the main computational effort in finding $P_j$ is in calculating the $g_j$, and hence the cost of $\partial P_j/\partial d_k$ is mostly in computing $(\partial g_j/\partial d_k)_{\theta_i}$.

In most cases, however, the finite difference approximation is the only practical approach to finding the gradient, and we should consider the non-gradient methods (see the remarks in Section 2.12).

### An Example

The example problem E.4, the 3-bar truss with a loading envelope, was solved for both the loadings described in Chapter 1 by using the integrated penalty function. The $\phi$-function used was simply

$$\phi(X,r) = F - r\left[\sum_{j=1}^{3}\int_{0}^{\theta^{(u)}}\frac{1}{g_j}\,d\theta + \sum_{j=4}^{6}\frac{0.1}{g_j}\right],$$

where the $g_j, j = 1,2,\ldots,6$, are as defined by Eqs. (1.48).

For both cases the initial value of $r$ was 1000 and the drop-down factor $c$ was 0.1. The starting design for case 1 was $(A_1,A_2,A_3) = (2,3,4)$; and for case 2, (4,3,4). The results for case 1, the two-lobed loading envelope, are given in Table 3.6.

**Table 3.6. The 3-bar truss with loading envelope, case 1**

| $r$ | $A_1$ | $A_2$ | $A_3$ | $\phi$ | $F$ |
|---|---|---|---|---|---|
| Starting | 2 | 3 | 4 | 247.1 | 114.8 |
| $10^3$ | 2.671 | 3.170 | 2.671 | 237.6 | 107.3 |
| $10^2$ | 0.878 | 1.021 | 0.878 | 70.6 | 35.0 |
| $10^1$ | 0.768 | 0.534 | 0.768 | 32.2 | 27.1 |
| $10^0$ | 0.798 | 0.405 | 0.798 | 27.2 | 26.6 |
| $10^{-1}$ | 0.797 | 0.404 | 0.797 | 26.7 | 26.6 |
| $10^{-2}$ | 0.7968 | 0.4035 | 0.7968 | 26.57 | 26.57 |

The stresses, $g$-functions, and $1/g$'s are plotted in Fig. 3.24 for members 1 and 2 (the member 3 plots are a mirror image about $\theta = 90°$). The noteworthy features of the resulting design are that: (a) it is symmetric; (b) members 1 and 3 are fully stressed but member 2 is not; and (c) the result is almost identical with one obtained for the two distinct load cases[19] shown in Fig. 3.25. Thus if we had surmised that the critical loads of the envelope were maximum at $\theta = 45°$ and 135° and had solved the problem for these two ordinary con-

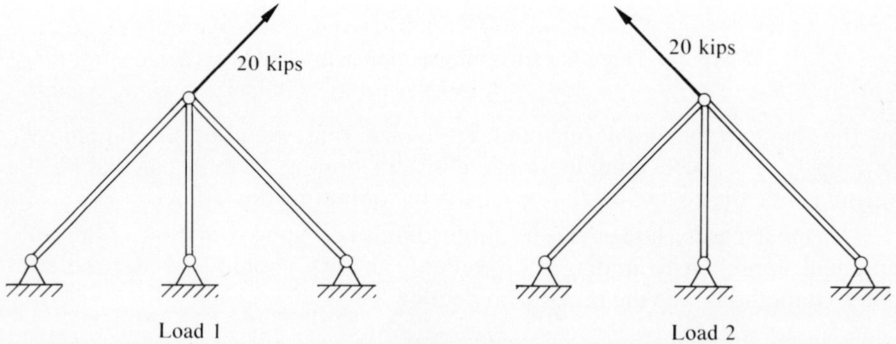


**Figure 3.25**

[19] Schmit (1964).

straints (i.e., without a parameter), the result would have been nearly the same. Although it could be considered quibbling, the optimum design for the distinct load case $(A_1,A_2,A_3) = (0.788, 0.410, 0.788)$ will not quite bear all the loads implied by the envelope, but it doesn't miss by much.

The results for the case of the elliptical envelope are given in Table 3.7. In this problem, member 1 takes its maximum stress of +20 ksi at $\theta = 32°$ (vs. the maximum *load* of 20 kips at 30°); member 2 takes +20 ksi at 73° (when the load is only 15.76 kips); and member 3 takes its maximum absolute stress of −20 ksi at $\theta = 350°$ (when the load is 16.35 kips). This design is "fully stressed" in the sense that each member reaches its maximum stress level for some load position.

**Table 3.7. The 3-bar truss with loading envelope, case 2**

| $r$ | $A_1$ | $A_2$ | $A_3$ | $\phi$ | $F$ |
|---|---|---|---|---|---|
| Starting | 4 | 3 | 4 | 273.9 | 143.1 |
| $10^3$ | 2.682 | 3.172 | 2.677 | 261.4 | 107.5 |
| $10^2$ | 0.916 | 1.020 | 0.884 | 73.3 | 35.6 |
| $10^1$ | 0.876 | 0.392 | 0.586 | 31.1 | 24.6 |
| $10^0$ | 0.901 | 0.211 | 0.605 | 24.4 | 23.4 |
| $10^{-1}$ | 0.903 | 0.197 | 0.605 | 23.4 | 23.3 |

While it is true that if the critical loads were known in advance the design could be optimized with ordinary constraints, this is not usually possible. The approach illustrated here is the only viable method presently available for the general parametric constraint.

## 3.7 PENALTY FUNCTIONS FOR EQUALITY CONSTRAINTS

In Section 1.6, we discussed equality constraints in certain problems and a form of problem statement called the integrated formulation. To review briefly, we must perform a complicated or time-consuming analysis in many design problems in order to relate a set of values for the $g_j$ to a particular set of values of the design variables $\boldsymbol{D}$. Often this analysis involves the solution of a system of algebraic equations of the form

$$I_j(\boldsymbol{D},\boldsymbol{W}) = 0\,, \qquad j = 1,2,\ldots,t\,, \tag{3.58}$$

for the behavior variables $\boldsymbol{W}$ for a given $\boldsymbol{D}$; the $g_j$ are then computed from their explicit dependence on $\boldsymbol{W}$. A problem of this type is given in Example E.3, the planar truss, in which ten linear equations in ten unknowns must be solved at each new design for which the stresses and displacements are to be determined. If we apply the penalty function method to the direct formulation, each computation of the $\phi$-function requires a new solution. For problems of the size considered practical from the analysis point of view in the aerospace and similarly sophisticated industries, repeating such simultaneous solutions a great many times is prohibitively expensive. Furthermore, in an increasing number of situations, the simultaneous equations are nonlinear in the behavior variables $\boldsymbol{W}$ and we must apply iterative solution methods.

This latter fact, that iterative solution methods can or must be used, has motivated the development of penalty functions that include equality constraints. Almost all such methods are based on the idea that one way of solving the equations

$$I_j(\boldsymbol{W}) = 0\,, \qquad j = 1,2,\ldots,t\,, \tag{3.59}$$

for $\boldsymbol{W}$ is to solve a minimization problem: Find $\boldsymbol{W}$ such that

$$\sum_{j=1}^{t} I_j^2 \to \min\,.$$

If the above minimum is zero, then the corresponding $\boldsymbol{W}$ is a solution to Eq. (3.59). The term to be minimized is sometimes called the *residual* of the Eqs. (3.59):

$$R(\boldsymbol{Y}) \equiv \sum_{j=1}^{t} R_j^2(\boldsymbol{Y}) \equiv \sum_{j=1}^{t} I_j^2\,, \tag{3.60}$$

where the dependence of $R$ upon $\boldsymbol{Y} \equiv (\boldsymbol{D},\boldsymbol{W})$ reflects the fact that it is a function of both the design variables $\boldsymbol{D}$ and the behavior variables $\boldsymbol{W}$.

Solving the equation for $\boldsymbol{W}$ by minimizing $R$ is not the most efficacious approach if the only purpose is to obtain a solution. This is because the residual is often a poorly conditioned function in $\boldsymbol{W}$-space.[20] In linear problems $\mathbf{K}\boldsymbol{W} = \boldsymbol{P}$, the "conditioning," or measure of difficulty, in obtaining accurate solutions is ordinarily related to the ratio of largest to smallest eigenvalue of the matrix of coefficients $\mathbf{K}$. However, in residual minimization, it is related to the ratio of largest to smallest eigenvalues of $\mathbf{K}^2$ ($\mathbf{K}$ being symmetric). Thus if $\mathbf{K}$ has a conditioning number of 100, the residual has one of 10,000, which is much worse.

In many engineering problems, the equations $l_j(\boldsymbol{W}) = 0$ can be derived from a minimum principle[21] $\pi(\boldsymbol{W}) \to$ min:

$$\partial\pi(\boldsymbol{W})/\partial w_j \equiv l_j(\boldsymbol{W}) = 0\,, \tag{3.61}$$

and $\pi$ has better conditioning than $R$ in Eq. (3.60). Unfortunately, no way has

[20] Fox and Stanton (1968).

[21] In a linear structures problem, the concept might be the minimum potential energy principle $\pi = \frac{1}{2}\boldsymbol{W}^T\mathbf{K}\boldsymbol{W} - \boldsymbol{W}^T\boldsymbol{P}$, whereas $R = (\mathbf{K}\boldsymbol{W} - \boldsymbol{P})^T(\mathbf{K}\boldsymbol{W} - \boldsymbol{P}) = \boldsymbol{W}^T\mathbf{K}^2\boldsymbol{W} - 2\boldsymbol{P}^T\mathbf{K}\boldsymbol{W} + \boldsymbol{P}^T\boldsymbol{P}$. In this form it is evident that the degradation of conditioning comes about in the quadratic terms $\boldsymbol{W}^T\mathbf{K}\boldsymbol{W}$ vs. $\boldsymbol{W}^T\mathbf{K}^2\boldsymbol{W}$.

yet been found to utilize the original minimum principle in a penalty function.

Several penalty functions for equality constraints are described in the literature and some of them will be briefly presented here. The last one to be discussed (an interior penalty function method) is preferred by the author and will be given slightly more attention than the others.

Fiacco and McCormick[22] report some success with the formulation

$$\phi(Y,r) = F - r \sum_{j=1}^{m} \frac{1}{g_j} + \frac{1}{r^{1/2}} \sum_{j=1}^{t} l_j^2 , \tag{3.62}$$

where $\phi$ is minimized for a decreasing sequence of values of $r$.

As $r$ is made small, the second term does its familiar job of allowing the minimum to approach the constraints from the inside, and the third term successively forces a satisfaction of $R = 0$. The justification for the $-\frac{1}{2}$ power on $r$ in the third term is given by Fiacco and McCormick (1964).

The method works in principle and has been used successfully in a number of problems. However, in many cases it presents an extremely difficult minimization problem, and scale disparities between the terms $F - r \Sigma 1/g_j$ and $r^{-1/2} \Sigma l_j^2$ are hard to resolve.

An exterior penalty function of the same type has been proposed as

$$\phi(Y,r) = F + r \left\{ \sum_{j=1}^{m} \langle g_j \rangle^2 + \sum_{j=1}^{t} l_j^2 \right\} , \tag{3.63}$$

which would be minimized for an increasing sequence of values of $r$. This formulation would doubtless suffer from the same problem as the interior function.

A different approach to the problem is to present the residuals as the function to be minimized, subject to the usual constraints $g_j \leqslant 0, j = 1,2, \ldots, m$, plus a new constraint $F - F_0 \leqslant 0$, where $F_0$ is a constant selected as a goal for the objective function in a particular cycle of minimization. Thus the problem now is to find $\boldsymbol{Y}$ such that $R(\boldsymbol{Y}) \rightarrow$ min, subject to

$$g_j(Y) \leqslant 0 , \qquad j = 1,2, \ldots, m ,$$
$$F - F_0 \leqslant 0 .$$

If a $\boldsymbol{Y}$ for which $R(\boldsymbol{Y}) = 0$ is obtained as a solution to this problem, then we have an acceptable design and its correct analysis, a design whose objective function has a value less than $F_0$. Optimization is carried out by solving the problem for a succession of decreasing values of $F_0$ until we find one for which $R_{\min}(\boldsymbol{Y}) > 0$. The optimum design lies between the last two values of $F_0$, and if the steps taken in $F_0$ are small enough we can take the last successful design as a reasonable approximation to the optimum.

[22] Fiacco and McCormick (1963).

An exterior penalty function approach to the problem has the form

$$\phi(Y,r) = R + r\left\{\sum_{j=1}^{m} \langle g_j \rangle^2 + \langle F - F_0 \rangle^2\right\}. \tag{3.64}$$

Engineering applications of this approach have been made with a modicum of success.[23] However, the method occasionally breaks down completely and unexpectedly with the appearance of an induced relative minimum.

The operation of the method is to pick values of $F_0$ and $r$ and to minimize $\phi$; if $R$ is acceptably small at the minimum and if the constraints are satisfied, then a new value of $F_0$ is chosen and the process repeated; if not, $r$ is increased and a new attempt to drive $\phi$ to zero is made. In practice, we can often select *a priori* a single value of $r$ and keep it constant throughout the process.

Much of the work that has gone into developing technical applications of the method has been concerned with a proper weighing of the penalty terms.[23] The special weighing balances the permissable violation tolerance for the constraints with that for $R = 0$.

Aside from the usual difficulties of being a hard minimization problem, the method, as we said before, suffers from artificially induced relative minima. In other words, the minimization process converges to an apparent minimum of $\phi$ at which $R \neq 0$ when there exists a $Y$ for which $R = 0$ and when the constraints, including $F - F_0 \leqslant 0$, are satisfied. These conditions cause the process to be falsely terminated and thwarts the optimization.

Finally, we discuss an interior penalty function method for the residual minimization form of the optimization problem:[24]

$$\phi = R - r\left\{\sum_{j=1}^{m} \frac{1}{g_j} + \frac{1}{(F - F_0)}\right\}. \tag{3.65}$$

This formulation too has been applied to a number of engineering problems, and it seems to be successful in a wider variety of cases than the exterior form. The operation of the method is as follows:

1. From an initial quasi-feasible point,[25] minimize $\phi(Y,r,F_0)$.
2. At the minimizing point $Y_M$, check the value of $R$: if $R$ (or some other measure of the satisfaction of $l_j(Y) = 0$) is acceptably close to zero, compute $\bar{F} \equiv F(Y_M)$, choose a new $F_0 < \bar{F}$ and proceed to step 3; otherwise, reduce $r$ and proceed to step 4.

---

[23] Fox and Schmit (1966). See also Schmit and Fox (1965).

[24] Schrader (1968).

[25] We will call a point satisfying $g_j \leqslant 0$ and $F - F_0 \leqslant 0$ a quasi-feasible point, since it does not satisfy $l_j(Y) = 0$.

3. Generate a point $\boldsymbol{Y}$ which satisfies $g_j \leqslant 0, j = 1,2,\ldots, m$, and $F - F_0 \leqslant 0$, and return to step 1.
4. Check the termination criterion; if it is not satisfied, return to step 1; otherwise, terminate.

This algorithm is also outlined in Fig. (3.26).

Like all penalty functions involving the residual, the minimization implied by block A is difficult. However, scaling (see Section 2.9) improves the situation considerably.

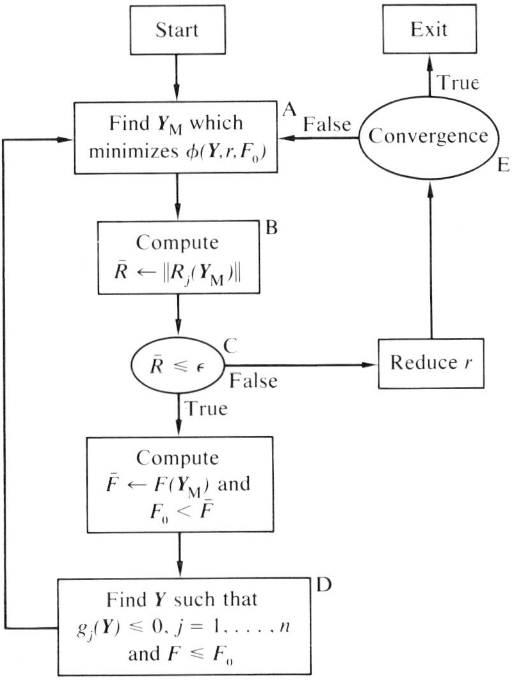


**Figure 3.26**

If we can compute or approximate $\partial^2\phi/\partial Y_i^{\,2}$ occasionally, then we can base a scaling on these factors. With this improvement, the conditioning of the function can often be enhanced to the point where the conjugate gradient method can serve as the minimizer. This may be important in many problems because the method tends to produce large minimization problems (i.e., $\boldsymbol{Y}$ may have many components).

The measure of satisfaction of the equations indicated in blocks B and C of Fig. 3.26 can be other than the least-squares measure implied by $R$ itself; e.g., $\bar{R}$ could be designated as $\bar{R} = \max_j(|l_j|)$ or $\bar{R} = \max_j(|l_j|/\epsilon_j)$, where the

$\epsilon_j$ are weighing factors or actual tolerances for the various equations. If the $\epsilon_j$ are individual tolerances, then $\bar{R}$ is simply compared with 1 in block C. This type of measure may be more appropriate in some engineering problems than the least-squares measure, because the equations often have physical meaning and we can choose the $\epsilon_j$ with a fair amount of judgment.

Block D can be the most troublesome step in the entire process. To start with, since $F_0$ has been lowered, $\boldsymbol{Y}_M$ no longer satisfies the constraint $F - F_0 \leqslant 0$. Stepping $\boldsymbol{Y}$ in the direction $-\nabla F$ will rectify this, but may cause violation of the other constraints, $g_j \leqslant 0$. In some problems, special directions in $\boldsymbol{Y}$-space are available that will always reduce the $g_j$ and $F$ simultaneously, though not, of course, while keeping $l_k = 0$. For example, consider a structures problem[26] in which $\boldsymbol{Y} = (\boldsymbol{D}, \boldsymbol{W})$ and $\boldsymbol{W}$ is a vector of displacement degrees of freedom. As the magnitude of the components of $\boldsymbol{W}$ is reduced toward zero, $g$-functions which represent yield stress, buckling stress, and displacement constraints can be reduced. Moreover, if the components of $\boldsymbol{D}$ are member areas or volume, we can reduce $F$ by reducing the components of $\boldsymbol{D}$. While such simple ideas are not always applicable, many problems do have similar special directions.

If a quasi-feasible point is not readily available or obtainable from tricks such as those described above, we can apply the ideas for finding a starting point that were discussed in Section 3.5. In this case, the approach is particularly straightforward, since $\boldsymbol{Y}_M$ already satisfies $g_j \leqslant 0$. All we need to do is operate on the function

$$\phi = F - r \sum_{j=1}^{m} \frac{1}{g_j} \tag{3.66}$$

for a sequence of values of $r$ until we obtain a $\boldsymbol{Y}$ with a value of $F \leqslant F_0$. At this point, we can resume the minimization of the original problem.

Bear in mind that it is desirable to stay as close as possible to a satisfaction of the $l_j = 0$ during the process of obtaining a quasi-feasible point. This, of course, is because the whole idea of the sequential minimization process is to be able to utilize good starting points for the individual minimizations.

Finally, we consider the convergence check of block E. The basic idea of convergence of the method is that after $r$ has been reduced a number of times, the residual function $R$ should be converging to its constrained minimum. If this minimum is nonzero, then convergence of the algorithm has been passed, so to speak. In other words, if the residual cannot be made to vanish in $g_j \leqslant 0$, $F - F_0 \leqslant 0$, there is no design with a lower value of the objective function than $F_0$ that also satisfies all the constraints.

We can do the convergence check by any of the techniques suitable for checking convergence of the inequality constrained problem done by the interior penalty function method. The extrapolation technique is perhaps the

[26] Schrader (1968).

most useful. With it, we can use the values of $R$ for several $r$ minimizations to estimate the final minimum value of $R$ for the current value of $F_0$. If the estimated values of $R$ appear to be reliable, then we can use their zero vs. nonzero property as the convergence criterion.

There are many ways to handle the different segments of a program that is using the unconstrained minimization approach to equality and inequality constrained problems. It is definitely a situation in which we must tailor the algorithm to the problem in order to be successful. These approaches to the general equality constrained problem[27] represent a state-of-the-art situation; the problem is not really solved, but some useful approaches are available.

## EXERCISES

**3.1** Apply a minimization algorithm to the transformed objective function of the post office parcel problem (i.e., minimize $F$ of Eq. 3.13 with respect to $\gamma_1$, $\gamma_2$, and $\gamma_3$).

**3.2** Assume in the post office parcel problem that $W = D$, and sketch the 2-dimensional design space in the variables $D$ and $L$. Show the constraints and function contours.

**3.3** An interior penalty function of the form

$$\phi(X) = F(X) - r\sum_{j=1}^{s}\frac{1}{g_j(X)},$$

where $X$ is a three-component vector, has been minimized for $r_1 = 9$ and $r_2 = 1$, with the results

$$X_1 = \begin{pmatrix} 1 \\ 2 \\ 2 \end{pmatrix} \qquad X_2 = \begin{pmatrix} \frac{1}{2} \\ \frac{1}{2} \\ 1 \end{pmatrix}.$$

Use the extrapolation to $r = 0$ to estimate the true optimum.
[*Answer*: $X_{\text{extrapolated}} = (\frac{1}{4}, -\frac{1}{4}, \frac{1}{2})$.]

**3.4** Assume $H(r) = A + Br^{1/2} + Cr$ (see Eq. 3.44) and that the $X_M$ are available corresponding to three previous minima for three values of $r$. Assume also that $r_{i+1} = cr_i$ and that $c$ is constant. Derive equations for $A$, $B$, and $C$.

**3.5** Write a computer program to apply the exterior penalty function method to the 2-bar truss problem (E.1). Follow the path produced by the program on Figs. 3.7–3.10 and in Table 3.1.

**3.6** Write a program to apply the interior penalty function method in Exercise 1.6. Take $L = 300$ in., $W = 50$ lb/in., $\sigma_b = 30{,}000$ psi, $\sigma_c = 100{,}000$ psi, $E = 3.0 \times 10^7$ psi, and $\alpha = 100$. Assume one cost unit per in$^3$ of beam material. Run two series of cases, one with $h = 10.00$ in. and the other with $h = 20.00$ in. Solve the problem for the maximum allowable deflection, $\Delta_M = 1.0$ in., 1.5 in., 2.0 in., and $\infty$. Compare these solutions with the result for a beam with no cable. The answers given in Table 3.8 are the average of

[27] Certain special equality constraints can be handled rigorously and in a straightforward manner. See Chapter 4.

**Table 3.8. Solutions to the propped cantilever problem**

| $h = 20.0$ | | | Optimum designs with cable | | | No cable designs | |
|---|---|---|---|---|---|---|---|
| $\Delta_M$ | $b$ | $H$ | $A$ | Cost | Active constraints | Cost | Active constraints |
| 1.0 | 0.854 | 328 | 0.102 | 9,630 | buckling, deflection | 15,187 | deflection |
| 1.5 | 0.784 | 343 | 0.054 | 7,160 | buckling, deflection | 10,125 | deflection |
| 2.0 | 0.759 | 309 | 0.037 | 6,140 | beam stress, cable stress | 7,593 | deflection |
| $\infty$ | 0.759 | 309 | 0.037 | 6,140 | beam stress, cable stress | 6,750 | beam stress |
| $h = 10.0$ | | | | | | | |
| 1.0 | 1.659 | 297 | 0.165 | 11,930 | deflection | 60,750 | deflection |
| 1.5 | 1.522 | 299 | 0.094 | 8,560 | beam stress, deflection | 40,500 | deflection |
| 2.0 | 1.711 | 303 | 0.066 | 7,940 | beam stress, cable stress | 30,375 | deflection |
| $\infty$ | 1.711 | 303 | 0.066 | 7,940 | beam stress, cable stress | 13,500 | beam stress |

several runs with various alterations of the program. Because the solution region appears to be flat, there may be some variation in the answers.

It is interesting to note that if the cost of the cable connections and installation are known, we can determine whether it is cheaper to use a cable or not for a particular depth and deflection limit.

**3.7** Write a computer program utilizing the interior penalty function and the integral form for parametric constraints, reproducing the results of Tables 3.6 and 3.7.

**3.8** Write a computer program utilizing the method of Eq. (3.65) to solve Example E.3. Form a residual function from Eqs. (1.34) and write (program) the constraint functions by directly using Eqs. (1.37). That is, write

$$g_1 = \frac{E}{100} u_1 - 20{,}000 \,,$$

$$g_2 = 15{,}000 - \frac{E}{100} u_1 \,,$$

$$g_3 = \frac{E}{200} (u_1 - v_1) - 20{,}000 \,,$$

and so on. Ignore displacement constraints, but in order to insure a statically stable structure, insert a constraint $A_i > 0.01$ in., $i = 1,2,\ldots,7$. Note that even though there are 17 variables in the problem (10 behavior + 7 design), the gradient of the penalty function can be calculated rather easily because the system of equations is linear. In view of this, it is recommended that the variable metric method be used. [*Answer*: $A_1 = 0.283$ in$^2$, $A_2 = 0.542$ in$^2$, $A_3 = 0.01$ in$^2$, $A_4 = 0.738$ in$^2$, $A_5 = 0.970$ in$^2$, $A_6 = 1.384$ in$^2$, $A_7 = 0.727$ in$^2$, and $F = 1151$ lb.]

**3.9** Solve Exercise 1.6(a) using the interior penalty function method. Assume constant $\sigma_e$ and $\sigma_w$ instead of the variable formulas given in Exercise 1.6. Take $G = 12.0 \times 10^6$ psi, $\sigma_w = 12.0 \times 10^4$ psi, $\sigma_e = 6.0 \times 10^4$ psi, $S_f = 1.15$, $h_0 = 2.0$ in., $\delta_0 = \frac{1}{4}$ in., $D_m = 1.0$ in. [*Answer*: $d = 0.204$ in., $D = 0.796$ in., $n = 8.57$, $h_f = 2.26$ in., $P_0 = 158.5$ lb.]

## REFERENCES

Box, M. J., "A New Method of Constrained Optimization and a Comparison with Other Methods," *Computer J.* **8** (1), 42–52 (1965)

Fiacco, A. V., and G. P. McCormick, "Programming under Nonlinear Constraints by Unconstrained Minimization: A Primal-Dual Method," Research Analysis Corporation, Bethesda, Md., Tech. Paper RAC-TP-96 (1963)

Fiacco, A. V., and G. P. McCormick, "Computational Algorithm for the Sequential Unconstrained Minimization Technique for Nonlinear Programming," *Man. Sci.* **10** (4), 601–617 (1964)

Fiacco, A. V., and G. P. McCormick, *Nonlinear Programming: Sequential Unconstrained Minimization Techniques*, Wiley, New York (1969)

Fox, R. L., and L. A. Schmit, Jr., "Advances in the Integrated Approach to Structural Synthesis," *J. of Spacecraft and Rockets* **3** (6), 858–866 (1966)

Fox, R. L., and E. L. Stanton, "Developments in Structural Analysis by Direct Energy Minimization," *AIAA J.* **6** (6), 1036–1042 (1968)

Hadley, G., *Linear Programming*, Addison-Wesley, Reading, Mass. (1962)

Hadley, G., *Nonlinear and Dynamic Programming*, Addison-Wesley, Reading, Mass. (1964)

Moses, F., "Optimum Design for Structural Safety," 8th IABSE Congress, New York (Sept. 1968)

Moses, F., and D. E. Kinser, "Optimum Structural Design with Failure Probability Constraints," *AIAA J.* **5** (6), 1152–1158 (1967)

Rutishauser, H., F. L. Bauer, and E. Stiefel, "New Aspects in Numerical Quadrature," *Proc. of Symposia in Applied Math. (1962)* **15**, 199–218, Amer. Math. Soc., Providence, R.I. (1963)

Schmit, L. A., "A Comment on 'Completely Automatic Weight Minimization Method for High-Speed Digital Computers,'" *J. Aircraft* **1** (6), 375–377 (1964)

Schmit, L. A., and R. L. Fox, "An Integrated Approach to Structural Synthesis and Analysis," *AIAA J.* **3** (6), 1104–1112 (1965)

Schrader, M. J., "An Algorithm for the Minimum Weight Design of the General Truss," Case Western Reserve University, Master's Thesis (June 1968)

Thornton, W. A., and L. A. Schmit, Jr., "Structural Synthesis of an Ablating Thermostructural Panel," AIAA/ASME 9th Conference on Structures, Structural Dynamics, and Materials, Palm Springs, Calif. (1968)

Zangwill, W. I., "Nonlinear Programming via Penalty Functions," *Man. Sci.* **13** (5), 344–358 (1967)

Zoutendijk, G., "Nonlinear Programming: A Numerical Survey," *J. SIAM Control* **4** (1), 194–210 (1966)

CHAPTER 4

# DIRECT METHODS FOR CONSTRAINED PROBLEMS

In Chapter 3 we discussed a class of methods for solving the inequality and mixed equality and inequality constrained optimization problems. All the methods were based on the trick of somehow converting a problem to an unconstrained minimization problem. In the present chapter we discuss a number of what could be loosely called *direct methods*. In these approaches, we consider the constraints as limiting surfaces or subspaces.

First we discuss a powerful test for a constrained minimum called the Kuhn-Tucker conditions. This test allows us to check a design point for optimality; furthermore, a study of it helps us to better understand the optimization problem and gives us an insight into some of the solution methods. The projection matrix is presented and its relation to the Kuhn-Tucker conditions is discussed.

Next there is a discussion of methods of feasible directions. These methods include some of the most effective direct approaches to the general nonlinear programming problem that currently exist.

These sections are followed by a discussion of the gradient projection method. While this technique is effective in only a limited range of problems, it is probably the best method available for problems with linear constraints (equality or inequality) and a general nonlinear objective function.

Next we discuss the so-called linear programming problem and the basic algorithm for its solution. Of all methods of solving mathematical programming problems, this is the best understood and most nearly foolproof. The class of linear problems, in view of the nature of engineering design, is severely limited; on the other hand, the method can be used to solve subsidiary problems arising in the feasible direction method and to solve a variety of approximations to nonlinear problems.

## 4.1 LAGRANGE MULTIPLIERS, KUHN-TUCKER CONDITIONS, AND PROJECTIONS

As we have seen, a valuable computational tool would be a test to ascertain whether a given vector $X$ is at least a local minimum in a constrained optimization problem. Such a test, providing necessary conditions for a local minimum, is available for problems satisfying certain rather general conditions. Before discussing them, let us review a closely connected topic.

**Lagrange Multipliers**

Consider the problem of finding an $X_M$ such that $F(X_M)$ is a minimum and the single *equality* constraint $l(X_M) = 0$ is satisfied. We can view the problem geometrically as one of finding a point $X_M$ such that all small "moves" from $X_M$ in the surface $l(X) = 0$ produce an increase or no change in $F$. An infinitesimal vector $dr \equiv (dx_1, dx_2, \ldots, dx_n)$ is "in" the surface $l(X) = 0$ if it is perpendicular to a normal to the surface at that point. Consider a Taylor series expansion of $l(X_M + dr)$:

$$l(X_M + dr) = l(X_M) + dr^T \nabla l(X_M) + \mathcal{O}(dr^2) \,. \tag{4.1}$$

Dropping the higher-order infinitesimals and noting that $l(X_M) = 0$, we have

$$\nabla l(X_M)^T dr = 0 \,. \tag{4.2}$$

(See Fig. 4.1.) At the desired point, all such vectors must also produce no change in $F$ and thus

$$dF = \nabla F^T dr = 0 \,. \tag{4.3}$$

In particular, we seek a point $X_M$ where $l(X_M) = 0$ and for which $\nabla F_M{}^T dr = 0$ for all $dr$ satisfying $\nabla l_M{}^T dr = 0$.

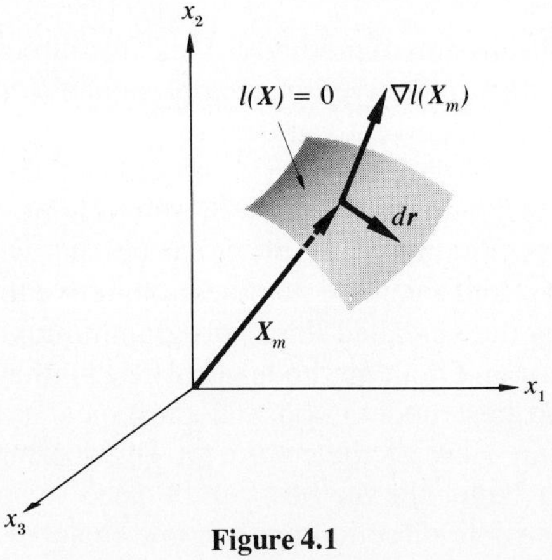


**Figure 4.1**

The requirements could be used in their original form to formulate the actual equations to be solved. That is, solve $l(X) = 0$ for

$$x_j = f(x_1, \ldots, x_{j-1}, x_{j+1}, \ldots, x_n)$$

for some $j$; substitute this into $F(X)$, transforming it into

$$\bar{F}(x_1, x_2, \ldots, x_{j-1}, x_{j+1}, \ldots, x_n),$$

and then solve the $n-1$ simultaneous equations

$$\partial \bar{F}/\partial x_i = 0\,, \qquad i = 1,2,\ldots,j-1,j+1,\ldots,n\,, \tag{4.4}$$

for the remaining $n-1$ values of $x_i$.

However, by introducing another variable called a *Lagrange multiplier*, we can simplify the problem formulation and, in some cases, simplify the computation of the solution.

We can state the requirements of the problem in the following way: Find $X_M$ that is: (1) in $l(X)=0$, and (2) for which $\nabla F$ and $\nabla l$ are related in such a way that $\nabla F^T dr = 0$ for all $dr$ satisfying $\nabla l^T dr = 0$.

We now eliminate d$r$ from the problem by finding the relationship that must hold between $\nabla F$ and $\nabla l$ in order for condition (2) to be satisfied. First note that the two equations

$$\nabla F^T dr = 0\,, \tag{4.5}$$

$$\nabla l^T dr = 0\,, \tag{4.6}$$

can be added in any proportion, and the sum used in place of one of the original equations. Thus the two equations

$$\nabla F^T dr + \lambda \nabla l^T dr = (\nabla F + \lambda \nabla l)^T dr = 0\,, \tag{4.7}$$

$$\nabla l^T dr = 0\,, \tag{4.8}$$

state the same thing as Eqs. (4.5) and (4.6) for *any* choice of the constant $\lambda$.

Suppose we solve Eq. (4.8) for one of the components of $dr$, say $dx_k$:

$$dx_k = \frac{-1}{\partial l/\partial x_k} \sum_{i \neq k}^{n} \frac{\partial l}{\partial x_i}\, dx_i\,, \tag{4.9}$$

which assumes that $\partial l/\partial x_k$ is nonzero. This restricts the choice of $k$ to one for which the gradient component $\partial l/\partial x_k$ does not vanish; if they all vanish, then some other criterion must take the place of Eq. (4.6), since we derived it by assuming $\nabla l \neq \mathbf{0}$.[1]

Now substitute Eq. (4.9) into Eq. (4.7), producing, after collecting terms,

$$\sum_{\substack{i=1,\\ i\neq k}}^{n} \left[ \left( \frac{\partial F}{\partial x_i} + \lambda \frac{\partial l}{\partial x_i} \right) - \left( \frac{\partial F}{\partial x_k} + \lambda \frac{\partial l}{\partial x_k} \right) \frac{\partial l/\partial x_i}{\partial l/\partial x_k} \right] dx_i = 0\,. \tag{4.10}$$

Since Eq. (4.7) is to be satisfied for any arbitrary choice of $\lambda$, assume that it is chosen so that

$$\frac{\partial F}{\partial x_k} + \lambda \frac{\partial l}{\partial x_k} = 0\,. \tag{4.11}$$

[1] For example, assume that $\nabla l = \mathbf{0}$ but that $[\partial^2 l/\partial x_i \partial x_j] \equiv \mathbf{J}$ is nonvanishing; Eq. (4.6) might be replaced by $dr^T \mathbf{J} dr = 0$.

The $n-1$ quantities $dx_i$, $i = 1,2, \ldots, k-1, k+1, \ldots, n$, can be chosen in any arbitrary way, and if $dx_k$ is obtained from Eq. (4.9), the resulting $dr$ will satisfy Eq. (4.8). Thus the $n-1$ $dx_i$ in Eq. (4.10) are arbitrary, and for the sum to vanish for all choices, their coefficients must be zero. This produces the conditions

$$\frac{\partial F}{\partial x_i} + \lambda \frac{\partial l}{\partial x_i} = 0\,, \qquad i = 1, \ldots, k-1, k+1, \ldots, n\,. \tag{4.12}$$

Since

$$\frac{\partial F}{\partial x_k} + \lambda \frac{\partial l}{\partial x_k} \tag{4.13}$$

has already been set to zero by the choice of $\lambda$, this produces the following condition in order for $X_M$ to be a minimum point of $F$ in $l(X) = 0$: There must exist a $\lambda$ for which

$$\frac{\partial F}{\partial x_i} + \lambda \frac{\partial l}{\partial x_i} = 0\,, \qquad i = 1, \ldots, n \tag{4.14}$$

or

$$\nabla F + \lambda \nabla l = \mathbf{0}\,. \tag{4.15}$$

Thus we have $n+1$ equations for the $n+1$ variables $x_1, x_2, \ldots, x_n, \lambda$: Eqs. (4.14) together with $l(X) = 0$.

We can repeat the above arguments in the case of several equality constraints $l_j(X) = 0, j = 1,2, \ldots, m$, yielding the conditions

$$\nabla F + \sum_{j=1}^{m} \lambda_j \nabla l_j = \mathbf{0}\,, \tag{4.16}$$

$$l_j(X) = 0\,, \qquad j = 1,2, \ldots, m\,. \tag{4.17}$$

It is instructive to view the conditions another way. Note that they can be given a different form if we define

$$\phi(X, \boldsymbol{\lambda}) \equiv F + \sum_{j=1}^{m} \lambda_j l_j \tag{4.18}$$

and state the problem as one of finding a stationary point of $\phi$ over all $x_i$ and $\lambda_j$ ($\phi$ is called the Lagrangian function). Thus

$$\frac{\partial \phi}{\partial x_i} \equiv \frac{\partial F}{\partial x_i} + \sum_{j=1}^{m} \lambda_j \frac{\partial l_j}{\partial x_i} = 0\,, \qquad i = 1,2, \ldots, n\,, \tag{4.16$'$}$$

$$\frac{\partial \phi}{\partial \lambda_j} \equiv l_j = 0\,, \qquad j = 1,2, \ldots, m\,. \tag{4.17$'$}$$

As an example of the method, consider $F = \frac{1}{2}(x_1{}^2 + x_2{}^2 + x_3{}^2)$, $l_1 = x_1 - x_2$, and $l_2 = x_1 + x_2 + x_3 - 1$ for which

$$\phi = \tfrac{1}{2}(x_1{}^2 + x_2{}^2 + x_3{}^2) + \lambda_1(x_1 - x_2) + \lambda_2(x_1 + x_2 + x_3 - 1\ ).$$

Then Eqs. (4.16) and (4.17) become

$$\frac{\partial \phi}{\partial x_i}: \quad \begin{aligned} x_1 + \lambda_1 + \lambda_2 &= 0, \\ x_2 - \lambda_1 + \lambda_2 &= 0, \\ x_3 + \lambda_2 &= 0; \end{aligned}$$

$$\frac{\partial \phi}{\partial \lambda_j}: \quad \begin{aligned} x_1 - x_2 &= 0, \\ x_1 + x_2 + x_3 - 1 &= 0. \end{aligned}$$

Solving the first three equations for $x_i$ in terms of the $\lambda$'s and substituting into the last two, we have

$$-\lambda_1 - \lambda_2 - \lambda_1 + \lambda_2 = 0,$$
$$-\lambda_1 - \lambda_2 + \lambda_1 - \lambda_2 - \lambda_2 - 1 = 0,$$

which yield

$$\lambda_1 = 0, \qquad \lambda_2 = -\tfrac{1}{3}, \qquad x_1 = x_2 = x_3 = \tfrac{1}{3}.$$

This approach, incidently, is the usual way to solve the Lagrange multiplier equations: solve the system $\partial\phi/\partial x_i = 0$ for the $x_i$ and substitute the results into $\partial\phi/\partial\lambda_j = 0$ to solve for $\lambda_j$ and finally back substitute for the $x_i$.

The implication of $\lambda_1 = 0$ in our example is worth noting. It results from the fact that the first constraint is redundant for this problem; in other words, we get the same answer if we ignore $l_1 = 0$ and just minimize $F$ subject to $l_2 = 0$.

In the general problem, of course, we do not often obtain such a simple set of equations to solve; they are usually coupled and nonlinear. Because of this, the Lagrange multiplier method is not very useful for solving constrained minimization problems.

It should also be noted that not all solutions of Eqs. (4.16) and (4.17) will be constrained minima, since these conditions also pertain to constrained maxima and saddle points. Further tests are necessary to ensure that a point is a minimum.

A geometric interpretation of the vector Eq. (4.16) is useful. If we are considering a point on the intersection of the surfaces $l_j(X) = 0$, then Eq. (4.16) means that at the minimum, the gradient of $F$ must be expressible as a linear combination of the normals to the surfaces. This interpretation is plausible because it implies that $\nabla F$ has no component perpendicular to all the $\nabla l_j$, and consequently there is no direction in which $F$ can be reduced without moving out of the intersection of the surfaces. Sometimes we describe this situation by saying that *$\nabla F$ is contained in the subspace spanned by the vectors $\nabla l_j$*.

**Inequality Constraints**

We can apply the concept of Lagrange multipliers to inequality constraints $g_j(X) \leqslant 0$ by the artifice of using so-called slack variables. Note that these inequalities are satisfied if the equalities

$$l_j(X, s_j) \equiv s_j^2 + g_j(X) = 0 \tag{4.19}$$

are satisfied, where the $s_j$ are new, real-valued variables. The $s_j$ are called slack variables because they give a measure of the "distance" or "slack" from point $X$ to the constraint boundary:[2] if $s_j = 0$, then $g_j(X)$ must equal zero; if $s_j \neq 0$, then $g_j(X)$ must be negative; and, of course, $g_j(X)$ cannot be positive if Eq. (4.19) is to be satisfied.

Applying the Lagrange multiplier method to the slack equalities, we define the function

$$\phi(X, S, \boldsymbol{\lambda}) = F + \sum_{j=1}^{m} \lambda_j (s_j^2 + g_j), \tag{4.20}$$

which has the following stationary conditions:

$$\frac{\partial \phi}{\partial x_i} \equiv \frac{\partial F}{\partial x_i} + \sum_{j=1}^{m} \lambda_j \frac{\partial g_j}{\partial x_i} = 0, \qquad i = 1, 2, \ldots, n, \tag{4.21a}$$

$$\frac{\partial \phi}{\partial s_j} \equiv 2\lambda_j s_j = 0, \qquad j = 1, 2, \ldots, m, \tag{4.21b}$$

$$\frac{\partial \phi}{\partial \lambda_k} \equiv (s_k^2 + g_k) = 0, \qquad k = 1, 2, \ldots, m. \tag{4.21c}$$

Equations (4.21c) ensure the inequalities $g_j \leqslant 0$. Equations (4.21b) state that either $s_j$ or $\lambda_j$ is zero, which implies that either the constraint is active ($g_j = 0$) and must be considered in testing the subspace containing $\nabla F$, or it is inactive ($\lambda_j = 0$) and is to be ignored in checking the subspace. Equations (4.21a) require that $\nabla F$ lie in the subspace spanned by those $\nabla g_j$ which correspond to the active constraints.

We seek a test which we can apply to a proposed minimum point rather than a set of equations which is to be solved. Therefore we will distill Eqs. (4.21) somewhat. First, let us define a set of integers $J$ as the subscripts of those constraints $g_j$ that are active at the point being tested. Thus

$$g_j(X) = 0\,, \qquad j \in J, \tag{4.22}$$

where $j \in J$ is read "$j$ contained in the set $J$." With this we can say $X$ *may* be a minimum if it is feasible (i.e., if $g_j \leqslant 0$, $j = 1, 2, \ldots, m$), and if there exist $\lambda_j$ such that

$$\nabla F + \sum_{j \in J} \lambda_j \nabla g_j = \mathbf{0}\,. \tag{4.23}$$

This test may be further sharpened to exclude situations in which Eq. (4.23) is satisfied and yet $X$ is not a local minimum.

To help clarify the general statement that follows, we consider the geometrical implications of two situations. First, imagine a point in a 3-dimensional space $X = (x_1, x_2, x_3)$ at which two inequality constraints are active

---

[2] In linear programming (Section 4.4) we define slack variables in a slightly different form, but the basic idea is the same.

(e.g., $g_1 = 0$, $g_2 = 0$). At this point the gradients of the constraints $\nabla g_1$ and $\nabla g_2$, unless they are colinear, define a plane: the subspace of all vectors that can be written as a linear combination of $\nabla g_1$ and $\nabla g_2$. Further, the gradient of the objective function $\nabla F$ at this point must either lie in this plane or not. If it does not lie in the plane, then the direction of steepest descent $-\nabla F$ has a component perpendicular to both constraint normals, and the function $F$ may be decreased by moving perpendicularly to these vectors. This condition agrees with the result of the Lagrange multiplier analysis; that is, the point is not optimal if $\nabla F$ cannot be written as a linear combination of the normals to the active constraints. Consider next the case where $\nabla F$ does lie in the plane defined by the two constraint normals. There are two possibilities: (1) $-\nabla F$ falls in the sector of the plane included between the acute angle made by $\nabla g_1$ and $\nabla g_2$, or (2) $-\nabla F$ lies outside this sector. If it lies outside the sector, there is a component of $-\nabla F$ that is directed away from both constraints, and the point is not optimal because the function may be decreased without moving toward the constraints. Putting this another way, there exist vectors of descent (i.e., $V$ such that $-\nabla F^T V > 0$) which make obtuse angles with both constraint normals (i.e., $V^T \nabla g_1 < 0$, $V^T \nabla g_2 < 0$). This situation is characterized by the fact that in writing $-\nabla F$ as a linear combination of the constraint normals, at least one of the constants $\lambda_1$ or $\lambda_2$ in

$$-\nabla F = \lambda_1 \nabla g_1 + \lambda_2 \nabla g_2 \tag{4.24}$$

will be negative. This is made clearer by a study of Fig. 4.2, which can be thought of as the 2-dimensional subspace defined by $\nabla g_1$ and $\nabla g_2$.

If $-\nabla F$ lies in the sector defined by $\nabla g_1$ and $\nabla g_2$, the point is a local optimum, barring certain exceptional situations. This is because there is no vector of descent making an obtuse angle with both constraint normals, and hence

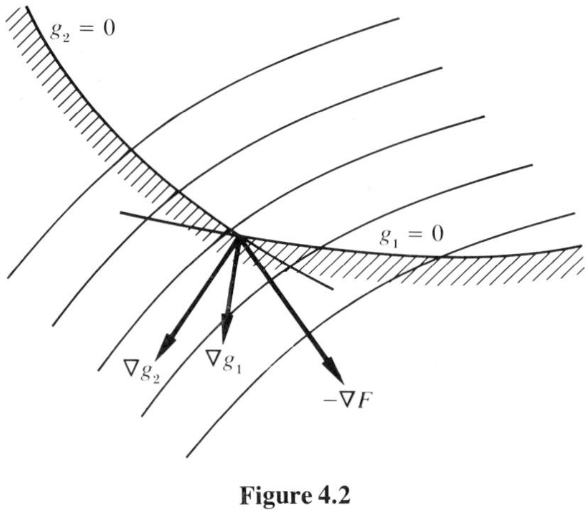


**Figure 4.2**

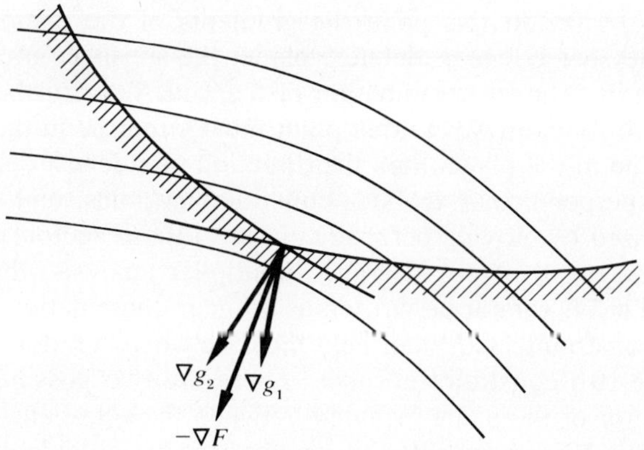


**Figure 4.3**

we cannot make any move that reduces the objective function in the feasible domain (see Fig. 4.3).

Imagine next a point in a 3-dimensional space at which three constraints are active. The normals $\nabla g_1$, $\nabla g_2$, and $\nabla g_3$ to these constraints, if they are not coplanar or colinear, span the 3-dimensional space. This means that at the point in question, the direction of steepest descent $-\nabla F$ (indeed any vector) can be written as a linear combination of the normals. The three vectors $\nabla g_1$, $\nabla g_2$, and $\nabla g_3$ form what is called a *cone*, although it is really more like a three-sided pyramid with its apex at the point. Any cross section of the cone is a triangle. Now imagine the vector $-\nabla F$; it can fall within the cone or outside of it. That is, if we visualize any cross section of the cone, $-\nabla F$ intersects the plane of this cross section at a point that lies inside the triangle or outside of it. If the steepest descent direction lies outside the cone, then a move can be made in some descent directions without penetrating the constraints. On the other hand, if $-\nabla F$ lies inside the cone, there does not exist a $V$ such that $-\nabla F^T V > 0$ and $\nabla g_i^T V < 0$, $i = 1,2,3$. In other words, there is no direction of descent that makes an obtuse angle with all the constraints. Finally, note that $-\nabla F$ can be written as a nonnegative linear combination of $\nabla g_i$ if and only if it is within the cone.

These ideas generalize to $n$ dimensions and $m$ constraints, and we can state the powerful *Kuhn-Tucker conditions*[3] for a relative minimum as

$$\frac{\partial F}{\partial x_i} + \sum_{j \in J} \lambda_j \frac{\partial g_j}{\partial x_i} = 0\,, \qquad i = 1,2,\ldots,n\,, \tag{4.25a}$$

$$\lambda_j \geqslant 0\,, \qquad j \in J\,. \tag{4.25b}$$

[3] For further discussion, see Hadley (1964).

Equations (4.25a) require that $\nabla F$ lie in the subspace of the $\nabla g_j$ and the inequalities, and Eqs. (4.25b) ascertain that the active constraints are really obstructing a move in a direction of descent. These are necessary conditions for a point to be a relative minimum, but they are not sufficient to ensure a relative minimum (as is illustrated by the case of point $Q$ in Fig. 3.3). There is a class of problems, called convex programming problems, for which the Kuhn-Tucker conditions are necessary and sufficient for a global minimum.

**Convex Programming Problems**

A set of points, say those bounded by $g_j(X) \leqslant 0$, is called *convex* if the line segment joining any two points $X_1$ and $X_2$ is contained entirely within the set. This concept can be written in mathematical shorthand as: The set $S$ is convex if for all $X_1 \in S$, $X_2 \in S$, and $0 < \alpha < 1$, the point $\alpha X_1 + (1-\alpha)X_2 \equiv Y \in S$. The set may be bounded or unbounded and may be an $r$-dimensional subspace of an $n$-dimensional space (e.g., a plane in a 3-space).

A function $F(X)$ is said to be convex if, on the line connecting every pair of points $X_1$ and $X_2$ in its domain of definition, the function is less than or equal to a linear interpolation of $F(X_1) \equiv f_1$ and $F(X_2) \equiv f_2$. In other words, the function is convex if

$$F[\alpha X_2 + (1-\alpha)X_1] \leqslant \alpha f_2 + (1-\alpha)f_1, \qquad 0 < \alpha < 1, \tag{4.26}$$

where the right-hand side is recognized as a linear interpolation of the function along the line from $X_1$ and $X_2$, and the argument of the function on the left-hand side is some point on the line between $X_1$ and $X_2$. Figure 4.4 illustrates the idea. If a function $F$ is convex, then $-F$ is concave, but note that these two designations do not include all situations. A function may be neither convex nor concave.

A *convex programming problem* for minimization is one with a convex feasible domain and a convex objective function. This is assured if $F$ and the

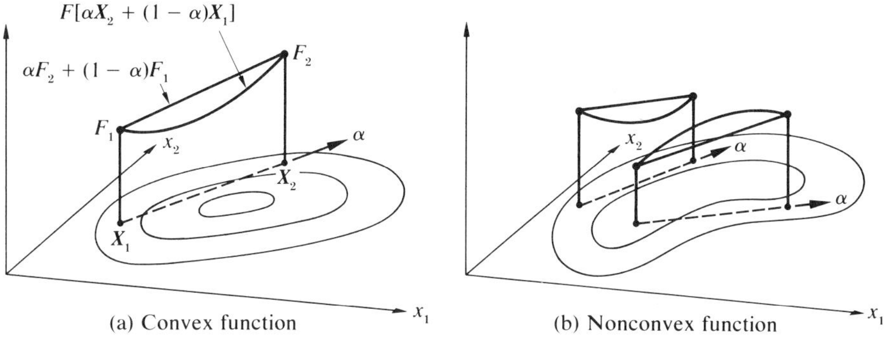


**Figure 4.4**

$g_j$ are convex functions. It can be shown that the intersection of convex domains is convex: since the individual domains $g_1 \leqslant 0$ or $g_2 \leqslant 0$ are convex, then if $g_1$ and $g_2$ are convex, the domain that is defined by both $g_1 \leqslant 0$ and $g_2 \leqslant 0$ is also convex. A problem with equality constraints is convex if the $l_i(\boldsymbol{X})$ are linear and if $F$ and the $g_j$ are convex. The intersection of linear equality constraints (i.e., hyperplanes) is a convex subspace by the same argument that we used above, since a single hyperplane is a convex domain. Other equality constraints may intersect a convex domain (consider two curved surfaces that intersect in a straight line), but this is an unusual situation.

If a programming problem is known to be convex, than a great many advantages accrue. For example, there are no relative minima or saddle points, and the Kuhn-Tucker conditions are necessary and sufficient for a global minimum. However, it is often difficult to ascertain whether the functions in an engineering problem are convex. Even if a problem is not a convex program, it may still have only a global minimum, or it may be solvable for its relative minima, which provide useful information.

The lesson here is that if a problem can be easily shown to be convex, life will be greatly simplified for the problem solver, but if it is not convex or cannot be shown to be convex, it is still often possible to obtain useful answers and even optima. Usually, if a physical problem is intelligently formulated, it has answers.

**Computing the Kuhn-Tucker Multipliers**

Practical application of the necessary conditions (Eqs. 4.25) as a test for a minimum usually requires the solution of simultaneous linear equations for the $\lambda_j$. For convenience, let us denote

$$b_i \equiv -\partial F/\partial x_i, \tag{4.27}$$

or, in vector form,

$$\boldsymbol{B} \equiv -\nabla F, \tag{4.28}$$

$$n_{ij} \equiv \partial g_j/\partial x_i. \tag{4.29}$$

Also denote

$$\nabla g_j \equiv \boldsymbol{A}_j \equiv (n_{1j}, \ldots, n_{nj}). \tag{4.30}$$

Thus $\mathbf{N}$ is an $n \times r$ matrix

$$\mathbf{N} \equiv [n_{ij}] = [\boldsymbol{A}_1, \boldsymbol{A}_2, \ldots, \boldsymbol{A}_r], \tag{4.31}$$

where the constraints have been renumbered so that the $r$ active ones correspond to $j = 1, 2, \ldots, r$.

The linear equations (4.25a) become

$$\sum_{j=1}^{r} n_{ij}\lambda_j = b_i, \qquad i = 1, 2, \ldots, n, \tag{4.32}$$

or, in matrix form,

$$\mathbf{N}\boldsymbol{\lambda} = \boldsymbol{B}. \tag{4.33}$$

We thus have $n$ equations in the $r$ unknowns $\lambda_j$. Typically, in engineering problems, the optimum lies at a point where fewer than $n$ constraints are active. Thus $r < n$ and the system is overdetermined. There are three possibilities in such cases: (1) Eqs. (4.32) have a unique solution, (2) they have no solution (i.e., no $\boldsymbol{\lambda}$ satisfies all the equations), or (3) the solutions are indeterminate. Situations (1) and (2) are the normal results we expect when testing the Kuhn-Tucker conditions; situation (3) is exceptional and results only when the $A_j$ (i.e., $\nabla g_j$) are not all independent. As an example of the third situation, consider a point in a 3-dimensional space where the three normals $\nabla g_1$, $\nabla g_2$, and $\nabla g_3$ are coplanar; if $-\nabla F$ lies in the same plane, there is an infinite number of combinations of the normals that give $-\nabla F$. On the other hand, if $-\nabla F$ falls outside the plane, then no combination gives $-\nabla F$ and this is a case (2) situation. The technique we will illustrate for finding the $\lambda_j$ requires precautions if the $A_j$ are not independent; but first we will proceed as though they were.

To set up an approach for finding $\boldsymbol{\lambda}$, we will define the residual vector for Eqs. (4.32), form the square of its length, and then look at the conditions for its length to be a minimum. Consider the residual vector

$$R \equiv \mathbf{N}\boldsymbol{\lambda} - B \tag{4.34}$$

and the square of its length

$$\begin{aligned} L(\boldsymbol{\lambda}) \equiv |R|^2 &= (\mathbf{N}\boldsymbol{\lambda} - B)^T(\mathbf{N}\boldsymbol{\lambda} - B) \\ &= \boldsymbol{\lambda}^T\mathbf{N}^T\mathbf{N}\boldsymbol{\lambda} - 2\boldsymbol{\lambda}^T\mathbf{N}^T B + B^T B. \end{aligned} \tag{4.35}$$

The stationary conditions for $L$ as a function of $\boldsymbol{\lambda}$ are $\partial L/\partial\lambda_i = 0$, or

$$\nabla L = 2\mathbf{N}^T\mathbf{N}\boldsymbol{\lambda} - 2\mathbf{N}^T B = 0, \tag{4.36}$$

from which the factor of 2 can be eliminated. The $r \times r$ matrix $\mathbf{N}^T\mathbf{N}$ is interesting: its elements are the "dot" products $A_i^T A_j$, and it is nonsingular exactly when the $A_i$ are linearly independent vectors.

Whenever $\mathbf{N}^T\mathbf{N}$ is nonsingular, a solution for the Lagrange multipliers is possible:

$$\boldsymbol{\lambda} = (\mathbf{N}^T\mathbf{N})^{-1}\mathbf{N}^T B. \tag{4.37}$$

The $\boldsymbol{\lambda}$ vector always minimizes the sum of the squares of the residuals, but it may not satisfy the original equations. To check this, we substitute Eq. (4.37) into Eq. (4.33), and if $B$ can be written as a linear combination of the $A_j$, then

$$\mathbf{N}(\mathbf{N}^T\mathbf{N})^{-1}\mathbf{N}^T B = B, \tag{4.38}$$

which can be written as

$$[\mathbf{I} - \mathbf{N}(\mathbf{N}^T\mathbf{N})^{-1}\mathbf{N}^T]B = 0. \tag{4.39}$$

Of course, the result may not be zero, in which case the Kuhn-Tucker conditions are unsatisfied.

Thus one possible approach to testing for satisfaction of the Kuhn-Tucker conditions is to solve for $\boldsymbol{\lambda}$ by inverting $\mathbf{N}^T\mathbf{N}$ and computing $\boldsymbol{\lambda}$ from Eq. (4.37).

Then if all components are positive, and if $\boldsymbol{\lambda}$ satisfies Eq. (4.33), the Kuhn-Tucker conditions are satisfied.

Because of the special nature of the matrices involved, some simple recursive procedures are available for computing $(\mathbf{N}^T\mathbf{N})^{-1}$ or $[\mathbf{I}-\mathbf{N}(\mathbf{N}^T\mathbf{N})^{-1}\mathbf{N}^T]$. These are discussed in Section 4.3 along with other characteristics of these matrices. For the present, we assume that ordinary approaches for computing an inverse will be used.

Before leaving the discussion of Kuhn-Tucker conditions, we will find it useful to view the problem from a different direction. Consider a projection of the vector $\boldsymbol{B}$ onto the intersection of all the hyperplanes perpendicular to the $\boldsymbol{A}_j$ vectors. Call this projection $\boldsymbol{B}_p$, and write

$$\boldsymbol{B}_p = \boldsymbol{B} - \sum_{j=1}^{r} u_j \boldsymbol{A}_j = \boldsymbol{B} - \mathbf{N}\boldsymbol{U}, \tag{4.40}$$

where $u_j$ are scalar multipliers to be determined and $\boldsymbol{U} \equiv (u_1, \ldots, u_r)$. This expression is based on the proposition that $\boldsymbol{B}_p$ will be merely $\boldsymbol{B}$, with all components parallel to the $\boldsymbol{A}_j$ subtracted off. We determine $u_j$ from the fact that we require

$$\boldsymbol{A}_i^T \boldsymbol{B}_p = 0, \qquad i = 1, \ldots, r, \tag{4.41}$$

or

$$\boldsymbol{A}_i^T \boldsymbol{B} - \sum_{j=1}^{r} u_j \boldsymbol{A}_i^T \boldsymbol{A}_j = 0, \qquad i = 1, \ldots, r, \tag{4.42}$$

which lead to the matrix equation

$$\mathbf{N}^T\mathbf{N}\boldsymbol{U} = \mathbf{N}^T\boldsymbol{B}. \tag{4.43}$$

The solution

$$\boldsymbol{U} = (\mathbf{N}^T\mathbf{N})^{-1}\mathbf{N}^T\boldsymbol{B} \tag{4.44}$$

can be substituted into Eq. (4.40) to produce

$$\boldsymbol{B}_p = \boldsymbol{B} - \mathbf{N}(\mathbf{N}^T\mathbf{N})^{-1}\mathbf{N}^T\boldsymbol{B} = \{\mathbf{I} - \mathbf{N}(\mathbf{N}^T\mathbf{N})^{-1}\mathbf{N}^T\}\boldsymbol{B}, \tag{4.45}$$

where the term in brackets is identified as the *projection matrix* $\mathbf{P}$:

$$\mathbf{P} \equiv \{\mathbf{I} - \mathbf{N}(\mathbf{N}^T\mathbf{N})^{-1}\mathbf{N}^T\}. \tag{4.46}$$

Of course, the $u_i$ are recognized as the Lagrange multipliers. Equation (4.39) thus expresses the first part of the Kuhn-Tucker conditions by requiring that the projection of $\boldsymbol{B}$ onto the intersection of the constraints be the null vector. In Section 4.3, we will use the projection matrix directly as part of an algorithm for solving an optimization problem.

In summary, a test for optimality is available in the Kuhn-Tucker conditions of Eqs. (4.25), and a practical computational form exists as Eqs. (4.37) and (4.39). These conditions are necessary if a point is to be an optimum, and in the case of convex programming problems, they are also sufficient.

## 4.2 METHODS OF FEASIBLE DIRECTIONS

Of the direct methods of attack on general nonlinear inequality constrained optimization problems, the largest class is called *methods of feasible directions.* These methods consist of an iteration or step-by-step design evolution of the familiar form

$$\boldsymbol{X}_{q+1} = \boldsymbol{X}_q + \alpha \boldsymbol{S}_q, \tag{4.47}$$

where the direction $\boldsymbol{S}_q$ and the "distance of travel" $\alpha$ are always chosen so that $\boldsymbol{X}_{q+1}$ is in the feasible domain. They are called feasible direction methods because of certain properties of $\boldsymbol{S}_q$ which will now be described. First we consider two definitions:

1. A vector $\boldsymbol{S}$ is a *feasible direction* from the point $\boldsymbol{X}$ if at least a small step can be taken along it that does not immediately leave the feasible domain.
2. A vector $\boldsymbol{S}$ is a *usable feasible direction* from the point $\boldsymbol{X}$ if, in addition to definition 1,

$$\boldsymbol{S}^T \boldsymbol{\nabla} F < 0.$$

For problems with sufficiently smooth constraint surfaces, definition 1 is satisfied if

$$\boldsymbol{S}^T \boldsymbol{\nabla} g_j < 0 \tag{4.48}$$

or if a constraint is linear or "outward curving":

$$\boldsymbol{S}^T \boldsymbol{\nabla} g_j \leq 0. \tag{4.49}$$

The significance of interpretating definition 1 in this way is that the vector $\boldsymbol{S}$ must make an obtuse angle with all constraint normals except that, for the linear or outward curving ones, the angle may go to 90°. Any vector satisfying the strict inequality lies at least partly in the feasible region of the space. In other words, there is some $\alpha > 0$ for which $\boldsymbol{X}_{q+1}$ is in the feasible domain (see Fig. 4.5).

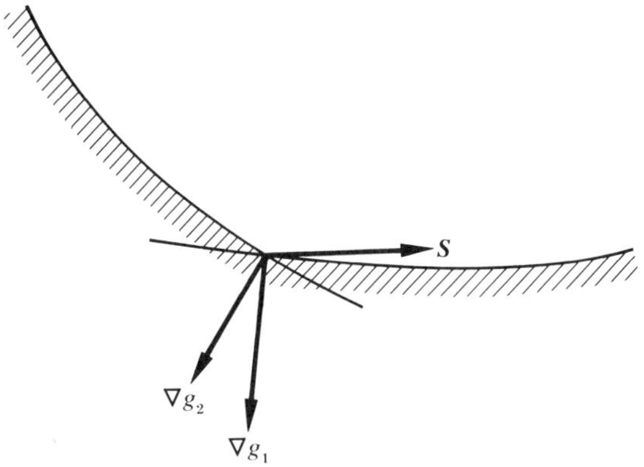


**Figure 4.5**

A vector satisfying the strict inequality of definition 2 is guaranteed to produce, for some $\alpha > 0$, an $X_{q+1}$ that reduces the value of $F$ (see Fig. 4.6). Sometimes we refer to a usable feasible *sector* of the space; by this we mean the intersection of all the halfspaces defined by Eqs. (4.47) and (4.48), as illustrated in Fig. 4.7.

Methods of feasible directions are those that produce an improving succession of feasible $X_q$ vectors by moving in a succession of usable feasible directions. There are two general parts to those algorithms. First, a usable feasible

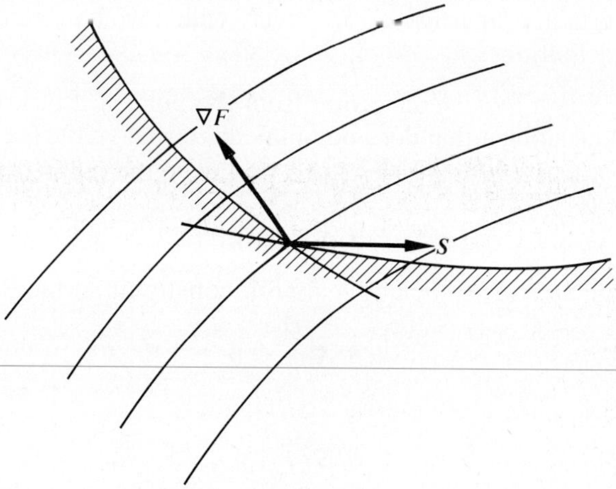


**Figure 4.6**

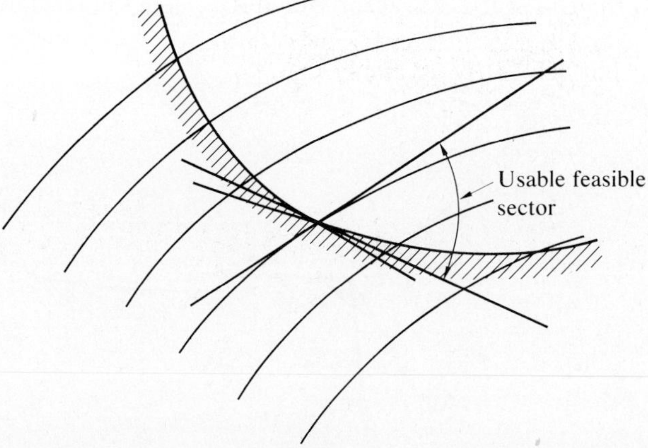


**Figure 4.7**

vector must be determined for each step of the iteration, and second, the step size must be determined.

It is assumed throughout that the derivatives $\partial g_j/\partial x_i$, which are the components of $\nabla g_j$, are available in some form. This is not as presumptuous as it may appear, since derivatives of many seemingly hopeless functions can be calculated. Chapter 5 will describe some tricks for getting exact derivatives of such quantities as stress, displacement, frequency, etc., with respect to the design variables. Also in Chapter 5 we discuss ways of computing derivatives by finite difference approximations. In this section, we briefly mention some ways to determine the direction, and then we consider in more detail the problems of step size selection. In later sections we will discuss details of the direction-finding problem, with different concepts for finding suitable $\boldsymbol{S}$ vectors.

**Finding a Direction**

Assuming we have attained a point $\boldsymbol{X}_q$ at which one or more $g_j = 0, j \in J$, and all others are negative, we then seek a vector $\boldsymbol{S}$ such that

$$\nabla g_j{}^T \boldsymbol{S} < 0, \qquad j \in J, \tag{4.50a}$$

$$\nabla F^T \boldsymbol{S} < 0. \tag{4.50b}$$

If there were no constraints active (i.e., if $J$ were empty), then $-\nabla F$ could be the same as $\boldsymbol{S}$ and the step would be in the direction of steepest descent. When, however, constraints are active, the determination of a suitable $\boldsymbol{S}$ requires the establishment of some sort of algorithm.

One simple possibility is to generate a random vector and test it against Eqs. (4.50a and b). While this approach may seem crude, it is certainly easy to program and is not too time-consuming, because of the simplicity of the relations to be checked. Other possibilities include the projection of $-\nabla F$ onto the intersection of the constraints and some other algorithms based on an optimization of the direction of travel itself. The latter, it has been observed with some skepticism, is an optimization problem within an optimization problem, but the secondary optimization problem is quite easy to solve and the results are usually good.

The projection approach starts with a direction vector assumed in a form so that all components parallel to the normals to the constraints are subtracted from the negative of the gradient to the objective function:

$$\boldsymbol{S} = -\nabla F - \sum_{j \in J} u_j \nabla g_j. \tag{4.51}$$

The $u_j$ can be determined from the conditions

$$\boldsymbol{S}^T \nabla g_j = 0, \qquad j \in J. \tag{4.52}$$

These simply require that the inequalities in Eq. (4.50a) hold with equality, i.e., that $\boldsymbol{S}$ be in each of the planes tangent to the binding constraint surfaces.

Solving these linear equations is precisely the same problem we faced earlier in this chapter in finding the values of the Kuhn-Tucker multipliers. Thus $S$ can be written

$$S = -\mathbf{P}\nabla F, \tag{4.53}$$

where **P** is the projection matrix as described in the previous section. It can be shown that this $S$ vector is the direction that maximizes

$$\cos\gamma \equiv \frac{-S^T\nabla F}{|S||\nabla F|} \tag{4.54}$$

or minimizes the "angle" between the vector $S$ and the direction of steepest descent, subject to the constraints in Eq. (4.50a). If the constraints are nonlinear, a second step is often necessary to bring $S$ the short distance required back into the feasible domain. This approach is very effective in problems with linear constraints, but because the second step is needed, it has serious shortcomings on the general nonlinear problem as discussed in Section 4.3, where the method is presented in more detail.

In problems with nonlinear constraints, algorithms for finding a search direction employ many of the ideas just discussed, but they accommodate the curvature of the constraint surfaces by imposing the strict inequalities in Eqs. (4.50a and b). This is an advantage in nonlinear problems because the vector $S$ points into the acceptable space for some finite distance (see Fig. 4.8). With this objective, the following *direction-finding problem* is posed:[4] Find the vector $S$ and scalar $\beta$ such that $\beta \to$ max and

$$\text{(i)}\quad S^T\nabla g_j + \theta_j\beta \leqslant 0, \qquad j \in J,$$

$$\text{(ii)}\quad S^T\nabla F + \beta \leqslant 0.$$

(iii) A measure of the length $S$ is bounded.

In this problem the $\theta_j$ are arbitrary positive scalar constants (it may be best to think of them as $+1$ for the present discussion). Clearly, if $\beta_{\max} > 0$, then the strict inequalities of Eqs. (4.50a and b) are satisfied, and the vector $S$ is a usable feasible direction.

Let us postpone further discussion of the solution to this direction-finding problem until Section 4.5 (it can be solved by linear programming). We will assume throughout the remainder of this section that a vector satisfying the strict inequalities of Eqs. (4.50a and b) is available and will discuss the problem of finding a step size. There is some interaction between these two parts of the algorithm, but it is relatively weak.

---

[4] See Zoutendijk (1960).

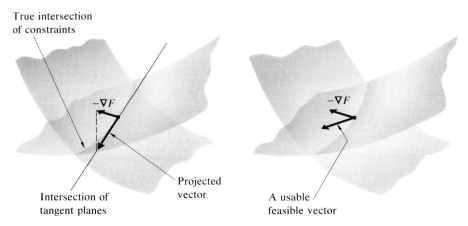

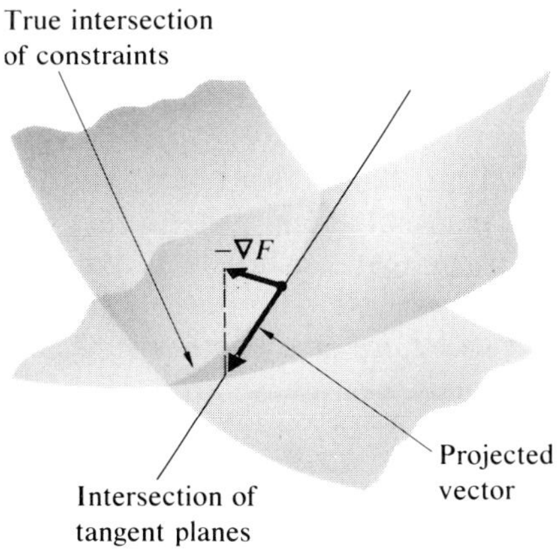


**Figure 4.8**

### Taking the Step

Assuming that a strictly usable feasible vector has been obtained by some means, the problem of selecting the step size can still be challenging. The object, of course, is to reduce the function $F$, probably as much as possible while keeping $\boldsymbol{X}$ in the feasible domain. This is to be accomplished without an excessive number of computations of the $g_j$ (i.e., without a large number of analyses). There are two possibilities for the outcome of such a step (see Fig. 4.9a and b):

1. At the point $\boldsymbol{X}_{q+1}$ (see Eq. 4.47), one or more of the $g_j$ are active.
2. The point $\boldsymbol{X}_{q+1}$ may be an uncontrained minimum with respect to $\alpha$.

In problems with linear objective functions, the first outcome is the only one possible, since a linear function has no unconstrained minima. As a matter of experience, outcome 1 also occurs in many engineering problems with non-linear objective functions. For this reason, we will first discuss some techniques

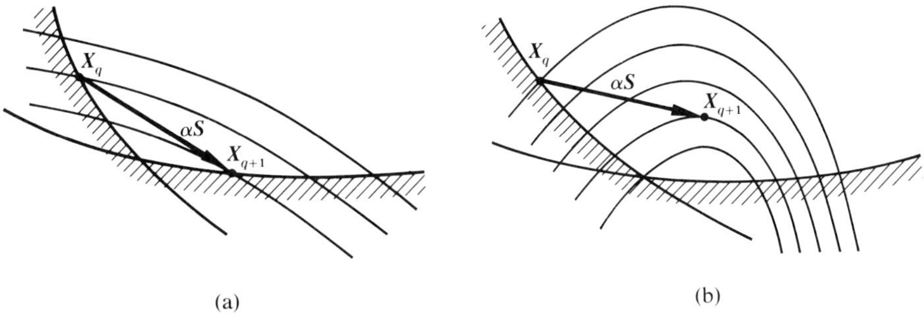


**Figure 4.9**

for the step size determination, on the assumption that $F$ is decreasing at all feasible points along $\boldsymbol{S}$. The implication of this assumption is that we thus seek as large a move as possible that does not violate the constraints and, in fact, we will always step from one set of constraints to another (see Fig. 4.10).[5]

To begin with, these algorithms are largely trial-and-error techniques and are more like complicated logical networks than numerical procedures. The general idea is to take a trial step $\alpha_t$ and check the constraints at the trial point; if they are in violation, interpolate or otherwise withdraw to attain a feasible point; if they are not bounded or in violation, take another step; and if they are bounded, determine a new direction.

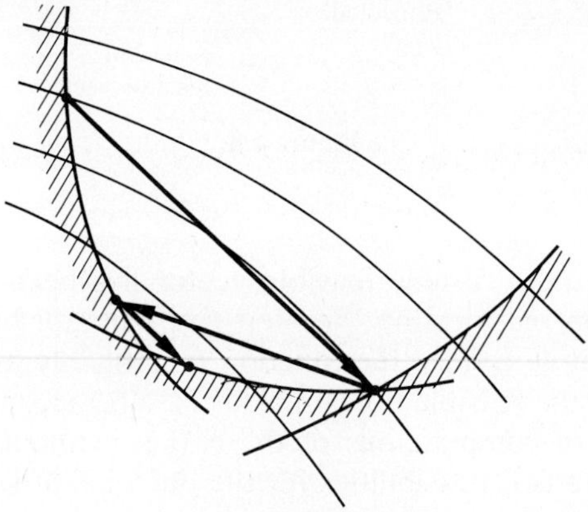

**Figure 4.10**

### The Initial Trial Step Size

The selection of an initial step size (if we assume the first outcome listed above) can be based on the results of previous iterations. For example, an average of the final $\alpha$ values for the last few steps can be used as the initial trial for the next step. This approach is often satisfactory, but it is not sensitive to the changes in the rate of variation of the function $F$ in different directions, nor is it sensitive to the rapid changes in possible step length that are characteristic of methods of feasible directions.

Another approach is to attempt to move a distance calculated to reduce the objective function a given amount. To do this, we approximate $F(\boldsymbol{X}_q+\alpha\boldsymbol{S})$ by a linear function

$$F(\alpha) \simeq a+b\alpha. \tag{4.55}$$

[5] Gellatly, Gallagher, and Luberacki (1964) have adopted a different approach in which the object is to go only half as far as the constraints and then enter a steepest descent mode of travel.

Given the information

$$\bar{F} \equiv F(0) = F(X_q), \tag{4.56}$$

$$\bar{F}' \equiv \left.\frac{dF}{d\alpha}\right|_{\alpha=0} = S^T\nabla F, \tag{4.57}$$

we have

$$F(\alpha) \simeq \bar{F} + \bar{F}'\alpha. \tag{4.58}$$

Assume that the approximation is sufficiently accurate. Then, in order to attain a reduction in $F$ of $\Delta$, we select $\alpha_t$ according to

$$\bar{F} + \bar{F}'\alpha_t = F_0 - \Delta \tag{4.59}$$

or

$$\alpha_t = -\,\Delta/\bar{F}'. \tag{4.60}$$

If we prefer, a fractional reduction defined by $\Delta = \Delta_f|\bar{F}|$ can be specified as

$$\alpha_t = -\frac{|\bar{F}|}{\bar{F}'}\,\Delta_f. \tag{4.61}$$

In either case, $\alpha_t$ would be positive since $\bar{F}'$ is negative from satisfaction of the strict inequality of Eq. (4.50b), and both $\Delta$ and $\Delta_f$ are positive. Typically, $\Delta_f$ is taken at about 0.05 to 0.1 (a 5 to 10% change). Note that $\alpha_t$ will be large if $S$ is nearly perpendicular to $-\nabla F$, and smaller as it is more nearly parallel to $-\nabla F$. The idea produces reasonable results in many cases and is often the best approach for engineering problems.

Finally, another simple idea for the initial trial step is to pick $\alpha_t$ so that the maximum component of $\alpha_t S_q$ produces some predetermined change. This scheme can ensure that all moves are significant design changes. The criterion

$$\alpha_t = \frac{\epsilon_t}{\max_i\,(s_{iq})} \tag{4.62}$$

is selected so that $\epsilon_t$ is some multiple of the minimum meaningful design change. If this change is different for different design variables, a fractional form for $\alpha_t$ is given by

$$\alpha_t = \frac{1}{\max_i\,(s_{iq}/\epsilon_{it})}, \tag{4.63}$$

where $\epsilon_{it}$ is the multiple of the minimum meaningful design change for the $i$th design variable.

**Correcting the Step**

Given some trial value of $\alpha_t$, the next operation is tentatively to take the step

$$X_t = X_q + \alpha_t S_q$$

and check the constraints at the new point. There are three possible results of this test:

1. The point is feasible and no constraints are active.
2. The point is feasible and constraints are active.
3. The point is infeasible.

If result 1 is the outcome, then another step may be taken in the same direction or, since no constraints are active, a step may be taken in the $-\nabla F$ direction. There is support for both approaches and the best strategy depends on the problem. Keeping the $S_q$ would be an advantage if the trial step is too short, as in Fig. 4.11. On the other hand, if the trial step is such that the design point is out in the middle of the space, steepest descent, as illustrated in Fig. 4.12, would be the best policy.

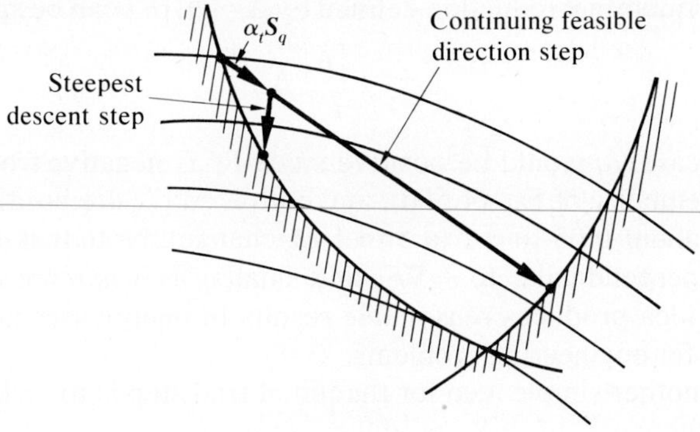


**Figure 4.11**

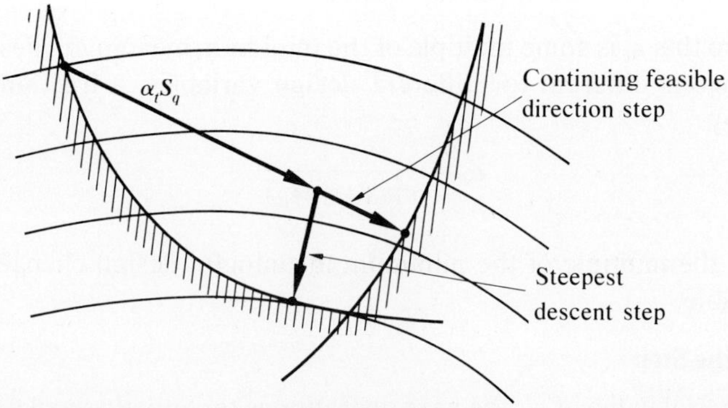


**Figure 4.12**

Result 2, as we mentioned previously, is the desired one and calls for a new solution to the direction-finding problem. It is not, however, a straightforward proposition to determine that the point is indeed bound. To see why, we need only consider the likelihood of obtaining a point with one or more $g_j$ *exactly* equal to zero. Will we consider the constraint active if $g_j = 10^{-3}, 10^{-6}$, etc.? We immediately see that some sort of margin is required if we are to make any progress at all, because many iterations may be necessary to get small values of $g_j$, and there are no rewards for doing so.

With this objective, we would consider a point to be bound if

$$|g_j| \leq \epsilon \tag{4.64}$$

or, as another possibility,

$$-\epsilon \leq g_j \leq 0. \tag{4.65}$$

Equation (4.64) allows a slight violation of the constraint, whereas Eq. (4.65) requires the point to be strictly feasible. In a sense, these criteria give the constraint some "thickness" and make it an easier target. We will take up this idea again later in this section, since there are some questions about the size and even about a strategy for picking $\epsilon$.

If result 3 is the outcome of a trial step, then presumably the step was too long, and it must be shortened to attain a bound point. Suppose for the moment that only one constraint is in violation. A simple and effective means of modifying the step is to interpolate the value of the offended constraint, say $g_k$. Denote

$$g_{0k} \equiv g_k(\boldsymbol{X}_q) < 0, \tag{4.66}$$

$$g_{tk} \equiv g_k(\boldsymbol{X}_q + \alpha_t \boldsymbol{S}) > 0. \tag{4.67}$$

Then we can derive an interpolation to find $\alpha$ such that $g_k(\boldsymbol{X}_q + \alpha \boldsymbol{S}) \simeq 0$ by assuming $g_k$ to be linear along $\boldsymbol{S}$:

$$g_k \simeq a + b\alpha, \tag{4.68}$$

from which

$$g_{0k} = a, \tag{4.69a}$$

$$g_{tk} = a + b\alpha_t, \tag{4.69b}$$

$$b = \frac{g_{tk} - g_{0k}}{\alpha_t}. \tag{4.70}$$

The desired $\alpha$ is obtained from setting Eq. (4.68) to zero:

$$g_{0k} + \frac{g_{tk} - g_{0k}}{\alpha_t}\alpha_I = 0, \tag{4.71}$$

from which we obtain

$$\alpha_I = -\frac{g_{0k}}{g_{tk} - g_{0k}}\alpha_t. \tag{4.72}$$

What we are really doing is approximating the analysis of the design along the line $S_q$ as a linear function of $\alpha$ and predicting that at $\alpha = \alpha_I$ the function goes to zero.[6]

If several constraints are in violation at the trial point, the worst (i.e., the largest) constraint would be interpolated. As an example of the interpolation process, let us consider a single step in the planar truss problem (Example E.3). The data shown in Table 4.1 give the starting point for the

**Table 4.1***

| | $S_q$ | $X_q$ | $X_t$ | $X_{q+1}$ |
|---|---|---|---|---|
| $A_1$ | $-1.0$ | 1.532 | 1.341 | 1.434 |
| $A_2, A_8$ | $-1.0$ | 0.812 | 0.621 | 0.715 |
| $A_3, A_9$ | $-1.0$ | 0.427 | 0.236 | 0.329 |
| $A_4, A_{10}$ | 1.0 | 0.812 | 1.003 | 0.910 |
| $A_5, A_{11}$ | $-1.0$ | 0.953 | 0.762 | 0.855 |
| $A_6, A_{12}$ | $-1.0$ | 1.287 | 1.096 | 1.190 |
| $A_7, A_{13}$ | 0.624 | 0.812 | 0.931 | 0.873 |
| $\sigma_4$ | — | 19.41 | 15.45 | 17.24 |
| $\sigma_5$ | — | $-13.13$ | $-16.78$ | $-14.73$ |
| $\sigma_6$ | — | $-13.75$ | $-16.49$ | $-14.97$ |
| $\alpha$ | — | 0.0 | 0.191 | 0.0977 |
| $F$ (weight) | — | 1540 | 1386 | 1461 |

* The optimum design for this problem is $A_1 = 0.283$, $A_2 = A_8 = 0.542$, $A_3 = A_9 = 0.01$, $A_4 = A_{10} = 0.738$, $A_5 = A_{11} = 0.970$, $A_6 = A_{12} = 1.384$, $A_7 = A_{13} = 0.727$, and $F = 1151$.

step, a usable feasible direction, the initial trial step, the successful interpolated step, and certain other information of interest. We recall that the stress limits were 20 ksi tension and $-15$ ksi compression. Note that the starting design for the step is bound in tensile stress in member 4 (see Fig. 1.11, on p. 22, for member identification). It is not bound with respect to any other constraints. The direction vector $S_q$ is a decrease in the areas of all members except $A_4$, $A_{10}$, $A_7$, and $A_{13}$. In these it calls for an increase. The trial vector $X_t$ represents an attempt to reduce the weight by 10%, but the stresses $\sigma_5$ and $\sigma_6$ are in violation of their lower bound. The stress $\sigma_5$ is slightly more in violation than is $\sigma_6$, and this was used for the interpolation. It is interesting that while

[6] If we are using the one-sided tolerance that considers the constraint active if $0 \geqslant g_j \geqslant -\epsilon$, we can shoot for the center of the tolerance zone with

$$\alpha_I = -(\epsilon/2 + g_{0k})/(g_{tk} - g_{0k})\,\alpha_t.$$

the interpolation is successful and $\sigma_5$ actually overshoots the $-15$ ksi target, $\sigma_6$ barely makes it. The design $\boldsymbol{X}_{q+1}$ represents a weight reduction of slightly more than 5%.

This example hints at an area of possible difficulty that must be allowed for in writing computer programs for this method: The constraint in worst violation at $\boldsymbol{X}_t$ may not be the binding one when $\boldsymbol{X}_{q+1}$ is finally determined. In other words, interpolating a $g_k$ (the worst at $\boldsymbol{X}_t$) may produce a point where $g_e$ is still in violation, and the interpolation must be repeated for $g_e$. It requires additional logic and some bookkeeping to provide for this possibility.

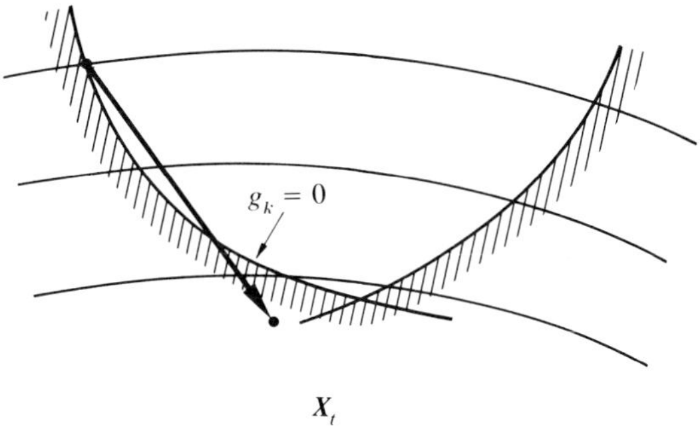


**Figure 4.13**

The interpolation method may also get into trouble if the situation depicted in Fig. 4.13 occurs. Here we have a violation of a constraint we have just left, and the formula for $\alpha_I$ (Eq. 4.72) breaks down because $g_{ok} \simeq 0$. To some extent, we can avoid this situation by a judicious choice for the $\theta_i$ in the direction-finding problem. We will see in Section 4.5 that the larger $\theta_i$ is taken, the deeper the direction $\boldsymbol{S}_q$ is forced into the feasible region.

In spite of these approaches, however, the situation may still occur, and a modification of the interpolation technique is necessary. Consider a plot of $g_k$ along the direction shown in Fig. 4.13 and as depicted in Fig. 4.14. The function is a small negative number at $\alpha = 0$; it is negative for some distance along $\boldsymbol{S}$ and then at $\bar{\alpha}$ it becomes zero and is increasing. The point we actually desire is given by $\bar{\alpha}$, and it is clear that a linear interpolation will only give us back $\alpha_I \simeq 0$.[7]

Viewing the situation in this way, we are led to approximate $g_k(\alpha)$ by a quadratic:

$$g_k \simeq a + b\alpha + c\alpha^2. \tag{4.73}$$

---

[7] If we use the formula $\alpha_I = -(\epsilon/2 + g_{0k})/(g_{tk} - g_{0k})\,\alpha_t$, we may actually get a negative value for $\alpha_I$.

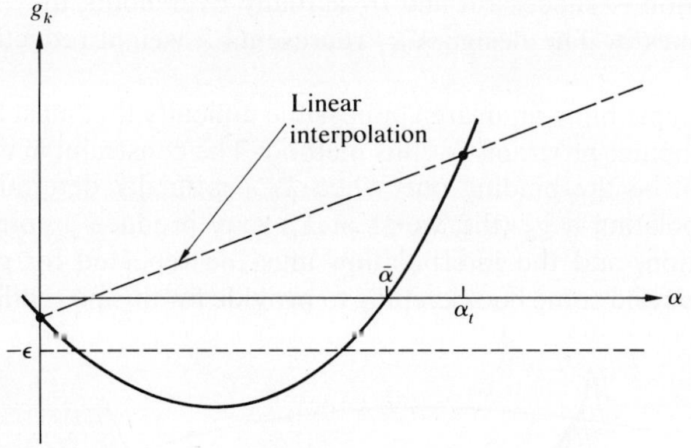


**Figure 4.14**

Allowing that $g_k(0)$ may not be quite zero, we have the following data available for the quadratic interpolation:

$$g_k(0) \equiv g_{0k} = a, \tag{4.74}$$

$$dg_k/d\alpha = \nabla g_k(0)^T S \equiv g'_{0k} = b, \tag{4.75}$$

$$g_k(\alpha_t) \equiv g_{tk} = a + b\alpha_t + c\alpha_t^2. \tag{4.76}$$

The last expansion implies

$$c = \frac{g_{tk} - g_{0k} - g'_{0k}\alpha_t}{\alpha_t^2}. \tag{4.77}$$

We obtain the desired point by setting the quadratic to zero, from which

$$a + b\alpha_I + c\alpha_I^2 = 0 \tag{4.78}$$

or

$$\alpha_I = \frac{-b \pm [b^2 - 4ac]^{1/2}}{2c}. \tag{4.79}$$

The discriminant $[b^2 - 4ac]$ will always be positive, as we can see in Fig. 4.14. If we choose the plus sign in the formula, we will have an approximation to $\alpha$ of Fig. 4.14. It may be better, however, to aim at the point $g_k = -\epsilon/2$ in order to allow for interpolation error in both directions. Then we can use the formula

$$a + b\alpha_I + c\alpha_I^2 = -\epsilon/2 \tag{4.80}$$

or

$$\alpha_I = \frac{-b + [b^2 - 4(a + \epsilon/2)c]^{1/2}}{2c}. \tag{4.81}$$

Here the discriminant may not always be positive, since the interpolating quadratic is not guaranteed to cross the line $-\epsilon/2$ (see Fig. 4.15). This may be an

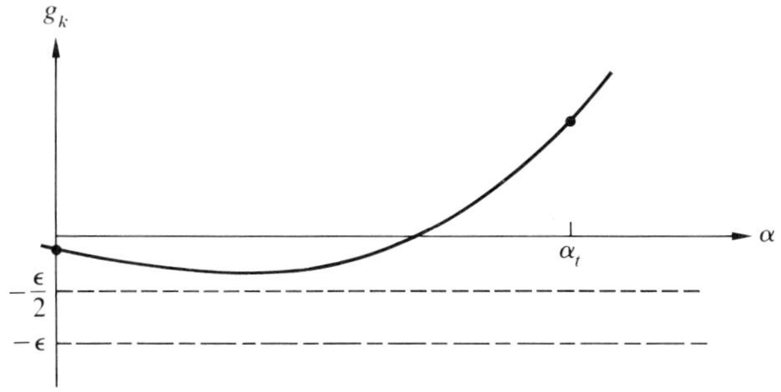


**Figure 4.15**

indication of a more serious problem since it implies that the $S$ vector never gets further away from the constraint than $\epsilon/2$ and hence that the direction $S$ is not very useful. Whether or not this is serious depends on the curvature of the constraints, and again we need some complicated logic in the program, including some alterations on the direction-finding portion (see Section 4.5). In spite of these difficulties, the second form (Eq. 4.81) is probably more useful, since it is about twice as likely to produce a feasible point as is the first formula.

**When $F$ has a Minimum along $S_q$**

Earlier we noted that there is a second possible outcome for the complete step in the event that $F$ has a proper minimum along $S_q$ in the feasible region (see Fig. 4.9b). In this case, one of the methods of 1-dimensional minimization (see Sections 2.4 and 2.8) should be applied to determine the value of $\alpha^*$. If the function is moderately eccentric, we may need to enter one of the more effective unconstrained minimization algorithms on a temporary basis until the constraints are again encountered. A particularly attractive approach is to use the variable metric method and retain the **H**-matrix as a transformation throughout the space.

Suppose that at some stage in the solution to a constrained optimization problem it is possible (or necessary) to take several successive iterations of the variable metric method:

$$X_{q+1} = X_q + \alpha_q^* \mathbf{H}_q \nabla F_q, \tag{4.82}$$

where we can determine $\alpha_q^*$ so as to minimize $F$ in the search direction without encountering the constraints. After this, we can use the **H**-matrix to advantage to produce a transformed objective gradient

$$\nabla \tilde{F} \equiv \mathbf{H} \nabla F \tag{4.83}$$

and transformed constraint gradients

$$\nabla \tilde{g}_j \equiv \mathbf{H} \nabla g_j \tag{4.84}$$

for the feasible direction method. For example, consider a two-variable problem in which the objective function is a quadratic: one step of Eq. (4.82) and the subsequent update of the **H**-matrix (see Section 2.11) produce a transformation matrix that everywhere aims the gradient at the unconstrained minimum of $F$.

It is possible to apply other unconstrained minimization methods to this aspect of the constrained problem. In fact, for some classes of problems, it may be best to approach the solution as one of unconstrained minimization and utilize the feasible direction concept only when the constraints block the way. This tends to be true in situations where the objective function is an eccentric and contorted function and the constraints are few and relatively smooth (see Fig. 4.16).

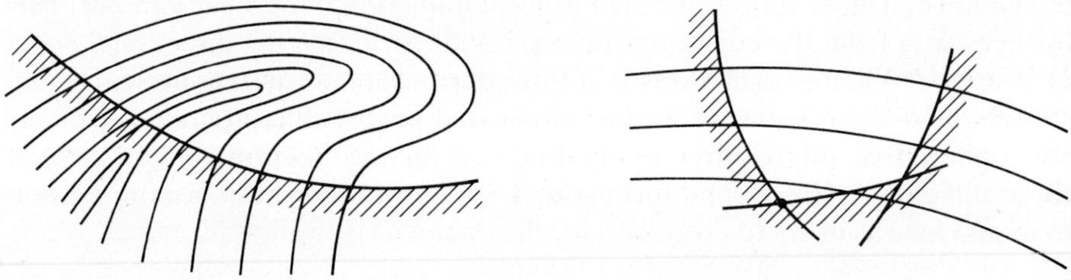

(a) (b)

**Figure 4.16**

As we mentioned earlier, most engineering problems seem to be the type in which the step properly terminates at the constraints rather than the more difficult type discussed above. A simple, if not foolproof, safeguard in doubtful situations is simply to determine the maximum $\alpha$ for which $X_{q+1}$ is in the feasible region, and then compute

$$\left(\frac{dF}{d\alpha}\right)_{X_{q+1}} = S_q{}^T\nabla F_{q+1}. \tag{4.85}$$

If this quantity is negative, then all is well, but if it is positive, then a minimum exists along the line segment $X_{q+1} - X_q$, and $\alpha^*$ should be computed by an interpolation or other means.

### A Strategy for Constraint Tolerances: The Zigzag

The practical necessity of using constraint margins (Eq. 4.64 or 4.65) opens up a number of new complications as well as possibilities for improvement of the algorithm. First, consider a phenomenon called, aptly, zigzagging. Visualize a 3-dimensional design space with two constraints as shown in Fig. 4.17. At point $A$, constraint 1 is active but not constraint 2, and vice versa at point $B$. The logical "downhill" direction with respect to the objective function is

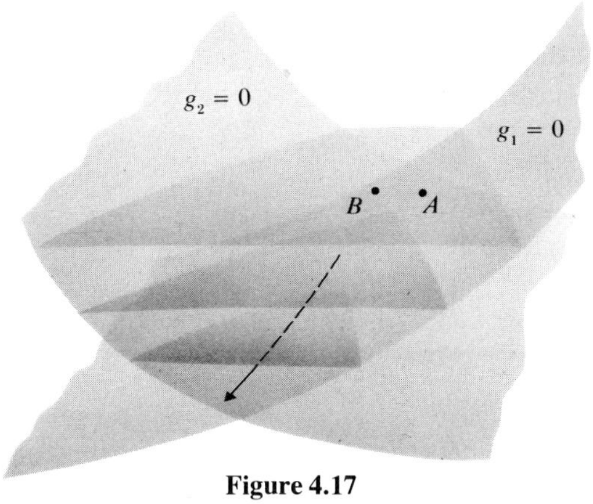


**Figure 4.17**

shown by the arrow, and the objective function by the horizontal planes. If the direction-finding problem is given only the gradients to the exactly active constraints at $A$ or $B$, then the usable feasible direction that results may point directly at the "almost active" constraint. This would produce a path as shown in Fig. 4.18.

One means of avoiding this situation is to use a substantial tolerance in the enumeration of the active constraints. Point $A$ or point $B$ could, by this approach, be considered bound on both $g_1$ and $g_2$, and the only usable feasible directions left would be those directed more or less along the intersection of the constraints. Thus the use of a reasonable tolerance provides some relief from the zigzag problem.

Another approach is to record the encounters of all constraints in a table, and when a constraint is active too many times in alternate succession, it is included in the set $J$ (of bound constraints) whether or not it is actually bound. This technique is quite a bit more complicated to program than the simple tolerance idea, and there is no evidence that it works significantly better.

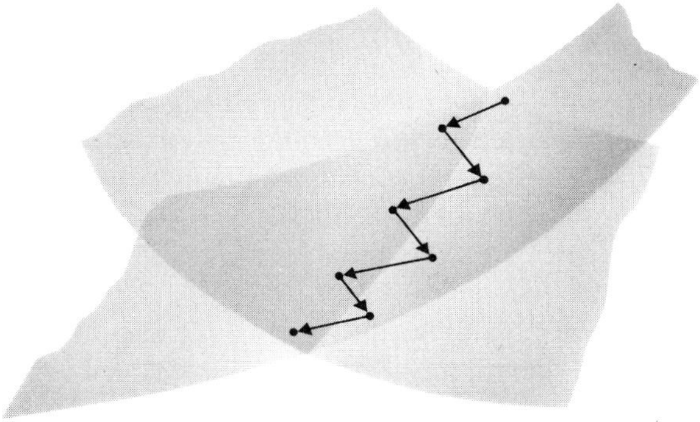

**Figure 4.18**

With either method, we ultimately reach a point where the gradient $\nabla F$ and the constraint normals whose indices are included in $J$ so delimit the direction-finding problem that it has no solutions. It will be shown in Section 4.5 that under ordinary circumstances this indicates that the Kuhn-Tucker conditions are satisfied. However, since the constraint indices included in $J$ are not only those of the truly binding constraints, this may be a false indication. What we must do is cut the constraint tolerance $\epsilon$ in half, for example (or in the case of the second approach, eliminate all nonactive constraints from $J$), and reattempt to solve the direction-finding problem. This process may be reiterated several times until $\epsilon$ is below a practical working limit.

**Summary of the Method**

The basic logic for a method of feasible directions is given in the flow diagram of Fig. 4.19. For this program, we assume that the initial design is an unbound feasible point, and hence the first passage through the logic would be that indicated by the heavy leaders. The constraint tolerance indicated by blocks A and B is the one-sided form (Eq. 4.65). The Boolean variable $\mathscr{I}$ is simply a flag to tell whether the free point just obtained is from an interpolation or simply an ordinary step. If it is from an interpolation, then the constraint was overshot by more than $\epsilon$. At such a juncture, the algorithm shown in the figure simply applies a new move equal in length to the interpolation step; other alternatives could be used.

Block C embodies the variation on the interpolation formula in which the center of the tolerance zone $g_k = -\epsilon/2$, $\epsilon > 0$, is the target rather than $g_k = 0$. This technique increases the likelihood of obtaining a feasible point.

The antizigzag feature shown in the flow diagram simply involves using a moderately large tolerance initially and then reducing it when the Kuhn-Tucker conditions are satisfied. If, after $\epsilon$ is reduced to a level of $\epsilon_f$, the Kuhn-Tucker conditions are still satisfied, we assume that the point is an approximation to a local minimum. The reason the test is placed where it is in the flow diagram is that the solution of the direction-finding problem contains the criterion for the Kuhn-Tucker condition.

The effectiveness of the algorithm is probably best measured by the number of times block D is transversed combined with some weighted number for the times block E is passed. Block F presumably consumes a small fraction of the total time, because the analysis block constitutes a major effort. If this is not true for a particular problem, then we may prefer an indirect method to the feasible direction technique.

There is a variety of possible ways to speed the execution of blocks D and E because of the way they are embedded in the design loop. Most of these attempt to salvage some of the information contained in the solutions of "nearby" designs, and hence they can considerably complicate the computer

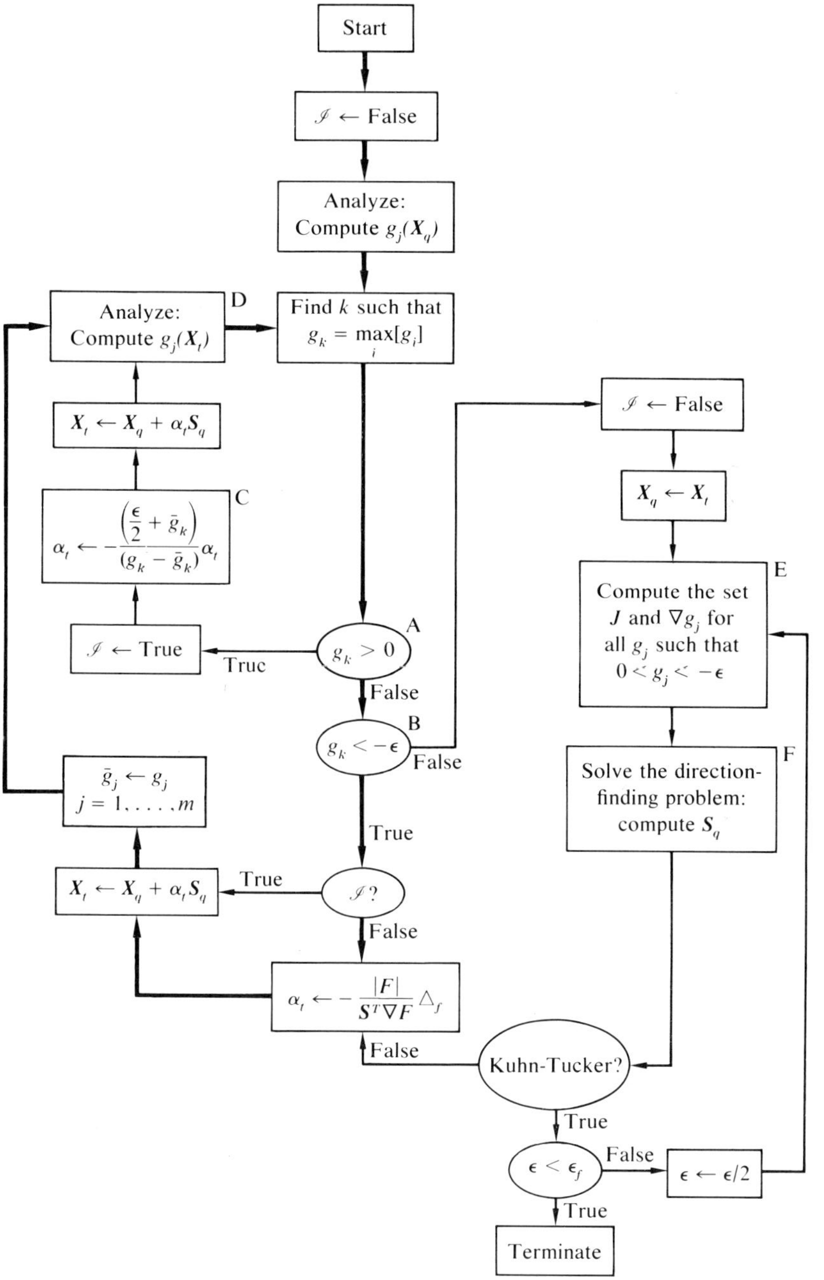

Start
$\mathscr{I} \leftarrow$ False
Analyze: Compute $g_j(X_q)$
Find $k$ such that $g_k = \max_i[g_i]$
Analyze: Compute $g_j(X_t)$
D
$X_t \leftarrow X_q + \alpha_t S_q$
$\alpha_t \leftarrow -\frac{\left(\frac{\epsilon}{2} + \bar{g}_k\right)}{(g_k - \bar{g}_k)}\alpha_t$
C
$\mathscr{I} \leftarrow$ True
Truc
$g_k > 0$
A
False
$g_k < -\epsilon$
B
False
True
$\bar{g}_j \leftarrow g_j$, $j = 1, \ldots, m$
$X_t \leftarrow X_q + \alpha_t S_q$
True
$\mathscr{I}$?
False
$\alpha_t \leftarrow -\frac{|F|}{S^T \nabla F} \triangle_f$
False
$\mathscr{I} \leftarrow$ False
$X_q \leftarrow X_t$
Compute the set $J$ and $\nabla g_j$ for all $g_j$ such that $0 < g_j < -\epsilon$
E
Solve the direction-finding problem: compute $S_q$
F
Kuhn-Tucker?
True
$\epsilon < \epsilon_f$
False
$\epsilon \leftarrow \epsilon/2$
True
Terminate


**Figure 4.19**

programs. Some of these ideas, which are problem dependent, are discussed in Chapter 5.

The diagram shown in Fig. 4.19 takes no account of the possibility of a minimum along $\boldsymbol{S}$. The test could be added between blocks E and F.

Finally the flow diagram has no provision for a situation in which a constraint active at $X_q$ is the worst violated at $X_t$. A test for this condition and the associated remedial action would be placed in a control statement just before block C.

In the next section, the gradient projection method is discussed. This technique is a special case of a feasible direction method, but it retains a certain flavor of the general method.

## 4.3 THE GRADIENT PROJECTION METHOD[8]

In previous sections, we introduced the projection of a vector and the projection matrix; in this section we discuss a direct method for solving the constrained minimization problem that uses the projection of $-\nabla F(X_q)$ onto the constraints that are binding at $X_q$. The method has been described[9] for the general nonlinear programming problem, but its effectiveness is mainly limited to problems in which the constraints $g_j(X)$ are linear functions of the $x_i$. We will assume such a case in this section.

If the functions $g_j$ are linear, they can be written

$$g_j(X) \equiv \sum_{i=1}^{n} a_{ij}x_i - b_j, \qquad j = 1, 2, \ldots, r, \tag{4.86}$$

and we can define a vector of constraint functions that are active at the point $X_q$ as

$$G_q = \mathbf{A}_q{}^T X - B, \tag{4.87}$$

where the subscript $q$ indicates that $\mathbf{A}_q$ contains only those columns associated with active constraints at $X_q$. The gradients of the $g_j$ are

$$\nabla g_j = (a_{1j}, a_{2j}, \ldots, a_{nj}), \tag{4.88}$$

or, by analogy with Eq. (4.30),

$$\nabla g_j \equiv A_j \equiv (n_{1j}, n_{2j}, \ldots, n_{nj}). \tag{4.89}$$

We note that the $\mathbf{A}$-matrix in Eq. (4.87) is exactly the $\mathbf{N}$-matrix of the projection operator of Eq. (4.46):

$$\mathbf{P} \equiv \{\mathbf{I} - \mathbf{N}(\mathbf{N}^T\mathbf{N})^{-1}\mathbf{N}^T\}$$

for linear constraints. Later in this section we will discuss the efficient computa-

[8] See Rosen (1960).
[9] See, for example, Rosen (1961).

tion of **P** and the situation in which the constraints are not independent. We will also consider the case in which there are active constraints that should nonetheless be omitted in the computation of **P**. Let us assume for now, however, that the **P**-matrix contains only contributions from those active constraints that would be violated by the vector $S = -\mathbf{P}\nabla F$ if they were not included, and that all constraints are independent.

We now show that if $X_q$ satisfies

$$\mathbf{A}_q^T X_q - B \equiv \mathbf{N}^T X_q - B = 0, \tag{4.90}$$

where **A** and **N** contain only the columns of active constraints at $X_q$, and if

$$X_{q+1} = X_q - \alpha \mathbf{P}\nabla F, \tag{4.91}$$

then the active constraints will be satisfied for all $\alpha$, i.e.,

$$\mathbf{N}^T X_{q+1} - B = 0. \tag{4.92}$$

Substitute Eq. (4.91) into the right-hand side of Eq. (4.92) to obtain

$$\begin{aligned} \mathbf{N}^T\{X_q + \alpha[\mathbf{I} - \mathbf{N}(\mathbf{N}^T\mathbf{N})^{-1}\mathbf{N}^T](-\nabla F)\} - B \\ = \mathbf{N}^T X_q - B + \alpha[\mathbf{N}^T - \mathbf{N}^T\mathbf{N}(\mathbf{N}^T\mathbf{N})^{-1}\mathbf{N}^T](-\nabla F), \end{aligned} \tag{4.93}$$

and note that the term in square brackets vanishes.

Thus if $X_q$ lies in the intersection of $r$ linear constraints, then any step of the form Eq. (4.91) yields a new vector in the intersection of the same constraints. If $F$ has no proper minimum along $S_q \equiv -\mathbf{P}\nabla F$, then the gradient projection algorithm consists of stepping as far as possible to a new constraint or constraints and then reprojecting $-\nabla F$ at the new point. That is, we step from $X_q$ to $X_{q+1}$ by choosing the largest $\alpha$ for which $X_{q+1}$ is feasible. If $F$ has a minimum in the feasible region along $S_q$, then we would go to this point.

### Computing the Step Length

Since the $g_j$ are linear in $X$, they are linear functions of $\alpha$ along $S_q$. To see this, note that

$$g_j(X) = A_j^T X - b_j \tag{4.94}$$

becomes

$$g_j(\alpha) = A_j^T(X_q + \alpha S_q) - b_j \tag{4.95}$$

along $S_q$. Expressed in another way,

$$g_j(\alpha) = A_j^T X_q - b_j + \alpha A_j^T S_q \tag{4.96}$$

$$= g_j(X_q) + \alpha A_j^T S_q. \tag{4.97}$$

Now for all constraints not active at $X_q$, we can compute the $\alpha_j$ that would cause $g_j(\alpha) = 0$:

$$\alpha_j = -\frac{g_j(X_q)}{A_j^T S_q}. \tag{4.98}$$

Since this computation would be done only for constraints that are not active and because the point $X_q$ is feasible, the $g_j$ are negative and the sign of $\alpha_j$ depends only on the sign of the scalar product $A_j^T S_q$. Noting that $A_j \equiv \nabla g_j$ and hence that

$$\frac{dg_j}{d\alpha} = A_j^T S_q, \tag{4.99}$$

we see that the sign of $\alpha_j$ depends on the rate of change of the $g_j$ with respect to $\alpha$. If this change is negative, then we are moving away from the constraint in the positive $\alpha$ direction, so we ignore this constraint in determining $\alpha$. With these ideas in mind, we determine the step length $\alpha_M$ from the following prescription:

$$\alpha_M = \min_{\substack{\alpha_j > 0 \\ j \notin J}} [\alpha_j], \tag{4.100}$$

with $\alpha_j$ as defined in Eq. (4.98). As a practical matter, the search on $\alpha_j$ in Eq. (4.100) should be carried out only over the inactive constraints because of the numerical problems associated with distinguishing true zero values from very small ones.

As with the general method of feasible directions, the step $\alpha_M$ may not be of "optimal" length if $F(\alpha)$ along $S_q$ has a minimum between $\alpha = 0$ and $\alpha = \alpha_M$. Thus at $\alpha_M$ the scalar product $S_q^T \nabla F(\alpha_M)$ should be calculated (if the objective function is nonlinear); if it is positive, an interpolation or other search for $\alpha^*$ between 0 and $\alpha_M$ should be undertaken.

Note that at the point given by $\alpha_M$ all the constraints whose normals contribute to the projection matrix at $X_q$ will be active, plus at least one new constraint corresponding to the $j$ that determines $\alpha_M$ in Eq. (4.100). Thus if all active constraints are always included in the projection matrix, the process will simply gather up constraints one at a time (it is unusual to hit several constraints simultaneously), never leaving a constraint once it is encountered, until the projection of $-\nabla F$ is zero. We assume that the step is always $\alpha_M$ instead of $\alpha^*$; if instead it is $\alpha^*$, the only difference is that a new constraint is not necessarily encountered at each move but none would ever be left. This point is of crucial importance to the effectiveness of the gradient projection method, since constraints encountered at earlier stages of the process may not be active at the optimum (see Fig. 4.20 for the desired performance).

### Leaving Constraints

We now discuss the procedure for dropping nonobstructing constraints from the projection. Recall that the projection of a vector $R$ onto the $r$ constraint surfaces defined by the normals $A_i$ can be written

$$R_p = R - \sum_{i=1}^{r} \lambda_i A_i = R - \mathbf{N}_r \boldsymbol{\lambda}, \tag{4.101}$$

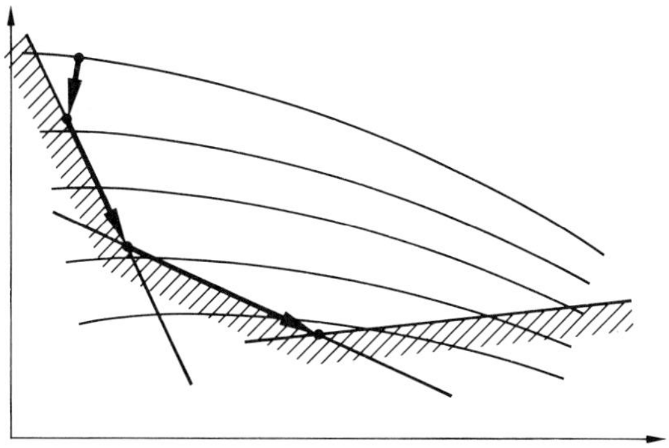

Figure 4.20

where

$$\mathbf{N}_r \equiv [A_1, \ldots, A_r] \tag{4.102}$$

$$\boldsymbol{\lambda} = (\mathbf{N}_r{}^T \mathbf{N}_r{}^T)^{-1} \mathbf{N}_r{}^T \boldsymbol{R}. \tag{4.103}$$

Let us assume henceforth that the constraints have been normalized so that

$$A_i{}^T A_i = 1, \qquad i = 1, 2, \ldots, r. \tag{4.104}$$

We see that the $\lambda_i$ are the amounts of each of the vectors $A_i$ to be subtracted from $\boldsymbol{R}$. If a particular $\lambda_l$ in this computation is negative, then the vector $A_l$ is added to produce the projection, and the constraint can be dropped. This idea is closely connected with the theory of the Kuhn-Tucker conditions; for if the projection of $-\nabla F$ is zero and all $\lambda_i \geqslant 0$, the point is a candidate for a local optimum. On the other hand, if one or more of the $\lambda_i$ are negative, then the point is not a local optimum.

The procedure for dropping constraints from the projection, whether or not $-\mathbf{P}\nabla F = \boldsymbol{0}$, is then simply to eliminate from the projection matrix the effect of a constraint associated with a negative $\lambda_i$. In other words, if we suppose $\lambda_i \geqslant 0$, $i = 1, 2, \ldots, r-1$, and $\lambda_r < 0$, then the improved projection matrix would be

$$\mathbf{P}_{r-1} \equiv [\mathbf{I} - \mathbf{N}_{r-1}(\mathbf{N}_{r-1}^T \mathbf{N}_{r-1})^{-1} \mathbf{N}_{r-1}^T], \tag{4.105}$$

where

$$\mathbf{N}_{r-1} \equiv [A_1, A_2, \ldots, A_{r-1}]. \tag{4.106}$$

The resulting projection will carry any vector $\boldsymbol{R}$ into a projection $\boldsymbol{R}_p$ such that

$$\boldsymbol{R}_p{}^T A_r < 0. \tag{4.107}$$

Hence $\boldsymbol{R}_p$ will be a feasible direction with respect to $A_r$. If there are several negative $\lambda$'s at a point, they must be eliminated one at a time. A reasonable rule for removing them is to take the most negative $\lambda_i$ first and compute the new $\mathbf{P}$-matrix and $\boldsymbol{\lambda}$; if there are still negative $\lambda$'s, repeat the procedure.

**Linear Dependence of Constraints**

If the projection matrix is made up of the normals of $r$ linearly independent constraints, and a new constraint $r+1$ is to be included in the projection, some difficulty arises if $A_{r+1}$ is linearly dependent on some set of the $A_i$, $i = 1, 2, \ldots, r$. This is evident when we consider that the matrix $(\mathbf{N}_{r+1}^T \mathbf{N}_{r+1})$ would be singular since some of its rows (or columns) would be linear combinations of others. A simple test for such dependence is to compute the projection $\mathbf{P}_r A_{r+1}$; if it is nonzero, then $A_{r+1}$ is linearly independent, and otherwise it is dependent. Thus, the projection matrix $\mathbf{P}_r$ would be identical with $\mathbf{P}_{r+1}$. There is, however, a difference in the $\boldsymbol{\lambda}$ vectors for different independent subsets of the dependent vectors. One subset may produce all positive $\lambda$'s, and another may produce some negative values for the $\lambda_j$.

As an example, take the three dependent vectors

$$A_1 = \begin{pmatrix} 1 \\ 1 \\ 2 \end{pmatrix}, \quad A_2 = \begin{pmatrix} 1 \\ 0 \\ 2 \end{pmatrix}, \quad A_3 = \begin{pmatrix} 0 \\ 1 \\ 0 \end{pmatrix}.$$

The vector $V = (3, 2, 6)$ can be written

$$V = 2A_1 + A_2,$$

but also

$$V = 3A_1 - A_3.$$

Thus $V$ is in the cone formed by $A_1$ and $A_2$ but not in that formed by $A_1$ and $A_3$.

**The Algorithm for the Gradient Projection Method**

Now we describe an algorithm for gradient projection. First, we assume that the constraints encountered are all independent, and then we describe the modifications necessary to allow for the possibility that they are not independent. We also assume that only one constraint is encountered at a time. In the last part of this section we will discuss efficient computation schemes for calculating $(\mathbf{N}^T\mathbf{N})^{-1}$ and $\mathbf{P}$, which, although not necessary to the working of the method, greatly enhance its efficiency compared to conventional computation.

Figure 4.21 shows the computational flow for the gradient projection method. We assume that the starting point is free (not bound) and hence $-\nabla F$ is a usable feasible direction. Blocks A through C compute the tentative step $\alpha_M$. This step is followed by a test to determine whether there is a minimum between $X$ and $X'$. If there is, it is located and a new projection is executed at the new point $X$. The index $r$ in block D is set to zero, indicating that no new constraint needs to be added to the projection. Otherwise (i.e., if the full step $\alpha_r = \alpha_M$ is taken), the projection section is entered with $r$, giving the index of the newly encountered constraint. In block E, the projection coefficients are

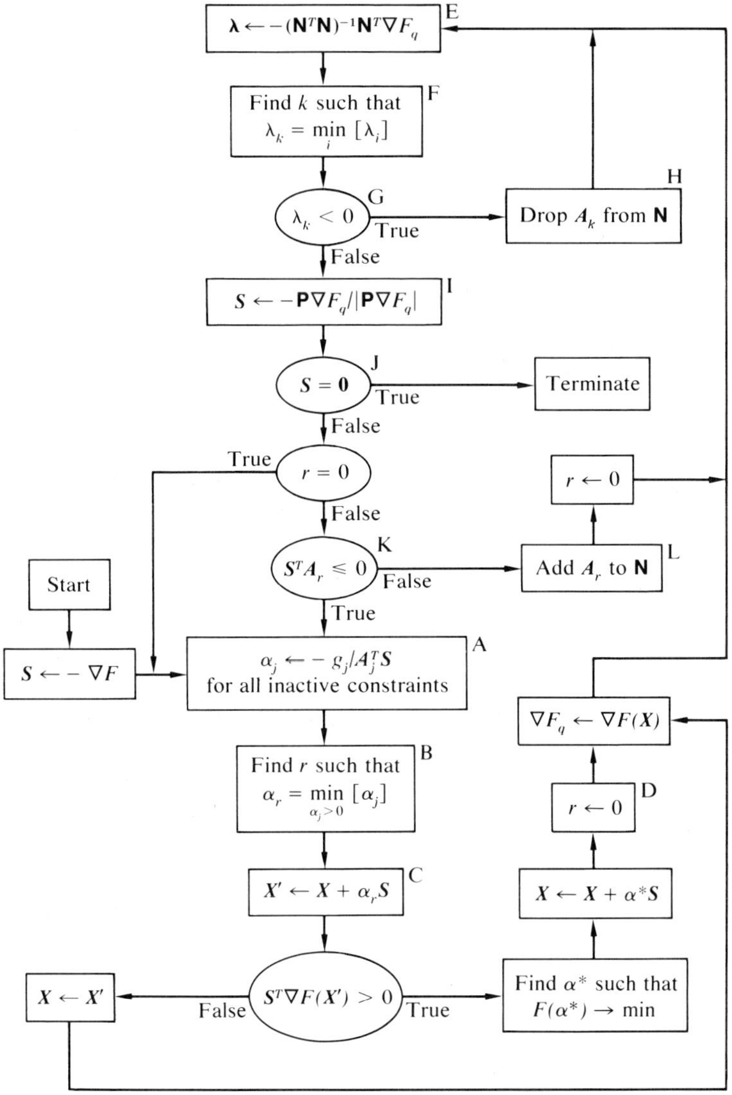


**Figure 4.21**

calculated without adding the new constraint. In F, G, and H, the constraint associated with the most negative coefficient is dropped and the coefficients are recalculated in block E. Once the **N** matrix associated with the nonnegative coefficients is established, the projection is done and tested for optimality (necessary conditions) in blocks I and J. If a new constraint is encountered just prior to the present computations ($r \neq 0$), then the $S$ vector is tested for feasibility with respect to it in block K. If $S$ is an infeasible direction, the constraint normal $A_r$ is added to the projection.

We have ignored several special cases and problem areas in this diagram. First, if the initial point is such that there are several binding constraints, it will have to be properly projected before entering block A. This presents no real problem, but complicates the program. Next, several $\alpha_j$ values in block B may equal $\alpha_r$, meaning that several constraints have been encountered simultaneously. We have to consider these constraints for inclusion in the next projection. Probably the best approach is to take first the constraints with the most positive product $S^T A_r$ in blocks K and L, and then proceed to work through the new constraints. In block K the product may be zero. This means that the vector $S$ already lies in the constraint surface $g_r(X) = 0$, and hence it is not needed in the projection. On the other hand, we should keep track of it, since it will be active at the new point. In this case it may be needed to obtain a feasible projection if some of the constraints upon which this particular constraint was dependent are dropped at a later point.

**Recursion Relations**

In utilizing the algorithm shown in Fig. 4.21 on an optimization problem, we must compute the projection matrix as well as the projection coefficients for a succession of vector sets. In the definition of these quantities, the matrix $(\mathbf{N}^T\mathbf{N})^{-1}$ plays the central role. Depending on the size of the problem, the repeated computation of this matrix can be time-consuming if done in a conventional way (e.g., Gauss elimination). The special structure of the matrix, however, allows us to use a recursive formulation. In particular, if we define

$$\mathbf{N}_r \equiv [A_1, \ldots, A_r], \tag{4.108}$$

we can compute both $(\mathbf{N}_{r-1}^T \mathbf{N}_{r-1})^{-1}$ and $(\mathbf{N}_{r+1}^T \mathbf{N}_{r+1})^{-1}$ if we know $(\mathbf{N}_r{}^T \mathbf{N}_r)^{-1}$. In other words, we can add or remove a vector from the set quite simply and without complete recalculation of the inverse matrix. Using these relations, we can assemble a complete inverse from scratch or, more important, since all the steps in the algorithm involve adding or removing one constraint at a time, they can form the sole computational basis for the method.

First consider a symmetric matrix $\mathbf{D}$, partitioned as

$$\mathbf{D} = \left[\begin{array}{c:c} \mathbf{D}_1 & \mathbf{D}_2 \\ \hdashline \mathbf{D}_2{}^T & \mathbf{D}_3 \end{array}\right], \tag{4.109}$$

where $\mathbf{D}_1$ and $\mathbf{D}_3$ are square submatrices. If $\mathbf{D}_1$ and

$$\mathbf{D}_0 \equiv \mathbf{D}_3 - \mathbf{D}_2{}^T \mathbf{D}_1{}^{-1} \mathbf{D}_2 \tag{4.110}$$

are nonsingular, then the inverse of $\mathbf{D}$ is

$$\mathbf{D}^{-1} \equiv \mathbf{B} = \left[\begin{array}{c|c} \mathbf{B}_1 & \mathbf{B}_2 \\ \hline \mathbf{B}_2{}^T & \mathbf{B}_3 \end{array}\right], \tag{4.111}$$

where

$$\mathbf{B}_1 = \mathbf{D}_1{}^{-1} + \mathbf{D}_1{}^{-1}\mathbf{D}_2\mathbf{D}_0{}^{-1}\mathbf{D}_2{}^T\mathbf{D}_1{}^{-1}, \tag{4.112}$$

$$\mathbf{B}_2 = -\,\mathbf{D}_1{}^{-1}\mathbf{D}_2\mathbf{D}_0{}^{-1}, \tag{4.113}$$

$$\mathbf{B}_3 = \mathbf{D}_0{}^{-1}. \tag{4.114}$$

The reader may wish to verify these equations. They can be solved for $\mathbf{D}_1{}^{-1}$ as

$$\mathbf{D}_1{}^{-1} = \mathbf{B}_1 - \mathbf{B}_2\mathbf{B}_3{}^{-1}\mathbf{B}_2{}^T. \tag{4.115}$$

Now suppose we have $(\mathbf{N}_r{}^T\mathbf{N}_r)^{-1}$ and we desire $(\mathbf{N}_{r-1}^T\mathbf{N}_{r-1})^{-1}$ (i.e., we are dropping a vector). We can define

$$\mathbf{D}_1 = \mathbf{N}_{r-1}^T\mathbf{N}_{r-1} \tag{4.116}$$

and

$$\mathbf{B} = (\mathbf{N}_r{}^T\mathbf{N}_r)^{-1} = \left[\begin{array}{c|c} \mathbf{B}_1 & \mathbf{B}_2 \\ \hline \mathbf{B}_2{}^T & \mathbf{B}_3 \end{array}\right]. \tag{4.117}$$

In particular, the partitions of $\mathbf{B}$ are such that $\mathbf{B}_1$ is an $(r-1) \times (r-1)$ matrix, $\mathbf{B}_2$ is an $r-1$ element vector, and $\mathbf{B}_3$ is a scalar. Equation (4.115) can then be used to compute the inverse of $\mathbf{D}_1$.

We can use this formula for computing the inverse regardless of which vector is to be dropped. Suppose we must eliminate $A_t$, $1 \leq t \leq r$; we simply interchange the $r$ and $t$ rows and columns of $\mathbf{B}$ and then perform the above recursion.

To add a new vector $A_{r+1}$, presuming that $(\mathbf{N}_r{}^T\mathbf{N}_r)^{-1}$ is known, we can resort to Eqs. (4.111), where we take

$$\mathbf{D} \equiv (\mathbf{N}_{r+1}^T\mathbf{N}_{r+1}), \tag{4.118}$$

$$\mathbf{D}_1{}^{-1} = (\mathbf{N}_r{}^T\mathbf{N}_r)^{-1}, \tag{4.119}$$

$$D_2 = \mathbf{N}_r{}^T A_{r+1} \text{ (a vector)}, \tag{4.120}$$

$$D_3 = A_{r+1}^T A_{r+1} = 1 \text{ (a scalar)}. \tag{4.121}$$

Note that if $A_{r+1}$ is linearly dependent on one or more of the $A_i$ already in $\mathbf{N}_r$, then the singularity of $(\mathbf{N}_{r+1}^T\mathbf{N}_{r+1})$ will show up as the value of $D_0$ being zero. From Eq. (4.120) we have

$$D_0 \equiv A_{r+1}^T A_{r+1} - A_{r+1}^T\mathbf{N}_r(\mathbf{N}_r{}^T\mathbf{N}_r)^{-1}\mathbf{N}_r{}^T A_{r+1}. \tag{4.122}$$

Since $A_{r+1}$ is linearly dependent on the $A_i$, we can write it as a linear combination:

$$A_{r+1} = \sum_{i=1}^{r} A_i u_i = \mathbf{N}_r U. \tag{4.123}$$

Substituting this into Eq. (4.122), we have

$$\begin{aligned} D_0 &= U^T \mathbf{N}_r^T \mathbf{N}_r U - U^T \mathbf{N}_r^T \mathbf{N}_r (\mathbf{N}_r^T \mathbf{N}_r)^{-1} \mathbf{N}_r^T \mathbf{N}_r U \\ &= U^T \mathbf{N}_r^T \mathbf{N}_r U - U^T \mathbf{N}_r^T \mathbf{N}_r U = 0. \end{aligned} \tag{4.124}$$

Another useful recursion relation is one that gives $P_{r+1}$, using only $P_r$ and $A_{r+1}$. Denote $\tilde{\mathbf{P}}_r$ as

$$\tilde{\mathbf{P}}_r \equiv \mathbf{N}_r (\mathbf{N}_r^T \mathbf{N}_r)^{-1} \mathbf{N}_r^T, \tag{4.125}$$

and then, denoting $(\mathbf{N}_{r+1}^T \mathbf{N}_{r+1})^{-1}$ as $\mathbf{B}$ again, we have

$$\tilde{\mathbf{P}}_{r+1} = [\mathbf{N}_r A_{r+1}] \begin{bmatrix} \mathbf{B}_1 & \mathbf{B}_2 \\ \mathbf{B}_2^T & \mathbf{B}_3 \end{bmatrix} \begin{bmatrix} \mathbf{N}_r^T \\ A_{r+1}^T \end{bmatrix}. \tag{4.126}$$

Substituting the definitions of the $\mathbf{B}$'s and carrying out the indicated products, we have

$$\tilde{\mathbf{P}}_{r+1} = \tilde{\mathbf{P}}_r + (\mathbf{P}_r A_{r+1})(\mathbf{P}_r A_{r+1})^T / D_0. \tag{4.127}$$

It can be easily seen that

$$\mathbf{P}_r(\mathbf{P}_r A_{r+1}) = \mathbf{P}_r A_{r+1}, \tag{4.128}$$

because the projection of a vector already in the intersection $(\mathbf{P}_r A_{r+1})$ into the intersection is the vector itself. Hence

$$A_{r+1}^T \mathbf{P}_r A_{r+1} = (\mathbf{P}_r A_{r+1})^T (\mathbf{P}_r A_{r+1}) = |\mathbf{P}_r A_{r+1}|^2. \tag{4.129}$$

Note from Eq. (4.122) that $D_0 = A_{r+1}^T \mathbf{P}_r A_{r+1}$. Then Eq. (4.127) becomes

$$\tilde{\mathbf{P}}_{r+1} = \tilde{\mathbf{P}}_r + \frac{(\mathbf{P}_r A_{r+1})(\mathbf{P}_r A_{r+1})^T}{|\mathbf{P}_r A_{r+1}|^2}. \tag{4.130}$$

If we let $E_{r+1}$ denote the unit vector

$$E_{r+1} = \mathbf{P}_r A_{r+1} / |\mathbf{P}_r A_{r+1}|, \tag{4.131}$$

we have

$$\tilde{\mathbf{P}}_{r+1} = \tilde{\mathbf{P}}_r + E_{r+1} E_{r+1}^T, \tag{4.132}$$

and then we finally have the very simple recursion to add a new vector to the projection,

$$\mathbf{P}_{r+1} = \mathbf{P}_r - E_{r+1} E_{r+1}^T. \tag{4.133}$$

Note that if $A_{r+1}$ is linearly dependent on the preceding $A_i$, then $\mathbf{P}_r A_{r+1}$ will be zero and the projection matrix will be unchanged.

### Nonlinear Constraints

The gradient projection method is highly effective when applied to problems with linear constraints and a reasonably well-behaved objective function. It has also been proposed as a method of solving problems with nonlinear constraints. The basic problem is that since the constraints may bulge outward with respect to the feasible region, the projected vector $-\mathbf{P}_r\nabla F$ makes the design infeasible even for very short moves (see Fig. 4.8a). What we must do in these cases is somehow sidestep back into the feasible region after taking a step. This process can involve some quite complicated logic and some very expensive computation if the "analysis" is at all difficult. Several algorithms have been proposed and tried but the method has proved ineffective for most of the general nonlinear programming problems arising in engineering design.

Occasionally, if the constraints are mild and easily computed perturbations of linear constraints, we can utilize the method with some clever programming. In such cases, however, one of the methods of successive linearization may be more effective.[10] These methods replace the original problem with a succession of linear programming problems by a variety of strategies. The completely linear problem can be solved very efficiently, and hence approaches that are based on linearization have an inherent appeal. The topic will be briefly discussed in the next section.

## 4.4 LINEAR PROGRAMMING

We have seen that when the constraint set is determined by linear functions, we can construct a systematic solution technique. If we consider problems in which the objective function is also linear, we have the ultimate in simplicity. Such problems are the best understood and have the most refined solution techniques of all mathematical programming problems. Unfortunately, many engineering design problems are nonlinear and hence not amenable to these methods, but no discussion of the subject of mathematical programming methods would be complete without some exposition of the so-called L-P (Linear Program) and its standard solution technique, the simplex method. It is extremely useful, of course, on truly linear optimization problems, and it is sometimes used to solve linear approximations to nonlinear problems. In addition, it is often used as a tool to solve subproblems arising in optimization, such as the direction-finding problem of the method of feasible directions. Finally, it is often a useful method for attacking some of the simultaneous equation problems of engineering, such as the determination of plastic collapse mechanism[11] in

[10] See Kelly (1960) for the method; Reinschmit, Cornell, and Brotchie (1966) for applications.

[11] See Dorn and Greenberg (1957).

structures, and perhaps the selection of a suitable "primary" structure in indeterminate structural analysis.

First, let us state the general problem: Find $X$ such that

$$F(X) = \sum_{i=1}^{n} c_i x_i \rightarrow \min, \tag{4.134}$$

subject to

$$\sum_{j=1}^{n} a_{ij} x_j \leq b_i, \qquad i = 1, 2, \ldots, m. \tag{4.135}$$

The constraints define a feasible region that is a convex polyhedron; that is, it is a convex region bounded by portions of some of the planes $\Sigma\, a_{ij} x_j = b_i$. A little reflection should reveal that if the region is bounded (that is, if the polyhedron is not open on a side), then the optimum value of $F$ is taken on at one of the apexes of the polyhedron. If the region is not bounded, then $F$ may still take on its minimum value at an apex, or it may approach $-\infty$. In this case the solution is said to be unbounded. If the L-P has a bounded solution, it will always take on its minimum at an apex; but it may take on this same value all along an "edge" joining two apexes or over the hyperplane containing three apexes, etc. These observations can be stated rigorously as theorems and are proven in most standard texts on linear programming.[12] See Fig. 4.22 for 2-dimensional examples of these situations.

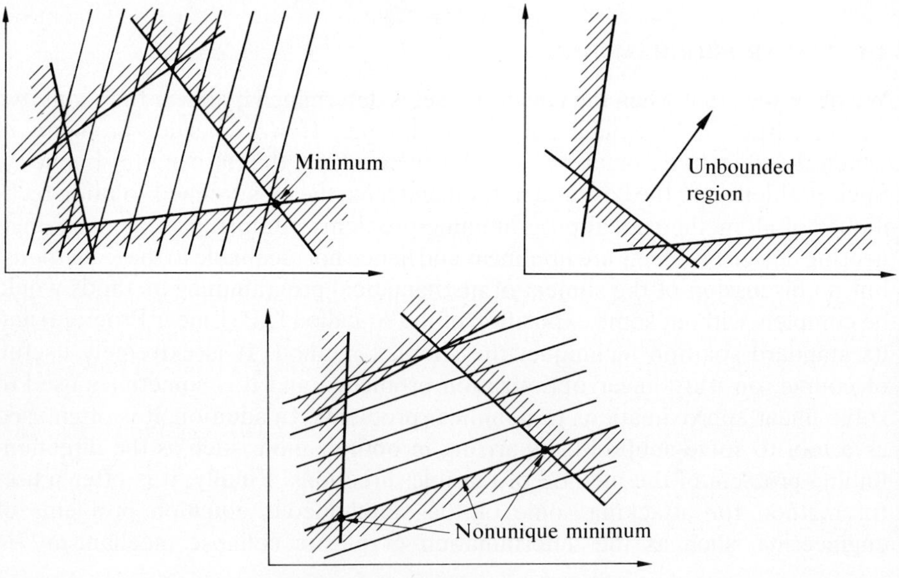


**Figure 4.22**

[12] See Hadley (1962) or Dantzig (1963).

**A Standard Form for Linear Programs**

For purposes of computation, a standard form of the linear program is utilized. It permits us to use a standard algorithm and simplifies the discussion of its application.

All linear programming problems, it will be shown, can be written in the following form: Find the $X \equiv (x_1, \ldots, x_n)$ that minimizes

$$F(X) = \sum_{j=1}^{n} c_j x_j, \tag{4.136a}$$

subject to

$$\sum_{j=1}^{n} a_{ij} x_j = b_i, \qquad i = 1, \ldots, m, \tag{4.137a}$$

$$x_j \geqslant 0, \qquad j = 1, \ldots, n. \tag{4.138a}$$

In matrix form, L-P problems can be written as follows: Find the $X$ that minimizes

$$F(X) = C^T X, \tag{4.136b}$$

subject to

$$\mathbf{A}X = B \tag{4.137b}$$

and, where a matrix or vector inequality is taken to apply to each element of the matrix or vector separately,

$$X \geqslant 0, \tag{4.138b}$$

where $\mathbf{A}$ is the $m \times n$ matrix of constants $a_{ij}$.

In all cases of interest, $m < n$ because if $m = n$ and none of the equations are redundant, there is only one solution to $\mathbf{A}X = B$. If $m > n$, then there are redundant equations that can be eliminated. With $m < n$, the system is underdetermined and in general possesses an infinity of solutions of which we seek the one that minimizes $F$. The nonnegativity constraints $X \geqslant 0$ are the only inequalities present in this standard form, and this feature greatly simplifies the solution method. In effect, we have rearranged the problem so that all the inequalities are distilled into the simple $x_j \geqslant 0$ constraints.

In order to put an arbitrary program into this form, we must do two things: (1) convert inequalities into equalities, and (2) transform the variables so that they are all nonnegative. To convert the inequalities to equalities, we introduce new $x$'s called *slack variables*. Suppose we have the inequality

$$a_{11}x_1 + a_{12}x_2 + \cdots + a_{1m}x_m \leqslant b_1.$$

We then define a new variable $x_{m+1} \geqslant 0$ such that

$$a_{11}x_1 + a_{12}x_2 + \cdots + a_{1m}x_m + x_{m+1} = b_1.$$

If we had a second similar inequality

$$a_{i1}x_1 + a_{i2}x_2 + \cdots + a_{im}x_m \leq b_i, \tag{4.139}$$

we would add a second slack variable

$$a_{i1}x_1 + a_{i2}x_2 + \cdots + a_{im}x_m + x_{m+2} = b_i, \tag{4.140}$$

and so on. If the inequality is of the form

$$a_{k1}x_1 + a_{k2}x_2 + \cdots + a_{km}x_m \geq b_k, \tag{4.141}$$

we subtract the slack variable

$$a_{k1}x_1 + a_{k2}x_2 + \cdots + a_{km}x_m - x_{m+l} = b_k. \tag{4.142}$$

Note that since the slacks must also be nonnegative, any $\boldsymbol{X}$ that satisfies the equalities also satisfies the original inequalities. The geometrical significance of this conversion can be seen in the following example: Suppose the constraints are of the form

$$2x_1 + x_2 \leq 2, \qquad x_1 \geq 0, \qquad x_2 \geq 0.$$

The feasible region is shown in Fig. 4.23(a), where the vertices of the region are points $A$, $B$, and $C$. After conversion, the constraint becomes

$$2x_1 + x_2 + x_3 = 2,$$

$$x_1 \geq 0, \qquad x_2 \geq 0, \qquad x_3 \geq 0,$$

where $x_3$ is the slack variable. The feasible region is now the portion of the plane cutting into the positive octant (see Fig. 4.23b), and the points $A'$, $B'$, and $C'$ correspond to the original vertices.

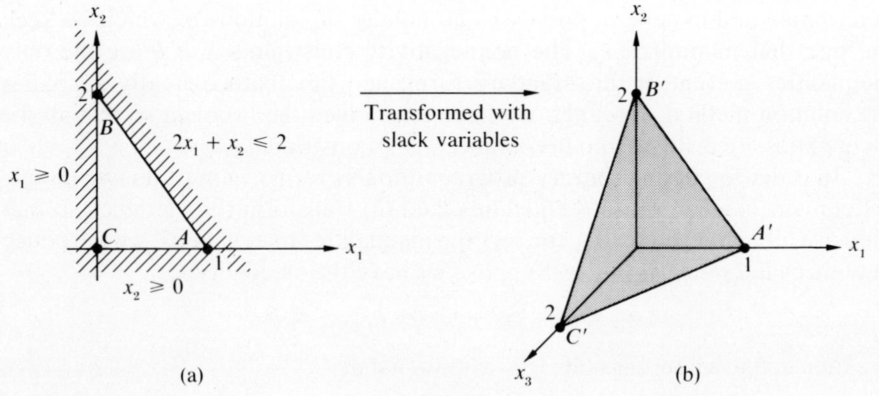


**Figure 4.23**

If the original problem has variables that are not required to be nonnegative, then we can write them as the difference between two nonnegative variables:

$$x_k = x_k' - x_k'', \tag{4.143}$$

where $x_k' \geqslant 0$ and $x_k'' \geqslant 0$. After the slacks and new nonnegative variables have been added, the variables are renumbered and the problem is in standard form, as in Eqs. (4.136), (4.137). Note that the new slacks would not ordinarily appear in the objective function, but the new nonnegative variables would, in general, appear there.

Once the linear programming problem is in standard form, we can generalize some of the ideas previously discussed. First, a number of standard definitions can be made.

1. A *feasible solution* is one that satisfies Eq. (4.137) and inequalities Eq. (4.138).
2. A *basic feasible solution* is a feasible solution with no more than $m$ nonzero $x_i$. In other words, it has at least $(n-m)$ $x_i$ that are zero.
3. A *nondegenerate basic feasible solution* has exactly $m$ positive $x_i$.

We can now state that *if the linear programming problem (converted to standard form) has a bounded solution, the minimum value of F is attained at one of the basic feasible solutions of the program.* This is an extremely powerful result, since there is a finite number of basic solutions; that is, there can be no more than the number of ways $m$ variables can be selected from a group of $n$ variables, or

$$\frac{n!}{(n-m)!m!} \equiv \binom{n}{m}. \tag{4.144}$$

Usually there are far fewer possibilities, since many combinations are infeasible.

For large $m$ and $n$, this is still a very large number, so what we need is a computational scheme that examines a sequence of basic feasible solutions, each of which corresponds to a lower value of $F$ until a minimum is reached. The simplex method of Dantzig[13] is a powerful scheme for obtaining a basic feasible solution; if the solution is not optimal, the method provides for finding a neighboring basic feasible solution which has a lower or equal value of $F$. The process is repeated until, in a finite number of steps (usually between $m$ and $2m$), an optimum is found.

To discuss the simplex method, we will need to know how to compute a basic feasible solution and how to go from one to a neighboring one. From the

[13] See Dantzig (1963) for a thorough presentation.

equations in their original form, we have

$$\begin{aligned} a_{11}x_1 + a_{12}x_2 + \cdots + a_{1n}x_n &= b_1 \\ a_{21}x_1 + a_{22}x_2 + \cdots + a_{2n}x_n &= b_2 \\ \vdots \qquad\qquad & \quad\ \vdots \\ a_{m1}x_1 + a_{m2}x_2 + \cdots + a_{mn}x_n &= b_m. \end{aligned} \tag{4.145}$$

It is not obvious what any one solution may be, to say nothing of a basic feasible solution. It is possible, however, to place the system into a form from which at least one solution can be readily deduced. We obtain this form by replacing the original system of equations with another system of the same size which is a linear combination of the equations of the original system. The operations necessary to accomplish this are familiar from elementary algebra. Suppose we select some variable $x_k$ and endeavor to eliminate it from all the equations except the $l$th. We can divide the $l$th equation by $a_{lk}$ and subtract $a_{ik}$ times the result from each of the other equations, $i = 1, 2, \ldots, m, i \neq l$. This produces the system

$$\begin{aligned} a'_{11}x_1 + a'_{12}x_2 + \cdots + 0x_k + \cdots + a'_{1n}x_n &= b'_1 \\ a'_{21}x_1 + a'_{22}x_2 + \cdots + 0x_k + \cdots + a_{2n}x_n &= b'_2 \\ \vdots \qquad\qquad\qquad\qquad & \quad\ \vdots \\ a'_{k1}x_1 + a'_{k2}x_2 + \cdots + 1x_k + \cdots + a'_{kn}x_n &= b'_k \\ \vdots \qquad\qquad\qquad\qquad & \quad\ \vdots \\ a'_{m}x_1 + a'_{m2}x_2 + \cdots + 0x_k + \cdots + a'_{mn}x_n &= b'_m \end{aligned} \tag{4.146}$$

where the primes indicate that the $a'_{ij}$ and $b'_j$ are changed from the original system. This procedure is called a *pivot operation*, and it produces a new system of equations that have exactly the same solutions as the original set. That is, any $\boldsymbol{X}$ which satisfies the original equations satisfies this system and conversely. The new system is then said to be *equivalent* to the old system.

Notice that if we take the system in Eq. (4.146) and, in a new equation, perform a second pivot on a new $x_t$, $t \neq k$ (i.e., we *pivot* on $a'_{st}$, $s \neq k$), we do not disturb any of the zeros or the 1 in the $k$th column. If we repeat these pivoting operations on the system (using a different equation and variable each time) until we have done it once for each equation, there will be $m$ columns, each containing zeros and a single 1. These can always be rearranged by renumbering the $x$'s (for discussion purposes) into the form

$$\begin{aligned} 1x_1 + 0x_2 + \cdots + 0x_m + a''_{1,m+1}x_{m+1} + \cdots + a''_{1n}x_n &= b''_1 \\ 0x_1 + 1x_2 + \cdots + 0x_m + a''_{2,m+1}x_{m+1} + \cdots + a''_{2n}x_n &= b''_2 \\ \vdots \qquad \vdots \qquad\quad \vdots \qquad\quad \vdots \qquad\qquad\quad \vdots \quad & \quad\ \vdots \\ 0x_1 + 0x_2 + \cdots + 1x_m + a''_{m,m+1}x_{m+1} + \cdots + a''_{mn}x_n &= b''_{mn}. \end{aligned} \tag{4.147}$$

Such a system is said to be *canonical*, or in *canonical form*. One solution to the still underdetermined system is always

$$x_i = b_i'', \qquad i = 1, 2, \ldots, m,$$
$$x_i = 0, \qquad i = m+1, m+2, \ldots, n. \tag{4.148}$$

This solution is called a *basic solution*, and the first $m$ of the $x_i$ are called *basic variables*. Of course, this is not the only solution, but it is the one most readily deduced from the equations in this form.[14] Even more interesting, in terms of linear programming, is the fact that if all the $b_i''$ are nonnegative, then the solution given by Eqs. (4.148) is a basic feasible solution: a candidate for an optimum point of the original linear programming problem in standard form.

Note that if we perform an additional pivot on the system after it is in canonical form, using $a_{st}''$ as the pivot term, $m < t$, and using any $s$, the new system is still in canonical form, but $x_t$ is now *in the basis*, and $x_s$ (which was a basic variable) is no longer basic. Thus an additional pivot on a canonical system allows us to go from one basic solution to another and in such a way that we exchange a nonbasic and a basic variable. It should be pointed out that the values of all basic variables change in general, but only one zero variable (nonbasic) becomes nonzero (basic) and vice versa.

(We have assumed throughout this discussion that we can choose any $a_{st}$ for a pivot operation, but, of course, if it is zero, then we cannot take the first step of dividing through by that term. Therefore, it is not always possible to go from a particular basic solution to all neighboring basic solutions.)

A small example should help clarify some of these points. Given the system

$$5x_1 - 4x_2 + 13x_3 - 2x_4 + x_5 = 20,$$
$$x_1 - x_2 + 5x_3 - x_4 + x_5 = 8. \tag{4.149}$$

If we pivot on $a_{11}$ we obtain

$$x_1 - \tfrac{4}{5}x_2 + \tfrac{13}{5}x_3 - \tfrac{2}{5}x_4 + \tfrac{1}{5}x_5 = 4,$$
$$0 - \tfrac{1}{5}x_2 + \tfrac{12}{5}x_3 - \tfrac{3}{5}x_4 + \tfrac{4}{5}x_5 = 4,$$

and then if we pivot on $a_{22}'$, we get

$$x_1 + 0 - 7x_3 + 2x_4 - \tfrac{15}{5}x_5 = -12,$$
$$0 + x_2 - 12x_3 + 3x_4 - 4x_5 = -20.$$

The basic solution is

$$x_1 = -12, \qquad x_2 = -20, \qquad x_3 = x_4 = x_5 = 0,$$

[14] For the reader familiar with simultaneous equation solution methods, this procedure amounts to a Gauss-Jordan reduction for the leading $m \times m$ matrix partition in **A**.

where $x_1$ and $x_2$ are the basic variables. Note that the point is not a basic *feasible* solution, since both $x_1$ and $x_2$ are negative.

If we now pivot on $a_{25}$, we obtain

$$x_1 - \tfrac{3}{4}x_2 + 2x_3 - \tfrac{1}{4}x_4 + 0 = 3,$$

$$0 - \tfrac{1}{4}x_2 + 3x_3 - \tfrac{3}{4}x_4 + x_5 = 5,$$

and the basic solution is

$$x_1 = 3, \qquad x_5 = 5, \qquad x_2 = x_3 = x_4 = 0,$$

which is a basic feasible solution because $x_1$ and $x_5$ are positive.

**Going from One Basic Feasible Solution to Another**

Given a system in canonical form corresponding to a basic feasible solution (as with the last form of the system in the previous example), we can easily pivot to a neighboring basic feasible solution if one exists. Consider a system in canonical form with a feasible basis and contemplate bringing some specific $x_t$ into the basis in place of some as yet undetermined $x_s$. Note first that all the $b_i$ are nonnegative because the present basis is feasible. We thus cannot pivot on any $a_{st}$ which is negative, since this would make $x_t$ negative in the basis $(x_t = b_t/a_{st})$.

Next note that we increase $x_t$ from zero to some positive value during the process and take some other $x_s$ (one of the present basic variables) to zero. If we are to keep the solution feasible, we cannot increase $x_t$ from zero by more than it takes to make the "first" $x_s$ just go to zero, since to increase it further would make $x_s$ negative. Suppose we take the canonical system and, keeping all nonbasic variables zero except $x_t$, examine the effect of increasing $x_t$ on the basic variables:

$$x_s = b_s - a_{st}x_t, \qquad s = 1, 2, \ldots, m; t > m. \tag{4.150}$$

The largest that $x_t$ can be made before $x_s$ diminishes below zero is

$$x_t = b_s/a_{st}, \tag{4.151}$$

if $a_{st}$ is positive (if $a_{st}$ is negative, no positive $x_t$ will make $x_s$ negative). Therefore, we must pivot on the $a_{st} > 0$, obtaining the minimum in

$$x_t = \min_{a_{it}>0} [b_i/a_{it}]. \tag{4.152}$$

In other words, since we wish to make $x_t$ basic (nonzero) in place of some other variable $x_s$ which will become nonbasic (zero), we must choose as the pivot row $s$ the one for which, by Eq. (4.150), $x_s = 0$ and all others are nonnegative. Hence the pivot row we choose must produce the minimum value in Eq.

(4.152). As an example, consider the previous canonical form

$$x_1 - \tfrac{3}{4}x_2 + 2x_3 - \tfrac{1}{4}x_4 + 0 = 3,$$

$$0 - \tfrac{1}{4}x_2 + 3x_3 - \tfrac{3}{4}x_4 + x_5 = 5.$$

Note first that we cannot bring $x_2$ or $x_4$ into the basis since all their coefficients are negative. We can, however, bring in $x_3$; then to determine the pivot row (i.e., the variable to leave the basis or become nonbasic), we compare $\frac{3}{2}$ and $\frac{5}{3}$. Since $\frac{3}{2}$ is the minimum $b_i/a_{it}$ ratio, we would pivot on $a_{13}$, producing

$$\tfrac{1}{2}x_1 - \tfrac{3}{8}x_2 + x_3 - \tfrac{1}{8}x_4 + 0 = \tfrac{3}{2},$$

$$-\tfrac{3}{8}x + \tfrac{7}{8}x_2 + 0 - \tfrac{3}{8}x_4 + x_5 = \tfrac{1}{2},$$

with the basic solution

$$x_3 = \tfrac{3}{2}, \qquad x_5 = \tfrac{1}{2}, \qquad x_1 = x_2 = x_4 = 0.$$

Note that if the pivot had been performed to eliminate $x_5$ instead of $x_1$ we would have

$$x_1 - \tfrac{7}{12}x_2 + 0 + \tfrac{1}{4}x_4 - \tfrac{2}{3}x_5 = -\tfrac{1}{3},$$

$$0 - \tfrac{1}{12}x_2 + x_3 - \tfrac{1}{4}x_4 + \tfrac{1}{3}x_5 = \tfrac{5}{3},$$

with the basic (infeasible) solution

$$x_1 = -\tfrac{1}{3}, \qquad x_3 = \tfrac{5}{3}, \qquad x_2 = x_4 = x_5 = 0.$$

It is important to note that all these forms of the original equations have the same solutions, but we are only considering the *basic* solutions, since these are trivially available from the canonical form. The reader may wish to verify that all the previously determined basic solutions

$$x_1 = -12, \qquad x_2 = -20, \qquad x_3 = x_4 = x_5 = 0,$$

$$x_1 = 3, \qquad x_5 = 5, \qquad x_2 = x_3 = x_4 = 0,$$

$$x_3 = \tfrac{3}{2}, \qquad x_5 = \tfrac{1}{2}, \qquad x_1 = x_2 = x_4 = 0,$$

are indeed solutions of Eqs. (4.149).

In summary, once it has been determined to bring the currently nonbasic variable $x_t$ into the basis, we pivot to a new basic feasible solution by following this procedure:

1. Compute $s$ such that

$$b_s/a_{st} = \min_{a_{it}>0} [b_i/a_{it}].$$

2. If no such $s$ exists (i.e., there are no $a_{it} > 0$), the pivot cannot be made because $x_t$ can be increased indefinitely without the solution becoming infeasible.

3. Otherwise, pivot on $a_{st}$ to the new basic feasible solution that includes $x_t$ in place of $x_s$.

We now know how to go from one basic feasible solution to another and could, in principle, determine all such solutions, compute the objective function at each, and select the one with the lowest value. Since this process could result in an enormous number of trials and since a simple alternative is available, we now examine the implications of the objective function.

**Including the Objective Function**

Since the objective function is merely a linear equation relating $F$ to the variables $x_i$, we can treat it in the same manner as we do the other equations of the system. Suppose we write

$$c_1x_1 + c_2x_2 + \cdots + c_nx_n - F = 0, \tag{4.153}$$

and, assuming the constraint equations are in canonical form, we eliminate the basic variables from the equation by successively subtracting $c_i$ times each equation from Eq. (4.153):

$$0 + 0 + \cdots + 0 + c'_{m+1}x_{m+1} + \cdots + c'_nx_n - F = - c_1b_1 - c_2b_2 - \cdots - c_mb_m. \tag{4.154}$$

Thus for the basic solution, we have

$$F = \sum_{i=1}^{m} c_ib_i, \tag{4.155}$$

since $x_{m+1} = x_{m+2} = \cdots = x_n = 0$. Often the objective function is thought of as appended to the last row of the system of equations and all pivots are carried out by eliminating down through this last row. If we do it in this way, the right-hand side of the last equation is always the negative of the value of the objective function for the basic solution.

Assume that the numerical example we have been working with has the objective function

$$F = x_1 + 6x_2 - 7x_3 + x_4 + 5x_5$$

and append it to the canonical form

$$x_1 - \tfrac{3}{4}x_2 + 2x_3 - \tfrac{1}{4}x_4 + 0 = 3,$$

$$0 - \tfrac{1}{4}x_2 + 3x_3 - \tfrac{3}{4}x_4 + x_5 = 5,$$

$$x_1 + 6x_2 - 7x_3 + x_4 + 5x_5 - F = 0.$$

After elimination, this becomes

$$x_1 - \tfrac{3}{4}x_2 + 2x_3 + \tfrac{1}{4}x_4 + 0 = 3,$$

$$0 - \tfrac{1}{4}x_2 + 3x_3 - \tfrac{3}{4}x_4 + x_5 = 5,$$
$$0 + 8x_2 - 24x_3 + 5x_4 + 0 - F = -28.$$

Hence for the basic feasible solution $x_1 = 3, x_3 = 5, x_2 = x_3 = x_4 = 0$, the objective function is 28.

**Improving a Basic Feasible Solution**

When the appended system is in canonical form, if any coefficient in the last (objective function) row is negative, then we can reduce $F$ by increasing the corresponding $x$ from zero while keeping all the other nonbasic variables at zero. In the above example, if we increase $x_3$, keeping $x_2$ and $x_4$ at zero and allowing $x_1$ and $x_5$ to take on whatever values are dictated by the constraints, the objective function is

$$F = 28 - 24x_3.$$

It can be decreased 24 times as much as $x_3$ can be increased.

We have already seen that we can increase $x_3$ from zero to $\frac{3}{2}$ by pivoting on $a_{13}$. Completing this pivot, including the last row, we have

$$\tfrac{1}{2}x_1 - \tfrac{3}{8}x_2 + x_3 - \tfrac{1}{8}x_4 + 0 = \tfrac{3}{2},$$
$$-\tfrac{12}{8}x_1 + \tfrac{7}{8}x_2 + 0 - \tfrac{3}{8}x_4 + x_5 = \tfrac{1}{2},$$
$$12x_1 - x_2 + 0 + 2x_4 + 0 - F = 8,$$

which shows that the objective function has been reduced to $-8$ for the basic feasible solution.

In general, the objective function will be reduced if any coefficient of the cleared objective function is negative and the pivot on that column is performed (unless the pivot row has a zero right-hand side, in which case it will remain unchanged).

**The Exceptional Cases**

If we pivot on a row for which the right-hand side $b_i$ is zero, we will not change the value of the objective function or of any of the variables of the basic solution. In such a case, the value of the basic variable corresponding to the zero $b_i$ is zero, and hence it is a *degenerate basic feasible solution.* In the *degenerate case* we get no reduction in the objective function even though we bring a variable into the basis which has a negative coefficient in the objective function. In the optimization procedure that we will describe subsequently, we will still opt to perform such pivots, since doing so may allow us to proceed to other nondegenerate pivots.

Another exceptional case occurs when all the $a_{st}$ in the column corresponding to a negative $c_t$ are also negative. In this case, we can increase $x_t$ indefinitely without causing any variable to become negative (see Eq. 4.150).

When we encounter such a case it is clear that we have an *unbounded solution*; that is, the objective function can be made as small (i.e., as negative) as desired without violating the constraints.

### The General Iterative Procedure

Starting with the system in canonical form with a feasible basis and the objective cleared, we now state a general procedure for going from one basis to an improved one, if one exists, and if not, to identify the optimality of the basis. We have noted that if any $c_t$ corresponding to a nonbasic variable is negative, the objective function will be reduced if we increase the associated variable from zero. Therefore, to improve the basis, we can bring any such $x_t$ into the basis. If more than one $c_t$ is negative, then we can choose among them, and the criterion most used today is to choose the $t$ for which

$$c_t = \min_j [c_j]. \tag{4.156}$$

This choice selects the variable for which the objective function reduces at the greatest rate. It should be noted that some other choice may occasionally produce a greater reduction in $F$ for this step since, because of the constraints, the alternative variable may be capable of more change. However, the above criterion is usually best, because it is simplest and because experience has shown it to be efficient overall.

If $c_t \equiv \min[c_j]$ is not negative, then there is no variable that can be increased to reduce the objective function; this situation is called the *optimality condition.*

We now know which variable to bring into the basis (assuming that some $c_t < 0$) and we have seen that we must eliminate the variable $x_s$ for which

$$b_s/a_{st} = \min_{a_{it}>0} [b_i/a_{it}], \tag{4.157}$$

and so we have a general iterative procedure for proceeding from any basic feasible solution to an optimal solution if one exists, or for determining the unboundedness of the solution if that is the case. The procedure is given by the flow diagram in Fig. 4.24. What to do in blocks A and C in the case of a tie for minimum is simply to select one of the candidates arbitrarily. Most computer algorithms for finding the minimum of some set of subscripted quantities will automatically produce an acceptable choice in such cases.

A note of caution about the procedure should be sounded: the tests for zero in blocks B and C must be given careful consideration, since it may be difficult to distinguish between very small numbers resulting only from round-off error and the numbers that are small but significant. This is usually handled in blocks B and C, respectively, by requiring

$$c_t < -\epsilon, \tag{4.158}$$

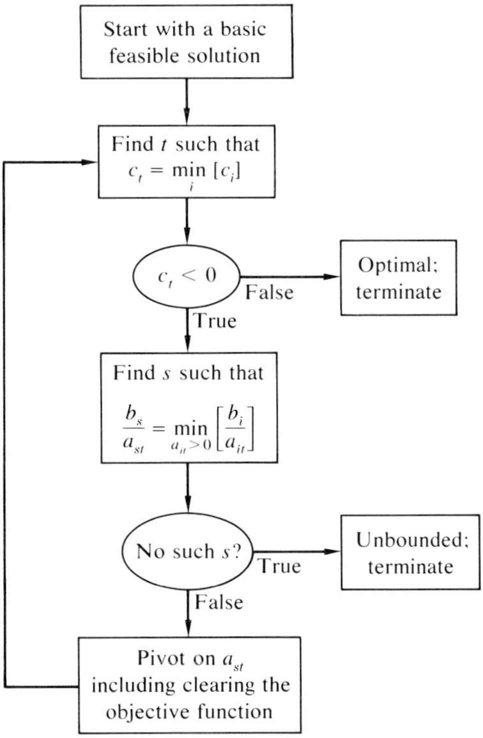


**Figure 4.24**

and

$$a_{it} > \epsilon, \tag{4.159}$$

where $\epsilon$ is a positive number selected to represent the expected roundoff in the problem; it will be problem dependent.

One of the topics given considerable discussion in the literature of linear programming is the efficient computation of the steps described by Fig. 4.24. Certainly the identity matrix portion of the canonical matrix **A** need not be stored or computed anew with each pivot, and by applying this fact, we can achieve considerable economy. There are a number of more important computational improvements that can be made;[15] however, a discussion of them is beyond the scope of this text. Most of these advanced techniques and concepts have as their objective the solution of problems with large numbers of variables and/or constraints; the method given here is adequate for problems of moderate size.

---

[15] See, for example, Hadley (1962).

## The Simplex Method

The general iteration process described here requires a basic feasible solution as a starting point, and so the simplex algorithm consists of two phases: Phase I to find a basic feasible solution if one exists and Phase II to find the optimal solution. Phase I consists of defining new variables called *artificial variables* and then eliminating them by the general iteration scheme. To see how this is done, consider the original system of equations (4.145) with a different new variable added to each equation:

$$\begin{aligned}
a_{11}x_1 + \cdots + a_{1n}x_n + x_{n+1} + 0 \quad + \cdots + 0 \quad &= b_1 \\
a_{21}x_1 + \cdots + a_{2n}x_n + 0 \quad + x_{n+2} + \cdots + 0 \quad &= b_2 \\
\cdot \qquad\qquad\qquad\qquad\qquad\qquad &\quad \cdot \\
\cdot \qquad\qquad\qquad\qquad\qquad\qquad &\quad \cdot \\
\cdot \qquad\qquad\qquad\qquad\qquad\qquad &\quad \cdot \\
a_{m1}x_1 + \cdots + a_{mn}x_n + 0 \quad + 0 \quad + \cdots + x_{n+m} &= b_m.
\end{aligned} \tag{4.160}$$

The "artificial" objective function is

$$F' = \sum_{i=n+1}^{m+n} x_i, \tag{4.161}$$

where $x_i$, $i = n + 1, \ldots, m + n$, are the artificial variables and form a basic solution $x_{n+i} = b_i$, $i = 1, 2, \ldots, m$; $x_i = 0$, $i = 1, 2, \ldots, n$. The basic solution is feasible if all $b_i$ are positive; this can be assured if we multiply all equations by sign $(b_i)$[16] before adding the artificial variables. If we append the artificial objective to the system and then clear it, we can then apply the general iterative procedure to minimize $F'$.

If the minimum of $F'$ is zero, then all the artificials have been eliminated from the basis and a new basic feasible solution is available which contains only $x_i$, $i = 1, 2, \ldots, n$. Then we can drop the artificials and append and clear the original objective function in preparation for Phase II. If the minimum of $F'$ is greater than zero, then no basic feasible solution to the original problem exists.

Often in converting inequalities to equalities by the addition of slack variables, we find that the slack variables can serve as part of an initial feasible basis. Consider the constraints

$$\begin{aligned}
x_1 \quad - x_2 + x_3 &\leqslant 5, \\
x_1 + 2x_2 - x_3 &\leqslant 10, \\
x_i \geqslant 0, \qquad i &= 1, 2, 3.
\end{aligned}$$

[16] Multiply by

$$\operatorname{sign}(b_i) = \begin{cases} +1, & b_i > 0, \\ \phantom{+}0, & b_i = 0, \quad \text{(do not multiply)} \\ -1, & b_i < 0. \end{cases}$$

Converting them to equalities, we have

$$\begin{aligned} x_1 - x_2 + x_3 + x_4 + 0 &= 5, \\ x_1 + 2x_2 - x_3 + 0 + x_5 &= 10, \\ x_i \geqslant 0, \qquad i &= 1, \ldots, 5, \end{aligned}$$

which give the immediate basic feasible solution

$$x_4 = 5, \qquad x_5 = 10, \qquad x_1 = x_2 = x_3 = 0.$$

This approach is not always possible. For example, if the right-hand side is negative or the inequalities are reversed and the right-hand side is positive, we cannot use this approach. The basic criterion, given a set of inequalities, is whether the origin is a feasible point.

If only some of the slack variables will serve as basic variables, then we need to add the artificials only to those equalities needing them.

As an example of the complete process of Phase I and II, we take the problem we have been using (Eqs. 4.149). The constraints are

$$\begin{aligned} 5x_1 - 4x_2 + 13x_3 - 2x_4 + x_5 &= 20. \\ x_1 - x_2 + 5x_3 - x_4 + x_5 &= 8. \end{aligned}$$

Adding the artificial variables $x_6$ and $x_7$ and appending the artificial objective function, we have

$$\begin{aligned} 5x_1 - 4x_2 + 13x_3 - 2x_4 + x_5 + x_6 + 0 &= 20, \\ x_1 - x_2 + 5x_3 - x_4 + x_5 + 0 + x_7 &= 8, \\ 0 + 0 + 0 + 0 + 0 + x_6 + x_7 - F' &= 0. \end{aligned}$$

Clearing the latter, we have as the starting system for Phase I:

$$\begin{aligned} 5x_1 - 4x_2 + \bigcirc\!\!\!\!\!\!13x_3 - 2x_4 + x_5 + x_6 + 0 &= 20, \\ x_1 - x_2 + 5x_3 - x_4 + x_5 + 0 + x_7 &= 8, \\ -6x_1 + 5x_2 - 18x_3 + 3x_4 - 2x_5 + \underset{*}{0} + \underset{*}{0} - F' &= -28, \end{aligned}$$

In (under $x_3$) Out (under $x_6$)

where the *'s call attention to the basic variables, the circled term is the next pivot, and "In" shows the new basic variable. Performing the pivot, we have

$$\begin{aligned} \tfrac{5}{13}x_1 - \tfrac{4}{13}x_2 + x_3 - \tfrac{2}{13}x_4 + \tfrac{1}{13}x_5 + \tfrac{1}{13}x_6 + 0 &= \tfrac{20}{13}, \\ -\tfrac{12}{13}x_1 + \tfrac{7}{13}x_2 + 0 - \tfrac{3}{13}x_4 + \bigcirc\!\!\!\!\!\!\tfrac{8}{13}x_5 - \tfrac{5}{13}x_6 + x_7 &= \tfrac{4}{13}, \\ \tfrac{12}{13}x_1 - \tfrac{7}{13}x_2 + \underset{*}{0} + \tfrac{3}{13}x_4 - \tfrac{8}{13}x_5 + \tfrac{18}{13}x_6 + \underset{*}{0} - F' &= -\tfrac{4}{13}. \end{aligned}$$

In (under $x_5$) Out (under $x_7$)

The next pivot produces

$$\begin{aligned}
\tfrac{1}{2}x_1 - \tfrac{3}{8}x_2 + x_3 - \tfrac{1}{8}x_4 + 0 + \tfrac{1}{8}x_6 - \tfrac{1}{8}x_7 &= \tfrac{3}{2},\\
-\tfrac{12}{8}x_1 + \tfrac{7}{8}x_2 + 0 - \tfrac{3}{8}x_4 + x_5 - \tfrac{5}{8}x_6 + \tfrac{13}{8}x_7 &= \tfrac{4}{8},\\
0 + 0 + \underset{*}{0} + 0 + \underset{*}{0} + x_6 + x_7 - F' &= 0,
\end{aligned}$$

and Phase I is complete. Dropping the artificial variables, appending the objective function

$$F = x_1 + 6x_2 - 7x_3 + x_4 + 5x_5,$$

and clearing, we have as the starting system for Phase II:

$$\begin{aligned}
\tfrac{1}{2}x_1 - \tfrac{3}{8}x_2 + x_3 - \tfrac{1}{8}x_4 + 0 &= \tfrac{3}{2},\\
-\tfrac{12}{8}x_1 + \boxed{\tfrac{7}{8}x_2} + 0 - \tfrac{3}{8}x_4 + x_5 &= \tfrac{4}{8},\\
12x_1 - x_2 + \underset{*}{0} + 2x_4 + \underset{*}{0} - F &= 8.
\end{aligned}$$

In Out

Performing the pivot, we have

$$\begin{aligned}
-\tfrac{1}{7}x_1 + 0 + x_3 - \tfrac{2}{7}x_4 + \tfrac{3}{7}x_5 &= \tfrac{12}{7},\\
-\tfrac{12}{7}x_1 + x_2 + 0 - \tfrac{3}{7}x_4 + \tfrac{8}{7}x_5 &= \tfrac{4}{7},\\
\tfrac{72}{7}x_1 + \underset{*}{0} + \underset{*}{0} + \tfrac{11}{7}x_4 + \tfrac{8}{7}x_5 - F &= \tfrac{60}{7},
\end{aligned}$$

which is the optimal form, since all $c_j > 0$. The solution is

$$x_2 = \tfrac{4}{7}, \qquad x_3 = \tfrac{12}{7}, \qquad x_1 = x_4 = x_5 = 0, \qquad F = -\tfrac{60}{7}.$$

**Linearization Approaches to Nonlinear Problems**

An attractive approach to some nonlinear programming problems is to linearize them in a way that permits the use of linear programming methods. We will discuss these ideas briefly.

Consider the original nonlinear problem: Find $X$ such that $F(X) \to \min$ subject to

$$g_j(X) \leqslant 0, \qquad j = 1, 2, \ldots, m.$$

Given some "reasonable" point $X_0$, which may be feasible or infeasible, expand

$$\begin{aligned}
F(X) &\simeq F(X_0) + \nabla F(X_0)^T(X - X_0) \equiv F^{(0)}(X),\\
g_j(X) &\simeq g_j(X_0) + \nabla g_j(X_0)^T(X - X_0) \equiv g_j^{(0)}(X).
\end{aligned} \tag{4.162}$$

The linear programming problem is as follows: Find $X$ such that $F^{(0)}(X) \to$ min subject to

$$g_j^{(0)}(X) \leq 0, \quad j = 1,2, \ldots, m.$$

This problem is expected to have a solution near the solution to the original problem. Call the solution point $X_1$, and expand

$$\begin{aligned} F^{(1)} &\equiv F(X_1) + \nabla F(X_1)^T (X - X_1), \\ g_j^{(1)} &\equiv g_j(X_1) + \nabla g_j(X_1)^T (X - X_1). \end{aligned} \tag{4.163}$$

Then solve this linear program: Find $X$ such that $F^{(1)}(X) \to$ min subject to

$$g_j^{(0)}(X) \leq 0, \qquad j = 1,2, \ldots, m,$$

$$g_j^{(1)}(X) \leq 0, \qquad j = 1,2, \ldots, m.$$

The process can be continued by adding new constraint approximations until the solution is seen to converge.

The reason for retaining the old approximation as new ones are generated is depicted in Fig. 4.25 for a single nonlinear constraint. The variations of the

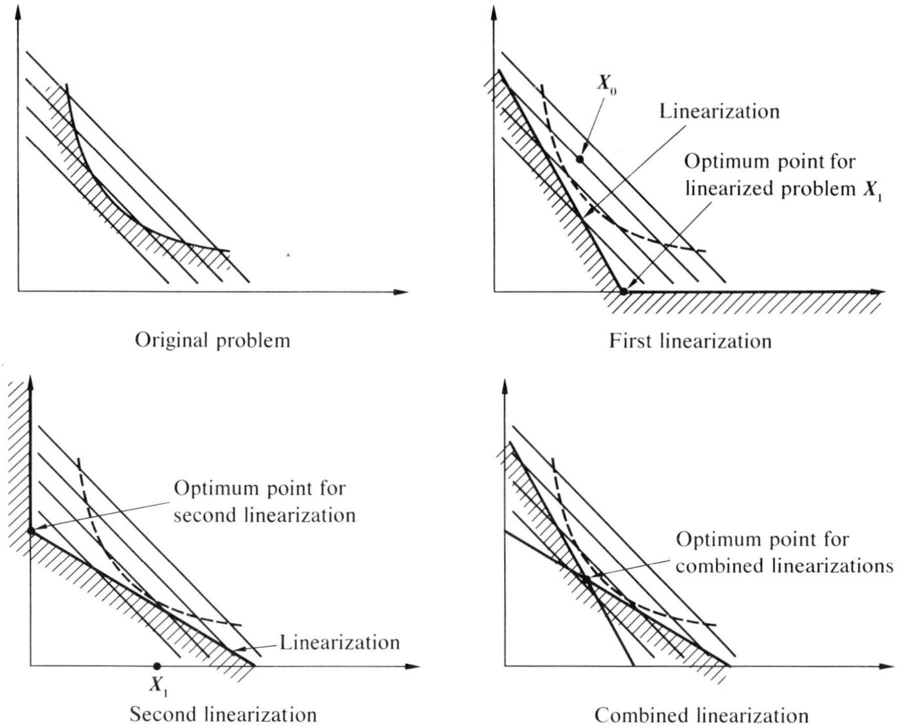


**Figure 4.25**

idea seem almost limitless:[17] some older or less meaningful linearizations can be dropped as the process progresses in order to keep the size of the problem from getting out of hand; several simultaneous linearizations can be made at the outset about selected points spread throughout the space; and an additional "box" of upper and lower bound constraints may be added to limit the total movement of the solution from the point about which the linearization is made.[18] This latter idea seems to be fairly effective; no old linearizations are retained but the box is moved about as the optimal solution to the linear program shifts, and ultimately we contract the box to obtain final convergence.

If the original nonlinear problem is a *convex program* and the $g$'s are convex functions, the general method will converge to the solution, provided the successive linearizations are retained.[19] A basic difficulty with the method in nonconvex problems is that some of the linearizations of the constraints may "cut off" feasible portions of the space that include the optimal solution.

The other main difficulty with the approach is that as constraints are accumulated, the size of the resulting linear programs can get very large. The problems that this brings can be alleviated somewhat by the more advanced linear programming methods, but it still remains a stumbling block in many cases.

Another objection to the approach from an engineering point of view is that even in convex problems the designs leading to the optimum are usually infeasible. The process of relinearization may have to be carried out many times before a useful design is available.

Despite these drawbacks, the so-called *cutting plane methods* have found favor among many workers because of their generality and the fact that in some cases they greatly reduce the number of analyses necessary to complete the optimization.

## 4.5 A LINEAR PROGRAMMING SOLUTION TO THE DIRECTION-FINDING PROBLEM OF FEASIBLE DIRECTIONS

We now take up briefly the solution of the direction-finding problem stated in Section 4.2 for the methods of feasible directions. Restating the problem, we want to find the vector $\mathbf{S}$ and scalar $\beta$ such that $\beta \to$ max, and

(i) $\mathbf{S}^T \nabla g_j + \theta_j \beta \leq 0, \quad j \in J,$

(ii) $\mathbf{S}^T \nabla F + \beta \leq 0$, and

(iii) some measure of $\mathbf{S}$ is bounded,

[17] See Moses (1964), Chan (1964), Rubenstein and Karagozian (1966), Pope (1968), and Reinschmidt, Cornell, and Brotchie (1966).

[18] See Griffith and Stewart (1961).

[19] See Kelly (1960).

where $J$ is the set of indices of all active constraints at the point from which a usable feasible direction is being sought, and $\nabla g_j$ and $\nabla F$ are evaluated at this point. If $\beta_{max}$ is positive, then the corresponding $S$ vector is a usable feasible direction. With the possible exception of (iii), the constraints as well as the objective function of this subsidiary problem are linear in the variables $s_i$ (the components of $S$) and $\beta$. Note that in the inequality $S^T\nabla F + \beta \leqslant 0$, the larger $\beta$ can be made, the smaller (more negative) $S^T\nabla F$ is made. If $S$ has a fixed or limited length, then the larger $\beta$ can be made, the more nearly aligned with $-\nabla F$ is $S$. Thus the purpose of maximizing on $\beta$ is to get the direction most nearly in line with the steepest descent direction.

The nonnegative constants $\theta_j$ in (i) prevent the vector $S$ from lying exactly in the plane perpendicular to $\nabla g_j$ so as to provide relief, when necessary, for the curvature of the constraints.

Sometimes the terminology used for the $\theta_j$ is *pushoff factors*, since they tend to "push" $S$ away from the constraint. The reason for a length limitation on $S$ is that, without it, $\beta$ can be made large without bound for any vector $\alpha S$ such that $\alpha S^T\nabla F \leqslant 0$.

The simplest form of length restriction on $S$ is to limit each component:

$$|s_i| \leqslant 1, \qquad i = 1, 2, \ldots, n, \tag{4.164}$$

or

$$\begin{aligned} s_i &\leqslant 1, \\ -1 &\leqslant s_i. \end{aligned} \tag{4.165}$$

Another form is the familiar Euclidean norm

$$|S| = \left(\sum_{i=1}^{n} s_i^{\,2}\right)^{1/2} \leqslant 1. \tag{4.166}$$

The former is a set of simple linear constraints while the latter is a quadratic constraint. The single quadratic constraint can be treated with linear programming by a technique described in Zoutendijk (1960), but we will consider here only the simple bounds $|s_j| \leqslant 1$. Though this constraint has a tendency to bias the resulting $S$ vector toward the corners of the hypercube defined by $|s_j| \leqslant 1$,[20] it generally produces good results.

To work with the resulting linear program in the standard form with nonnegativity constraints, we first define new variables related to the old by

$$s'_j = s_j + 1. \tag{4.167}$$

Thus we have

$$\beta \rightarrow \max,$$

[20] The reason for this bias is that the Euclidean length of vectors whose tips lie *on* the hypercube varies from a minimum of 1 at the center of the face to $\sqrt{n}$ at the corners.

$$S'^T\nabla g_j + \theta_j\beta \leqslant \sum_{i=1}^{n} \frac{\partial g_j}{\partial x_i}, \qquad j \in J, \tag{4.168}$$

$$S'^T\nabla F + \beta \leqslant \sum_{i=1}^{n} \frac{\partial F}{\partial x_i}, \tag{4.169}$$

$$s_i' \leqslant 2, \qquad i = 1, \ldots, n, \tag{4.170}$$

$$s_i' \geqslant 0, \qquad i = 1, \ldots, n. \tag{4.171}$$

After adding slacks we have the following linear program: Find $\boldsymbol{Y}$ such that $F = -y_{n+1} \to \min$ subject to

$$\mathbf{A}\boldsymbol{Y} = \boldsymbol{B}, \tag{4.172}$$

$$0 \leqslant y_i, \qquad i = 1, \ldots, t \tag{4.173}$$

where

$$y_i = s_i', \qquad i = 1, \ldots, n, \tag{4.174}$$

$$y_{n+1} = \beta, \tag{4.175}$$

and where $y_i$, $i = n+2, \ldots, t$, are slack variables, $t$ being the number of active constraints plus the number of variables plus 1.

Writing out the matrix $\mathbf{A}$, we have

$$\mathbf{A} = \begin{bmatrix} \partial g_1/\partial x_1 & \partial g\ /\partial x_2 \ldots & \partial g_1/\partial x_n & \theta_1 & 1\ 0 \ldots 0 & 0\ 0 \ldots 0\ 0 \\ \partial g_2/\partial x_1 & \ldots & \partial g_2/\partial x_n & \theta_2 & 0\ 1 \ldots 0 & 0\ 0 \ldots 0\ 0 \\ \cdot & \cdot & \cdot & \cdot & \cdot\ \cdot & \cdot\ \cdot\ \cdot & \cdot\ \cdot \\ \cdot & \cdot & \cdot & \cdot & \cdot\ \cdot & \cdot\ \cdot\ \cdot & \cdot\ \cdot \\ \cdot & \cdot & \cdot & \cdot & \cdot\ \cdot & \cdot\ \cdot\ \cdot & \cdot\ \cdot \\ \partial g_r/\partial x_1 & \ldots & \partial g_r/\partial x_n & \theta_r & 0\ 0 \ldots 1 & 0\ 0 \ldots 0\ 0 \\ \partial F/\partial x_1 & \ldots & \partial F/\partial x_n & 1 & 0\ 0 \ldots 0 & 1\ 0 \ldots 0\ 0 \\ 1 & 0 \ldots & 0 & 0 & 0\ 0 \ldots 0 & 0\ 1 \ldots 0\ 0 \\ 0 & 1 \ldots & 0 & 0 & 0\ 0 \ldots 0 & 0\ 0 \ldots 0\ 0 \\ \cdot & \cdot & \cdot & \cdot & \cdot\ \cdot & \cdot\ \cdot\ \cdot & \cdot\ \cdot \\ \cdot & \cdot & \cdot & \cdot & \cdot\ \cdot & \cdot\ \cdot\ \cdot & \cdot\ \cdot \\ \cdot & \cdot & \cdot & \cdot & \cdot\ \cdot & \cdot\ \cdot\ \cdot & \cdot\ \cdot \\ 0 & 0 \ldots & 1 & 0 & 0\ 0 \ldots 0 & 0\ 0 \ldots 0\ 1 \end{bmatrix} \tag{4.176}$$

and

$$\boldsymbol{B} = \left(\sum_i \frac{\partial g_1}{\partial x_i}, \sum_i \frac{\partial g_2}{\partial x_i}, \ldots, \sum_i \frac{\partial F}{\partial x_i}, 2, 2, \ldots, 2\right). \tag{4.177}$$

With the problem thus in standard form, the simplex method can be applied.

Note that for those variables where $\Sigma_i \, \partial g_j/\partial x_i \geqslant 0$, the slack variables can be used as a canonical basis, and where $\Sigma_i \, \partial g_j/\partial x_i < 0$, artificials must be added for Phase I.

There are more sophisticated approaches to this particular type of linear program,[21] but the brute force approach outlined above is in general sufficiently effective.

**The Kuhn-Tucker Conditions and Convergence**

We have noted that if $\beta_{\max} > 0$, then the corresponding vector $\boldsymbol{S}$ is a usable feasible direction; we will now show that if the Kuhn-Tucker conditions are satisfied, then $\beta_{\max} = 0$. The Kuhn-Tucker conditions for a local minimum are

$$\begin{aligned} &\text{(i)} \quad \nabla F + \sum_{j=1}^{r} \lambda_j \nabla g_j = 0, \\ &\text{(ii)} \quad \lambda_j > 0, \qquad j = 1, \ldots, r. \end{aligned} \tag{4.178}$$

We can show that if (i) and (ii) hold, then the inequalities

$$\begin{aligned} &\text{(iii)} \quad \boldsymbol{S}^T \nabla F < 0, \\ &\text{(iv)} \quad \boldsymbol{S}^T \nabla g_j < 0, \qquad j = 1, \ldots, r, \end{aligned} \tag{4.179}$$

cannot all simultaneously hold for any $\boldsymbol{S}$. To see this, note that (i) implies $\nabla F = -\Sigma \, \lambda_j \nabla g_j$, which if substituted into (iii) yields

$$-\sum_{j=1}^{r} \lambda_j \boldsymbol{S}^T \nabla g_j < 0 \,. \tag{4.180}$$

This cannot be true if all $\lambda_j > 0$ and if $\boldsymbol{S}^T \nabla g_j < 0$, as in (iv). Therefore, if the Kuhn-Tucker conditions are satisfied, there is no $\boldsymbol{S}$ satisfying (iii) and (iv).

The direction-finding problem always has the trivial solution $\boldsymbol{S} = \boldsymbol{0}$, $\beta = 0$, which produces

$$\boldsymbol{S}^T \nabla g_j + \theta_j \beta = 0 \,, \tag{4.181}$$

$$\boldsymbol{S}^T \nabla F + \beta = 0 \,. \tag{4.182}$$

Therefore, $\beta_{\max}$ always has a maximum of at least zero (i.e., a $\beta$ can always be found which is nonnegative). Thus if $\beta_{\max} = 0$, the Kuhn-Tucker conditions are satisfied.

As the optimum of the original optimization problem is approached, the value of $\beta_{\max}$ will diminish (though not necessarily monotonically) from some positive value toward zero. Theoretically, when the optimum (or some relative

---

[21] In particular, a linear program with constraints of the form $0 \leqslant x_i \leqslant b_i$ can be solved without bringing the bounds into the basis. Doing so reduces the computational effort considerably. See Hadley (1962) for details.

minimum in a general problem) is reached, $\beta_{max} = 0$. We will practically never get an exact zero, so we must decide how small to insist that $\beta_{max}$ be before we declare that the Kuhn-Tucker conditions are satisfied. The size of $\beta_{max}$ is related to the choice of the $\theta_j$ and the lengths of $\nabla F$ and $\nabla g_j$. It is useful to start off with a clean slate, so to speak, by normalizing $\nabla g_j$ and $\nabla F$ and assigning the $\theta_j$ to be 1. That is, by using $\boldsymbol{E}_j \equiv \nabla g_j / |\nabla g_j|$ and $\boldsymbol{P} \equiv \nabla F / |\nabla F|$ instead of the original vectors, and taking $\theta_j$ as 1, $\beta_{max}$ can be interpreted approximately as

$$\beta_{max} \simeq \cos \angle(\boldsymbol{S}, -\nabla F)\,. \tag{4.183}$$

The relation is only approximate because $|\boldsymbol{S}| \neq 1$ for the normalization chosen here. With this technique it is not uncommon to have $\beta_{max}$ numerically approach $10^{-6}$ or $10^{-8}$ when the optimum is reached. On the other hand, there is invariably some numerical error, certainly roundoff error and sometimes an approximation error, in computing $\nabla g_j$ and $\nabla F$. This can cause a situation where $\beta_{max}$ may be small but not vanishingly so (say 0.01 or 0.001), and yet no move can be made from the point in question; in other words, the vectors are not quite normal to their respective surfaces and hence cannot give an exact representation of the Kuhn-Tucker conditions. It is here that judgment must come into play to determine the most appropriate cut-off point in the process.

It is tempting to use the diminishing-return type of termination criterion for this method. In other words, when in the feasible-direction method the rate of reduction of the objective function diminishes from cycle to cycle, the diminished return is taken as a signal to terminate. While this may be useful as a conditional criterion, we must use it with care, since the method of feasible directions often works in fits and starts: it slows down while zigzagging, and then, when a group of simultaneously active constraints are gathered up, a large step is taken. Though the logic may become complicated, a practical scheme is one in which we use a combination of diminishing returns and a judicious choice of $\epsilon$ in $\beta_{max} < \epsilon$.

The multipliers $\theta_j$ were originally proposed[22] as a means of differentiating among the constraints with regard to their curvature. Figure 4.26(a) depicts a constraint with considerable curvature and Fig. 4.26(b) a constraint with little curvature. Given the same $\theta_j$, the usable feasible direction from $P$ (or $P'$) would be the same for both problems, although different directions are needed in each. In Fig. 4.26(a) a vector too nearly tangent to the constraint will immediately strike the same constraint again, whereas such a vector in Fig. 4.26(b) would be ideal. We can exercise some control over this aspect of the method of feasible directions by adjusting $\theta_j$: a large $\theta_j$ forces the usable feasible direction away from the constraint, and small $\theta_j$ allows the vector to

[22] Zoutendijk (1960).

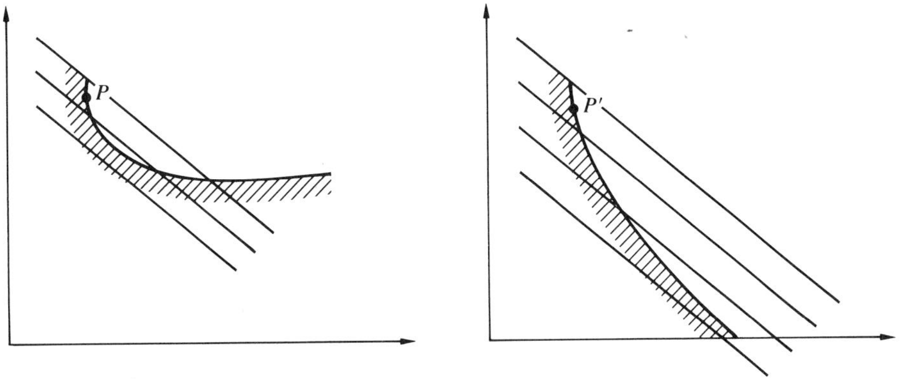


(a) (b)

**Figure 4.26**

approach tangency. (Indeed, the values of $\theta_j$ should be zero for all linear constraints in a mixed problem.) While the idea is appealing, it turns out to be difficult to incorporate the logical apparatus for the technique in a program. In general, we cannot pick reasoned values of the $\theta_j$ *a priori* (except for linear constraints) and must usually evolve them by taking account of the times a constraint just left is reencountered. For the constraints for which this happens frequently, the $\theta_j$ are increased.

While this sounds straightforward, consider the case in which the problem has only one active constraint; then the technique would escalate $\theta_j$ at each encounter, to the point where we could hardly find any direction of descent. Therefore, unless the problem has special characteristics, it is usually best to use a system of constant $\theta_j$ with the value of $+1$.

## EXERCISES

**4.1** Consider Example E.1 with the objective function and constraints given by Eqs. (3.26) to (3.28). Check the Kuhn-Tucker conditions at (a) $d = 3.30$, $H = 10.0$, and (b) $d = 1.88$, $H = 20.2$. Now assume that the yield stress of the material is $\sigma_y = 60{,}000$ psi and compute the Kuhn-Tucker conditions at (c) $d = 2.48$, $H = 30.0$, and (d) $d = 2.13$, $H = 43.8$.

**4.2** Given the following problem: Find $X = (x_1, x_2, x_3)$ such that $F(X) = x_1^2 + x_2^2 + x_3^2 \rightarrow \min$ and

$$\begin{aligned} 5 - x_1 - x_2 - x_3 &\leqslant 0\,, \\ 2 - x_2 x_3 &\leqslant 0\,, \\ -x_1 &\leqslant 0\,, \\ -x_2 &\leqslant 0\,, \\ 2 - x_3 &\leqslant 0\,. \end{aligned}$$

Check the Kuhn-Tucker conditions at (a) (2,1,2), (b) $(\frac{4}{3},\frac{2}{3},3)$, and (c) $(\frac{3}{2},\frac{3}{2},2)$. [*Answers*: (a) $\lambda_1 = 4, \lambda_2 = -1, \lambda_5 = 1$; (b) no $\lambda$'s exist; (c) $\lambda_1 = 3, \lambda_5 = 1$.]

**4.3** Apply the formalism of Eqs. (4.37) and (4.39) to the solution of Exercise 4.2.

**4.4** Verify the computation of $X_{q+1}$ in the last column of Table 4.1.

**4.5** Given a point in the 2-dimensional space $X = (x_1, x_2)$ with one constraint active and

$$\nabla g = (-1, -1)\,, \qquad \nabla F = (-\tfrac{1}{2}, 1)\,,$$

use the method of Section 4.5 to find a usable feasible direction.

**4.6** Graphically apply the gradient projection method to the problem in Exercise 1.2. Pick a nonoptimal feasible starting point and draw the steps that the gradient projection method would take. Follow these steps on a plot of the $(d,H)$ space.

**4.7** Given the system of equations

$$\begin{aligned} x_1 + 2x_2 + \ \ 8x_3 + \ \ x_4 &= 11\,, \\ 2x_1 + 5x_2 + 18x_3 + 2x_4 &= 26\,, \\ x_1 + 2x_2 + 11x_3 + 2x_4 &= 13\,, \end{aligned}$$

(a) pivot to the canonical form where $x_1$, $x_2$, and $x_4$ are basic. Is the solution feasible? (b) Pivot to the adjacent feasible solution. [*Answers*: (a) $x_1 = 1$, $x_2 = 4$, $x_3 = 0$, and $x_4 = 2$; (b) $x_1 = \frac{1}{3}, x_2 = \frac{8}{3}, x_3 = \frac{2}{3}$, and $x_4 = 0$.]

**4.8** Given the linear programming problem

$$\begin{aligned} F &= 5x_1 + x_2\,, \\ 2x_1 + x_2 &\geq 2\,, \\ -x_1 + x_2 &\leq 1\,, \\ x_1 + 2x_2 &\geq 2\,, \\ x_1, x_2 &\geq 0\,. \end{aligned}$$

a) Sketch the constraints and contours of the objective function and then inspect the optimum point. Follow the succeeding steps on this sketch.
b) Add slack variables to the constraints to convert the problem to standard form, and then, for those slacks that cannot be part of a basic feasible solution, add artificial variables in preparation for Phase I. [*Check*: This should bring the variables to 7 in number.]
c) Append the artificial objective function and clear it. [*Check*: It should be equal to 4.] Then minimize the artificials, bringing in $x_1$ on the first pivot. [*Check*: The optimum for the artificials is $x_1 = \frac{2}{3}, x_2 = \frac{2}{3}, x_3 = 0, x_4 = 1, x_5 = x_6 = x_7 = 0$.]
d) Append the original objective function and clear it [*Check*: Its value is 4 at this point.] Then minimize the objective function. [*Check*: The optimum is at $x_1 = \frac{1}{3}$, $x_2 = \frac{4}{3}, x_3 = x_4 = 0, x_5 = 1, F = 3$.]

**4.9** Solve Problem E.1 by the sequence of linear programs method. Use the starting point 3.0, 25.0 and perform a linearization, solve the resulting linear program, and then relinearize and solve the new linear program consisting of both constraint linearizations and the latest objective function linearization. Sketch the successive linearizations.

## REFERENCES

Chan, H. S. Y., "Optimum Structural Design and Linear Programming," Rep. 175, The College of Aeronautics, England (1964)

Dantzig, G., *Linear Programming and Extensions*, Princeton Univ. Press, Princeton, N. J. (1963)

Dorn, W. S., and H. J. Greenberg, "Linear Programming and Plastic Limit Analysis of Structures, *Quart. Appl. Math.* **15** (2), 155–167 (1957)

Gellatly, R. A., R. H. Gallagher, and W. A. Luberacki, "Development of a Procedure for Automated Synthesis of Minimum Weight Structures," AFFDL-TR-66-180 (December 1960)

Griffith, R. E., and R. A. Stewart, "A Nonlinear Programming Technique for the Optimization of Continuous Processing Systems," *Man. Sci.* **7**, 379–392 (1961)

Hadley, G., *Linear Programming*, Addison-Wesley, Reading, Mass. (1962)

Hadley, G., *Nonlinear and Dynamic Programming*, Addison-Wesley, Reading, Mass. (1964)

Kelly, J. E., "The Cutting-Plane Method for Solving Convex Programs," *J. Soc. Indus. Appl. Math.* **8**, 703–712 (1960)

Moses, F., "Optimum Design Using Linear Programming," *J. Struct. Div., ASCE* **92** (ST6), 89–104 (1964)

Pope, G. G., "The Design of Optimum Structures of Specified Basic Configuration, *Intern. J. Mech. Sci.*, **10** (4), 251–263 (1968)

Reinschmidt, K. F., C. A. Cornell, and J. F. Brotchie, "Iterative Design and Structural Optimization," *Proc. ASCE* **92** (ST6), 281–318 (1966)

Rosen, J. B., "The Gradient Projection Method for Nonlinear Programming, Part I," *J. Soc. Indus. Appl. Math.* **8**, 181–217 (1960)

Rosen, J. B., "The Gradient Projection Method for Nonlinear Programming, Part II, Nonlinear Constraints," *J. Soc. Indus. Appl. Math.* **9**, 414–432 (1961)

Rubinstein, M. F., and J. Karagozian, "Building Design Using Linear Programming," *J. Struct. Div., ASCE* **92** (ST6), 223–245 (1966)

Zoutendijk, G., *Methods of Feasible Directions*, Elsevier, Amsterdam (1960)

CHAPTER 5

# SPECIAL TECHNIQUES AND APPLICATIONS

In previous chapters, we discussed a variety of methods for solving optimization problems. Occasionally we touched on applications and special techniques which are valuable in utilizing the methods in particular engineering design problems. The present chapter is a potpourri of more such tricks and brief discussions of certain applications.

The list of special methods is almost endless and no attempt is made in this chapter to give a complete presentation of such techniques. An extensive bibliography on optimization methods is given in Lavi and Vogl (1966). A survey article by Sheu and Prager (1968) contains an extensive list of references on applications to structural design (both civil and aerospace). There are, no doubt, similar articles related to many other engineering fields.

One of the most important factors in optimization of engineering designs is, as we have frequently mentioned, the necessity of performing an analysis of each proposed design. We say we are doing an "analysis" when we calculate the value of the constraint functions $g_j(X)$ and the objective function $F(X)$. In some cases these may be very simple calculations requiring little computational effort. In other cases, however, they may be extremely arduous calculations. We will examine, in specific but representative problems, the ramifications of difficult analyses and ways of simplifying them, speeding them up, or approximating them. We will also discuss ways of calculating the derivatives of behavior quantities with respect to the design variables in the presence of a difficult analysis. Aside from this central theme, we will discuss a number of other practical considerations.

Section 5.1 explores the idea that there may be special directions of redesign in the design space which are oriented so that a complicated reanalysis becomes simple. The next section contains examples of rapid analysis and reanalysis methods that are of particular interest when embedded in an automated optimum design procedure. Section 5.3 deals with approximate analysis methods and the relationships among the degree of approximation, the way in which the approximation is done, and the method of optimization. Section 5.4 deals with the vital question of obtaining partial derivatives of the constraint functions with respect to the design variables. It is often not as difficult to compute these partial derivatives as it appears at first sight. The section also gives some useful formulas for partial derivatives of stresses, displacements, frequencies, etc. Section 5.5 deals briefly with the problem of the discrete valued variable. The final section, Section 5.6, deals with the overall question of picking a method. We attempt to take into account most of the important considerations in selecting a method, such as: the calendar time and man hours required to write the program, the running time of the resulting program, its applicability to other problems, and its reliability in finding an optimum design unassisted.

## 5.1 SPECIAL REDESIGN DIRECTIONS FOR SIMPLIFIED ANALYSES

The ideas discussed in this section are simple and warrant discussion mainly to alert the reader to the possibilities of such techniques. The basic idea is that there are directions or design modification vectors that can be applied to a current design and along which the reanalysis of the design is either trivial or at least greatly simplified compared to the computational effort required for a general design modification.

The simplest example of this type is probably dimensional scaling of structural designs. Consider a truss structure composed of straight, axial-load carrying members, pin-connected at the joints (as in Example E.3). If we have calculated the stresses in all the members and the deflections of all the joints for a given load condition and if we then change the areas of all the members of the structure by multiplying by a given factor, the stresses and deflections of the structure will change as the reciprocal of this factor. For example, if all the members are doubled in area, then all the stresses and deflections are reduced by half. This principle is often applicable to structural design; usually we can apply a factor to the design variables in such a way that the design need not really be reanalyzed in order to predict the behavior of the new design. By applying such a factor, we might simply scale a structural design downward until the first constraint is encountered, instead of traveling in steepest descent until we encounter a constraint. This, of course, assumes that weight or volume reduction is the objective and that we are using a direct method such as feasible directions.

Once we encounter a constraint in this type of travel, there is no purpose, of course, in using a direction in place of the gradient to the objective function in the direction-finding problem, since the resulting direction will not be one which simplifies the analysis. While the idea is appealing, it is far from a panacea, because most of the moves or redesigns that occur in the optimization process have to be in directions other than these directions. However, the possibility of saving analyses at various points in the problem should not be overlooked.

An example of such a mechanical redesign problem can be found in the 4-bar mechanism design problem (E.2). In this problem the analysis is not particularly difficult, but the numerical integration of the error function may consume a sizable portion of the overall computer time. The reference angles

$\alpha$ and $\beta$ do not change the shape of the output function but merely shift it in either the horizontal or vertical direction (see Fig. 5.1). Thus if the table of values of $\phi$ vs. $\theta$ are stored as they are calculated for particular values of the other design variables, then as $\alpha$ and $\beta$ alone are changed, we can use this same table of values to perform the numerical integration by applying the proper shift. In other words, by merely adding or subtracting an appropriate constant from the ordinate or the abscissa, we obtain the proper values for the integrand. In an attack on a problem similar to this one,[1] the following approach was adopted: Each time any of the links $a$, $b$, or $c$ was changed, $\alpha$ and $\beta$ were adjusted to minimize the total error, and the iterative process was then considered a function only of $a$, $b$, and $c$. This assumption is possible because the minimization of the error over $\alpha$ and $\beta$ is quite simple and requires very little computation, whereas changes in the length of the links entails considerably more computation.

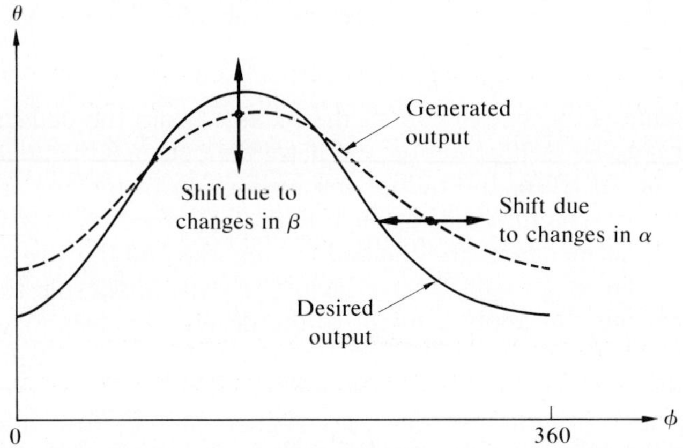


**Figure 5.1**

Thornton and Schmit (1968a) have solved a transient thermoelastic problem in which part of the analysis is either exactly or approximately independent of certain design variables. For a brief introduction to the problem, consider the cross section of an ablative heat shield, as shown in Fig. 5.2. The heat shield forms part of the thermal protection of a reentry vehicle, and the time-dependent thermal input corresponds to the heat load due to atmospheric reentry. The system is subject to a thermal input $q(t)$, and the heat shield unit consists of an ablating layer $a$, a sandwich structural layer $b$, a backwall insulation layer $c$, and the vehicle primary structure. In planform, the ablating panel is assumed to be long compared to its width, and the width is a design variable $x_6$, along with $x_1, \ldots, x_5$. The thermal problem is assumed

[1] See Timko (1966).

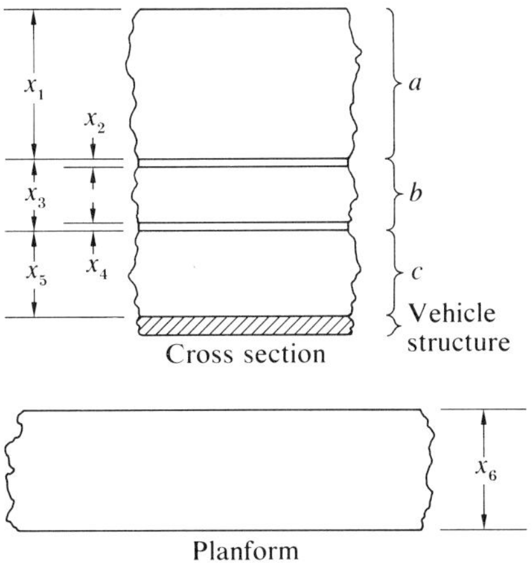


**Figure 5.2**

to be the 1-dimensional transient flow through the panel. The distance $x_6$, as the distance between supports, influences only the stress analysis. To analyze the system, it is necessary: (1) to perform a complete, time-dependent, thermal analysis of the heat shield in order to determine the thermal distribution as a function of time and throughout the layers, and (2) to determine, from the thermal distribution, the stress history throughout the composite heat shield. In actually doing the thermal analysis, we do not need to ascribe any significant thermal thickness to the metallic structural layers of $b$. Therefore, changes in the thickness of the faces of the structural layer have almost no effect on the transient thermal analysis. These design variables do, however, have an effect on the stress analysis, so we can use these facts to avoid recalculating the thermal analysis when changes involve only $x_2$, $x_4$, and $x_6$. The stress analysis is much simpler, since it does not require numerical integration in time, but it does have to be redone when the structural layer is changed. For the reader interested in more details of this particular problem, there is a fairly complete account of the analysis and optimization technique in a report by Thornton and Schmit (1968b).

**Separability**

In some problems, the special directions of redesign that simplify the analysis computation are associated with a fundamental property called *separability*. Suppose it is possible to write the constraints $g_j(X)$ in the form

$$g_j(X) = \sum_{i=1}^{n} G_{ij}(x_i) - b_j \,. \tag{5.1}$$

Then the computation of $g_j$ is simplified if we change only one variable. Such a constraint is said to be separable; if one variable changes, then only one

$G_{ij}(x_i)$ changes. If, in addition, the objective function is separable,

$$F(X) = \sum_{i=1}^{n} f_i(x_i) \,, \tag{5.2}$$

we have a *separable programming problem*. There is a great deal of literature regarding special methods for solving the separable problem.[2] It is a problem that recurs as either an exact or an approximate model of many economic and managerial problems. In these applications, the $G_{ij}(x_i)$ can often be identified as demands on a limited resource $b_j$ caused by performing $x_i$ of a certain activity, and $f_i(x_i)$ is the contribution to the overall objective made by the $x_i$. For example, suppose there is only the one constraint that the total dollars spent on a project must be less than $b$. Suppose further that the $x_i$ are the amount of certain facilities to be devoted to complete the $i$th part of the task and that $G_i(x_i)$ is the cost of using $x_i$ of these facilities [say, $x_i$ men to perform the $i$th job at a cost of $G_i(x_i)$]. (Note that the cost is not necessarily a linear function of the amount used: there may be overtime pay or premium rates for fast service or the cost of renting extra equipment.) Finally, suppose that $f_i(x_i)$ is the length of time it takes to complete the $i$th job using $x_i$ of the facility, and that the objective is to minimize the total time to completion. This is a typical separable programming problem, the type for which many of the special methods in the literature of separable and dynamic programming are suited. Though these methods are not especially difficult, they are beyond the objectives of this text.

## 5.2 SOME EXAMPLES OF RAPID REANALYSIS METHODS

In the context of automated optimization, the methods of analysis of engineering systems can often have different efficacies than they do in conventional applications. In this section we briefly discuss several standard ideas for the solution of simultaneous equation and eigenvalue problems which, while not necessarily the most effective approaches in general, may be especially suited to the design-analysis cycle inherent in optimization methods.

### Matrix Partitioning

Very often, particularly in structural problems, the solution of a matrix equation

$$\mathbf{K}Y = P \tag{5.3}$$

is the major step in the analysis process. In general, the elements of the matrix $\mathbf{K}$ are dependent on the design variables. Often, however, either because of a special direction of design modification or because of the nature of the prob-

[2] For an introduction, see Hadley (1964).

lem itself, relatively few of the elements change when the design is changed. When this is the case, an attractive approach to the solution of Eq. (5.3) is to partition it into two groups of submatrices: those that change and those that do not. Consider the partition:

$$\mathbf{K} = \left[\begin{array}{cccc|cccc} k_{11} & \cdot & \cdot & k_{1r} & k_{1r+1} & \cdot & \cdot & k_{1n} \\ k_{21} & \cdot & \cdot & k_{2r} & k_{2r+1} & \cdot & \cdot & k_{2n} \\ \cdot & & & \cdot & \cdot & & & \cdot \\ \cdot & & & \cdot & \cdot & & & \cdot \\ \cdot & & & \cdot & \cdot & & & \cdot \\ k_{r1} & \cdot & \cdot & k_{rr} & k_{rr+1} & \cdot & \cdot & k_{rn} \\ \hline k_{r+1} & \cdot & \cdot & k_{r+1r} & k_{r+1r+1} & \cdot & \cdot & k_{r+1n} \\ \cdot & & & \cdot & \cdot & & & \cdot \\ \cdot & & & \cdot & \cdot & & & \cdot \\ \cdot & & & \cdot & \cdot & & & \cdot \\ k_{n1} & \cdot & \cdot & k_{nr} & k_{nr+1} & \cdot & \cdot & k_{nn} \end{array}\right], \tag{5.4}$$

or

$$\mathbf{K} \equiv \begin{bmatrix} \mathbf{K}_{11} & \mathbf{K}_{12} \\ \mathbf{K}_{21} & \mathbf{K}_{22} \end{bmatrix}, \tag{5.5}$$

where, for example, the square matrix $\mathbf{K}_{22}$ is unchanging and $\mathbf{K}_{11}$, $\mathbf{K}_{12}$, $\mathbf{K}_{21}$ may vary from design to design. Assume further that $r$ is small compared to $n$. If we partition $\boldsymbol{Y}$ and $\boldsymbol{P}$, we can write Eq. (5.3) as

$$\mathbf{K}_{11}\boldsymbol{Y}_1 + \mathbf{K}_{12}\boldsymbol{Y}_2 = \boldsymbol{P}_1 , \tag{5.6}$$

$$\mathbf{K}_{21}\boldsymbol{Y}_1 + \mathbf{K}_{22}\boldsymbol{Y}_2 = \boldsymbol{P}_2 , \tag{5.7}$$

where $\boldsymbol{P}_1 = (p_1, p_2, \ldots, p_r)$, $\boldsymbol{P}_2 = (p_{r+1}, \ldots, p_n)$, and similarly for $\boldsymbol{Y}_1$ and $\boldsymbol{Y}_2$. From Eq. (5.7) we can write

$$\boldsymbol{Y}_2 = \mathbf{K}_{22}^{-1}[\boldsymbol{P}_2 - \mathbf{K}_{21}\boldsymbol{Y}_1] . \tag{5.8}$$

Substituting this into Eq. (5.6), we obtain

$$[\mathbf{K}_{11} - \mathbf{K}_{12}\mathbf{K}_{21}]\boldsymbol{Y}_1 = \boldsymbol{P}_1 - \mathbf{K}_{12}\mathbf{K}_{22}^{-1}\boldsymbol{P}_2 , \tag{5.9}$$

or, finally,

$$\boldsymbol{Y}_1 = [\mathbf{K}_{11} - \mathbf{K}_{12}\mathbf{K}_{21}]^{-1} [\boldsymbol{P}_1 - \mathbf{K}_{12}\mathbf{K}_{22}^{-1}\boldsymbol{P}_2] . \tag{5.10}$$

Thus once the initial solution, which involves finding $\mathbf{K}_{22}^{-1}$, is done, the largest matrix that we need to invert for the analysis of subsequent designs is the $r \times r$ matrix $[\mathbf{K}_{11} - \mathbf{K}_{12}\mathbf{K}_{21}]$. We assume, of course, that $\mathbf{K}_{22}^{-1}$ has been saved.

When conditions are right, this well-known approach is very effective in reducing the effort required for reanalysis. An example of its use is the design of a complex structure in which only a few of many members are to be changed.

There are a number of other ideas that are similar to the partitioning technique,[3] and many variations are possible.

**Iterative Solution Methods**

Because of the incremental nature of most automated optimum design processes, the analyses of the designs in the sequence often do not vary greatly from design to design. This fact makes the use of iterative analysis methods attractive because the analysis of the previous design is a good starting point for the iterative solution of the current design.

A typical method for the solution of simultaneous linear equations is Jacobi iteration.[4] The basic idea is simple: write the **K**-matrix of the original equations (5.3) as

$$\mathbf{K} \equiv \tilde{\mathbf{K}} + \mathbf{D}, \tag{5.11}$$

where **D** is a matrix which has as its diagonal the diagonal of **K** and which is zero elsewhere, and **K** is the matrix **K** except that its diagonal has been replaced by zeros.

The original equation can be written as

$$[\tilde{\mathbf{K}} + \mathbf{D}]Y = P, \tag{5.12}$$

from which we derive

$$Y = \mathbf{D}^{-1}[P - \tilde{\mathbf{K}}Y], \tag{5.13}$$

where $\mathbf{D}^{-1}$ is simply

$$\mathbf{D}^{-1} = \begin{bmatrix} \frac{1}{k_{11}} & & \bigcirc \\ & \frac{1}{k_{22}} & \\ \bigcirc & & \frac{1}{k_{nn}} \end{bmatrix}. \tag{5.14}$$

The Jacobi iteration is then defined as follows: Given an estimate $Y_q$ of the solution to Eq. (5.3), derive a new estimate as

$$Y_{q+1} = \mathbf{D}^{-1}[P - \tilde{\mathbf{K}}Y_q], \tag{5.15}$$

or simply

$$y_i^{(q+1)} = \frac{1}{k_{ii}}\left(p_i - \sum_{j \neq i} k_{ij} y_j^{(q)}\right), \qquad i = 1, 2, \ldots, n. \tag{5.16}$$

---

[3] See Melosh and Luik (1967 and 1968).

[4] See Isaacson and Keller (1966).

This iteration will always converge if

$$\left(\sum_{\substack{i=1\\i\neq j}}^{n} |k_{ji}|\right) \bigg/ |k_{jj}| < 1, \qquad i = 1, 2, \ldots, n. \tag{5.17}$$

The *rate* of convergence depends on the matrix **K**, but the total computation to convergence depends on both the rate and the nearness of the starting point $Y_0$ to the solution. Thus in an iterative design process, the solution for design $q$ can be used as a starting point for a new trial design $q+1$ in order to conserve computation.

The simple iterative method described here is only one of an extensive family of iterative procedures for linear equations.[5] For linear and nonlinear equations derivable from a minimum (or maximum) principle, some of the minimization methods of Chapter 2 are often very effective. Their usefulness, of course, is greatly enhanced by the use of a close starting point.

For nonlinear equations not derivable from a potential, the Newton-Raphson method is still applicable. If the equations are

$$l_i(X) = 0, \qquad i = 1, 2, \ldots, n, \tag{5.18}$$

then we can define $\mathbf{J}$ as $\mathbf{J} = [\partial l_i / \partial x_j]$, and the regular Newton-Raphson procedure continues as before. Good starting points are also very effective in speeding convergence here; they even assure convergence when a general starting point might lead to divergence.

### Linear Eigenvalue Problems

The solution of the linear eigenvalue problem

$$\mathbf{K}Y = \lambda \mathbf{M}Y \tag{5.19}$$

has been the subject of considerable study.[6] The problem is to determine the scalars $\lambda$ for which there exist $Y$ vectors satisfying the equation and often to find the corresponding $Y$. The sources of such problems are vibration and buckling problems, etc. Depending on the application, we may want to know the values of all of the $\lambda$ and $Y$ combinations, or simply the largest or smallest $\lambda$. In many cases, the computational effort is quite large, often far exceeding that for the solution of an equivalent number of simultaneous equations.

There are many iterative methods for solving this problem, and we mention just two. First, the well-known "power method" for obtaining the largest eigenvalue-eigenvector pair of the so-called *special eigenvalue problem*

$$\mathbf{K}Y = \lambda Y \tag{5.20}$$

[5] See Householder (1953) or Isaacson and Keller (1966).

[6] See Wilkinson (1965) for an extremely readable and complete account of this subject.

consists of an iteration

$$Z_{q+1} = KY_q,$$

$$Y_{q+1} = \frac{1}{z_j^{(q+1)}} Z_{q+1},$$

where $z_j^{(q+1)}$ is the $j$th component of $Z_{q+1}$ and $j$ is arbitrarily selected, usually so that $z_j^{(q+1)} \simeq \max_i [z_i^{(q+1)}]$. Ultimately, $z_j^{(q+1)}$ will converge to the largest $\lambda$ of the system, and $Y_{q+1}$ will be the same as $Y_q$ and thus will be the corresponding eigenvector. The method is quite simple to program and it often works well. On the other hand, convergence is sometimes slow and, though there are techniques for using the method to obtain the intermediate eigensolutions,[7] it is not in general regarded as the most effective means of solving the eigenproblem. Nevertheless, if good starting vectors are available, as from previous analysis of a similar design, it is possible to get convergence quite quickly and the method becomes a usable approach.

When the general eigenvalue problem (Eq. 5.19) arises in physical situations, we can usually convert it to the special form (Eq. 5.20) at reasonable but not negligible computational cost.

Another iterative technique for the general eigenproblem which is particularly attractive in structural vibration problems is the minimization of the Rayleigh quotient.[8] It is based on the idea that if we multiply Eq. (5.19) through by $X^T$ and solve for $\lambda$, we obtain

$$\lambda = R(X) \equiv \frac{X^T \mathbf{K} X}{X^T \mathbf{M} X}, \tag{5.21}$$

where the right-hand side is called the *Rayleigh quotient*. If $\mathbf{K}$ and $\mathbf{M}$ are positive definite, then $R(X)$ is a minimum when $X$ is the eigenvector corresponding to the smallest eigenvalue and a maximum for the largest eigenvalue-eigenvector.[9] A practical algorithm for minimization in this case turns out to be the conjugate gradient method. It is one of those rare, nonquadratic functions for which $\alpha^*$ can be computed exactly (see Exercise 2.6). Furthermore, the method causes extremely rapid convergence, especially when good starting points (approximate eigenvectors) are available. This is true even when the eigenvalues are closely spaced, a property which the power method does not possess. Minimization of the Rayleigh quotient can also be used to find intermediate eigensolutions, and it has special computational and computer storage advantages in finite element models of structural problems.

One of the intriguing and useful features of the method in structural

[7] See, for example, Wilkinson (1965).

[8] See Bradbury and Fletcher (1966) and Fox and Kapoor (1968a) for details of this method.

[9] Wilkinson (1965).

optimization problems in which we must consider vibration is that, as the design is changed, the natural frequencies of the structure (usually the square root of the eigenvalue) may change drastically, but usually the mode shapes change only gradually. Thus the minimization method has available to it, from a previous analysis, a potentially excellent set of starting vectors. All that we usually need to do is sort through the vectors corresponding to various eigenvalues of the previous analysis to find the one that produces the least $R(X)$, and use this as a starting point. Kapoor (1969) used this approach to advantage in the optimization of a structure subjected to a shock loading and under restrictions on the natural frequency and maximum stress and displacement.

## 5.3 APPROXIMATE ANALYSIS METHODS AND OPTIMIZATION

In a sense, all analysis methods used in engineering (or elsewhere for that matter) are approximate, but given a physical system and an engineering "need to know," we can usually distinguish between a so-called exact analysis and an approximate one. For one thing, we would call an analysis approximate if we obtain only an approximate solution to a mathematical model that was a close representation of the true physical situation. We would also deem an analysis approximate if the prime mathematical model is only an approximation to the true physical problem. In this section, we discuss a few of the possible interrelations between analysis accuracy and optimization. The basic theme is that we should avoid wasting computational effort to obtain accurate analyses of designs that are either grossly in violation of constraints or are quite far from having any constraints active; we will try to use approximate methods in these situations. Implicit in this approach, of course, is the concept that approximate methods require less computation than more accurate ones do. Some examples of forms of approximate solutions to accurate mathematical models are the use of coarse finite difference grids in lieu of a more accurate fine mesh, or the use of Euler integration in a dynamics problem instead of a high-order predictor-corrector formula. Another area of possible approximations is in conjunction with the iterative solution methods. Here we have a choice of convergence criterion and, depending on its stringency, we can obtain a "solution" in more or less time with more or less accuracy.

Examples of simpler models are low-order finite element representations of complex structures, stress concentration factors in place of true stress analysis, rigid elements in mechanical systems, and the neglect of shear deformation in the analysis of beams.

### Convergence of the Optimization Method vs. Analysis Accuracy

As the optimum design is evolved, it is common for the design to change from one with few constraints binding to one with relatively more active constraints. Suppose there are two analysis methods available: one a simple, approximate, but overly conservative technique[10] and the other a highly accurate one. If we are applying a direct method, say the method of feasible directions, we could work with the constraints arising from the approximate analysis either until convergence of the optimization or merely until a fair number of constraints becomes active; then we could switch to the accurate analysis for the final phases of the process. This can be done on a selective basis, resorting to the accurate analysis only when the associated constraint is active. The same idea can be used with a penalty function.

On the face of it, this may seem like an ideal solution to the problem with a difficult analysis, but there are flaws which become immediately apparent when one tries to apply the ideas. First, simple *conservative* analyses are often not available and the use of nonconservative approximations raises difficult problems for the optimization method. It means that the design process may wander into the infeasible region and encounter some logical, if not computational, difficulties in getting back into the feasible region. The use of exterior penalty function methods may be attractive in such cases. Second, experience with optimization methods reveals that the majority of computation often occurs in the final stages in which more accurate analysis methods are indicated; thus the computational effort we avoid might be only that relatively small part which occurs at the beginning of the design sequence.

There is some relation between simplifying the analysis by using an approximate one and simplifying the actual form of constraints, as in the linearization approach discussed in Section 4.4. Here we have merely discussed the reduction of the analysis effort, but have had to deal with nonlinear constraints, whereas in Section 4.4, we approximated the problem by a simpler *linear programming problem.*

**Reduced Vector Sets for Linear Problems**

An approximation idea for linear equations which has a special appeal in optimization problems is the use of *reduced bases* for the solution. The idea is similar to the use of a set of assumed modes in the solution of continuous problems.[11] Suppose we again have the problem

$$\mathbf{K}Y = P, \tag{5.22}$$

where $\mathbf{K}$ is a symmetric $n \times n$ matrix and $Y$ and $P$ are $n$-component vectors. If we make the approximating assumption

$$Y \simeq \sum_{j=1}^{r} \gamma_j V_j, \tag{5.23}$$

[10] By "conservative" we mean that an approximate analysis passes as feasible only feasible designs, but it may reject as infeasible some feasible designs. Some simple examples are the use of a maximum stress failure criterion in a situation where the distortion energy criterion is better, or the ignoring of damping in vibration problems.

[11] See Crandall (1956).

where $r < n$, $V_j$ are some "assumed modes" in the form of trial vectors or candidates for the solution of Eq. (5.22), and the $\gamma_j$ are participation factors for these modes, then we can derive a reduced problem by posing the question: What choice of the $\gamma_j$ makes the potential function

$$\phi(Y) = \tfrac{1}{2}Y^T\mathbf{K}Y + Y^TP \tag{5.24}$$

an extremum? Substituting Eq. (5.23) into Eq. (5.24), we have

$$\tilde{\phi}(\gamma) = \tfrac{1}{2}\gamma^T\tilde{\mathbf{K}}\gamma + \gamma^T\tilde{P}, \tag{5.25}$$

where $\tilde{\mathbf{K}}$ is the $r \times r$ matrix whose elements are $V_i^T\mathbf{K}V_j$, and $\tilde{P}$ is the $r$-vector whose components are $V_i^TP$.

The stationary conditions are the $r$ simultaneous equations $\nabla\tilde{\phi} = 0$, or

$$\tilde{\mathbf{K}}\gamma = \tilde{P}, \tag{5.26}$$

which are easier to solve, to the extent that $r$ is smaller than $n$.

The usefulness of this approach depends on our ability to select good trial vectors, and its application in the context of optimization makes this possible. Suppose the design process has been poking around in a particular area of the design space and a number of designs have been analyzed exactly (i.e., we have obtained the exact solution to Eq. 5.22). If we designate these solutions as the $V_j$, then we should be able to obtain a reasonably good approximate solution with relatively few vectors. As an example, suppose we have exact analyses of $X_q$ and $X_{q+1}$ in which $X_{q+1} = X_q + \alpha_q S_q$; then for other designs along $S_q$ between these two, we might approximate

$$Y \simeq \gamma_1 Y_q + \gamma_2 Y_{q+1}. \tag{5.27}$$

Note that if $X = (1-\delta)X_q + \delta X_{q+1}$, then the analyses of designs for $0 \leqslant \delta \leqslant 1$ pass from $\gamma_1 = 1$, $\gamma_2 = 0$, to $\gamma_1 = 0$, $\gamma_2 = 1$, as $\delta$ passes from 0 to 1 (although not necessarily linearly).

In structural applications, the finite element model dictated by the configuration of the structure often has far more degrees of freedom than are necessary to describe accurately the behavior of the structure. The scheme proposed here can help us avoid some of the penalty associated with this situation. A similar situation may exist for the finite difference equations of heat conduction and stress analysis, etc.

**Extrapolation of Solutions**

In the next section we will discuss a few examples in which derivatives of behavior functions with respect to design variables can be computed. We can use these derivatives to approximate solutions of nearby designs. Suppose $d_i$, $i = 1, \ldots, s$, are design variables and $\phi$ is some behavior function (stress, temperature, deflection, etc.) and that we have available the value of $\phi$ at some $D_q$, and that we also have the values of $\partial\phi/\partial d_i$, $i = 1, \ldots, s$ (i.e., $\nabla\phi$). We can then predict an approximate value of $\phi$ at some new design $\boldsymbol{D}_{q+1}$ obtained from the usual formula $\boldsymbol{D}_{q+1} = \boldsymbol{D}_q + \alpha_q \boldsymbol{S}_q$, by

$$\phi_{q+1} \simeq \phi_q + \alpha_q \boldsymbol{S}_q{}^T \nabla \phi_q, \tag{5.28}$$

where $\nabla \phi_q$ is $\nabla \phi$ evaluated at $\mathbf{D}_q$. The justification for this is the Taylor series expansion along $\boldsymbol{S}_q$ about $\alpha = 0$:

$$\phi = \phi_q + \alpha (d\phi/d\alpha)_q + \tfrac{1}{2}\alpha^2 (d^2\phi/d\alpha^2)_q + \cdots, \tag{5.29}$$

where Eq. (5.28) is merely the first two terms of Eq. (5.29) with $(d\phi/d\alpha)_q$ replaced by the equivalent $\boldsymbol{S}_q{}^T(\nabla\phi)_q$. We can apply the approximation to $g(\boldsymbol{D})$, the constraint functions themselves, or to any quantity which enters into the computation of the constraint functions.

For an example of the effectiveness of this means of approximate analysis, see Fox and Kapoor (1968a), where we illustrated the method by analyzing the vibration of a centilever beam and a truss structure.

## 5.4 DERIVATIVES OF RESPONSE QUANTITIES

Throughout the earlier chapters, the optimization methods presented often required the use of derivatives of the constraint function and of the objective function with respect to the design variables. We noted that when these are available, we can often use more efficient optimization methods. In this section, we discuss certain computational aspects of obtaining these quantities. First, we look at a few examples of the exact computation of derivatives in complex situations. These are presented because the particular formulas and procedures have some inherent value and because they may encourage the reader to attempt similar approaches in other problems. Next we look at some approximations to derivatives that we can use in cases where nothing else is available.

### Exact Derivatives of Solutions to Simultaneous Equations

Consider again the matrix problem

$$\mathbf{K}Y = P, \tag{5.30}$$

where $\mathbf{K}$ and possibly $P$ depend on the design variables $d_i$. The solution can be written, for convenience, as $Y = \mathbf{K}^{-1}P$. This $Y$, obtained either by matrix inversion or by other means, usually requires the application of a numerical algorithm, and obtaining $\partial Y/\partial d_i$ explicitly seems quite difficult. It develops, however, that it is surprisingly simple.[12] Taking the derivative of Eq. (5.30), we obtain

$$\mathbf{K}\frac{\partial Y}{\partial d_i} + \frac{\partial \mathbf{K}}{\partial d_i} Y = \frac{\partial P}{\partial d_i}, \tag{5.31}$$

[12] See Fox (1965).

where presumably $\partial\mathbf{K}/\partial d_i$ and $\partial\boldsymbol{P}/\partial d_i$ are known because the dependence of $\mathbf{K}$ and $\boldsymbol{P}$ on $d_i$ are known. Multiplying Eq. (5.31) through by $\mathbf{K}^{-1}$, which we also assume is known from the solution to Eq. (5.30) we have

$$\frac{\partial \boldsymbol{Y}}{\partial d_i} = \mathbf{K}^{-1}\left[\frac{\partial \boldsymbol{P}}{\partial d_i} - \frac{\partial \mathbf{K}}{\partial d_i}\boldsymbol{Y}\right], \tag{5.32}$$

which gives the desired derivative in terms of the known quantities $\partial\boldsymbol{P}/\partial d_i$, $\partial\mathbf{K}/\partial d_i$, $\boldsymbol{Y}$, and $\mathbf{K}^{-1}$. If, for computational reasons, we do not solve Eq. (5.30) by computing $\mathbf{K}^{-1}$ but rather by some other technique that obtains $\boldsymbol{Y}$ directly, then we can use the same technique to solve Eq. (5.31).

If $\boldsymbol{Y}$ is a vector of generalized displacements for a structural problem, then we usually obtain the stresses from a stress displacement relation of the form

$$\boldsymbol{\sigma} = \mathbf{R}\boldsymbol{Y}, \tag{5.33}$$

where $\boldsymbol{\sigma}$ is an $m$-component vector of stress resultants and $\mathbf{R}$ is an $m \times n$ matrix of stress-displacement relations. Obviously, $\partial\boldsymbol{\sigma}/\partial d_i$ is obtained from

$$\frac{\partial \boldsymbol{\sigma}}{\partial d_i} = \mathbf{R}\frac{\partial \boldsymbol{Y}}{\partial d_i}, \tag{5.34}$$

if we assume that the coefficients of $\mathbf{R}$ are independent of $d_i$.

Since the matrix $\mathbf{K}$ is assembled by a computer program in many problems, we may not know the specific dependence of the $k_{lj}$ on the $d_i$, and thus we often cannot calculate the $\partial k_{lj}/\partial d_i$ directly. One possibility is to calculate the quantities approximately by finite difference, as

$$\partial k_{lj}/\partial d_i \simeq (k_{lji} - k_{lj})/\Delta d_i\,, \tag{5.35}$$

where the notation (to be read "$k_{lj}$ evaluated at $d_1, \ldots$")

$$k_{lji} \equiv k_{lj}\,(d_1, \ldots, d_i + \Delta d_i, \ldots, d_r)$$

is introduced. This requires the assembly of a new matrix for the perturbed design but not its inversion; furthermore, this rather crude difference formula will actually be exact when the $k_{ij}$ are linearly dependent on the design variables, i.e., when

$$k_{lj} = \alpha_{lj1}d_1 + \alpha_{lj2}d_2 + \cdots + \alpha_{ljr}d_r. \tag{5.36}$$

In this situation, which is common in structural problems,

$$\partial k_{lj}/\partial d_i \equiv (k_{lji} - k_{ij})/\Delta d_i \equiv \alpha_{lji}, \tag{5.37}$$

and $\partial k_{lj}/\partial d_i$ needs to be evaluated only once, since it does not depend on $\boldsymbol{D}$. In fact, if the matrices $\mathbf{A}_i \equiv [\alpha_{lji}]$ are assembled and stored, the $\mathbf{K}$ matrix for any $\boldsymbol{D}$ can be assembled without using the original matrix assembly program by taking

$$\mathbf{K} = \sum_{i=1}^{S} \mathbf{A}_i d_i. \tag{5.38}$$

Note that if the linear dependence (Eq. 5.36) is known to hold, an efficient alternative to Eq. (5.35) is (to be read "$k_{lj}$ evaluated at 0, 0, . . .")

$$\partial k_{lj}/\partial d_i \equiv k_{lj}(0, 0, \ldots, 0, 1, 0, \ldots, 0), \tag{5.39}$$

where the 1 appears in the $i$th position of $\boldsymbol{D}$.

A similar development is possible when the dependence of the elements of $\mathbf{K}$ is known to be of the form

$$k_{lj} = \sum_{i=1}^{s} \beta_{lji}\, d_{i1}, d_{i2}, d_{i3}, \ldots, d_{iM}, \tag{5.40}$$

where the $d_{iM}$ are the design variables. This situation occurs, for example, in the stiffness matrix for a tubular truss structure in which $M = 2$ and the variables $d_{i1}$ and $d_{i2}$ are the mean diameter $D_i$ and the wall thickness $T_i$ for the $i$th member.[13]

Thus in matrix problems we can get derivatives of the solution for fairly low computational cost, and hence the use of the more advanced methods is feasible for this class of problem.

**Derivatives of Solutions to the Eigenproblem**

When the complete or partial solution to the general eigenproblem

$$\mathbf{K}Y - \lambda \mathbf{M}Y \tag{5.41}$$

is involved in the constraint functions or the objective function, we may need to take derivatives of the eigenvalues $\lambda_i$ with respect to the design variables.[14] We assume that both $\mathbf{K}$ and $\mathbf{M}$ are symmetric matrices. Denoting a particular eigenvalue by $\lambda_i$, its associated eigenvector by $Y_i$, and defining the matrix

$$\mathbf{F}_i = \mathbf{F}_i(\lambda_i, \boldsymbol{D}) \equiv [\mathbf{K} - \lambda_i \mathbf{M}], \tag{5.42}$$

we can write

$$\mathbf{F}_i Y_i = \boldsymbol{0}. \tag{5.43}$$

Premultiplying by $Y_i^T$ gives

$$Y_i^T \mathbf{F}_i Y_i = 0. \tag{5.44}$$

Differentiation with respect to $d_j$ yields

$$\frac{\partial Y_i}{\partial d_j} \mathbf{F}_i Y_i + Y_i^T \frac{\partial \mathbf{F}_i}{\partial d_j} Y_i + Y_i^T \mathbf{F}_i \frac{\partial Y_i}{\partial d_j} = 0. \tag{5.45}$$

The first and third terms of Eq. (5.45) are zero by virtue of Eq. (5.43), and thus

$$Y_i^T \frac{\partial \mathbf{F}_i}{\partial d_j} Y_i = 0. \tag{5.46}$$

---

[13] See Wright (1968) for the application of these ideas to the truss structure in a way that streamlines the computation for this particular problem.

[14] The approach presented here is essentially that shown by Fox and Kapoor (1968b).

Carrying out the differentiation of Eq. (5.42), we obtain

$$\frac{\partial \mathbf{F}_i}{\partial d_j} = \frac{\partial \mathbf{K}}{\partial d_j} - \lambda_i \frac{\partial \mathbf{M}}{\partial d_j} - \frac{\partial \lambda_i}{\partial d_j} \mathbf{M}. \tag{5.47}$$

If we assume that the eigenvectors have been made $\mathbf{M}$-orthonormal:

$$Y_i^T \mathbf{M} Y_i = 1, \tag{5.48}$$

then we get, upon substitution of Eq. (5.47) into Eq. (5.46),

$$Y_i^T \frac{\partial \mathbf{K}}{\partial d_j} Y_i - \lambda_i Y_i^T \frac{\partial \mathbf{M}}{\partial d_j} Y_i - \frac{\partial \lambda_i}{\partial d_j} = 0, \tag{5.49}$$

so that the solution is

$$\frac{\partial \lambda_i}{\partial d_j} = Y_i^T \left[ \frac{\partial \mathbf{K}}{\partial d_j} - \lambda_i \frac{\partial \mathbf{M}}{\partial d_j} \right] Y_i. \tag{5.50}$$

Thus the rate of change of an eigenvalue is given in simple form in terms of known quantities. This form has been used successfully in a number of optimization and other applications.[15]

**Derivatives of the Eigenvector**

As part of the process of finding derivatives of response quantities in some physical systems, we may need to compute the derivatives of the eigenvectors of Eq. (5.41). We will present two formulations for these derivatives, one that requires the inversion of an $n \times n$ matrix and another that requires a complete eigensolution for the exact derivative.

Differentiating and rearranging Eq. (5.43), we obtain

$$\mathbf{F}_i \frac{\partial Y_i}{\partial d_j} = - \frac{\partial \mathbf{F}_i}{\partial d_j} Y_i, \tag{5.51}$$

where $\partial \mathbf{F}_i / \partial d_j$ is given by Eq. (5.47). Also, by differentiating Eq. (5.48) we obtain the scalar equation

$$2 Y_i^T \mathbf{M} \frac{\partial Y_i}{\partial d_j} = - Y_i^T \frac{\partial \mathbf{M}}{\partial d_j} Y_i. \tag{5.52}$$

Note that $\mathbf{F}_i$ is a singular matrix of rank $n-1$ if the system of equations represented by Eq. (5.41) has distinct eigenvalues. Furthermore, it can be shown that Eq. (5.52) is linearly independent of the equations represented by Eq. (5.51). Taking these together, we obtain an overdetermined but consistent system that can be written in partitioned form as

$$\underset{(n+1) \times n}{\left[ \frac{\mathbf{F}_i}{2 Y_i^T \mathbf{M}} \right]} \underset{n \times 1}{\frac{\partial Y_i}{\partial d_j}} = - \underset{(n+1) \times n}{\left[ \frac{\partial \mathbf{F}_i / \partial d_j}{Y_i^T (\partial \mathbf{M} / \partial d_j)} \right]} \underset{n \times 1}{Y_i}. \tag{5.53}$$

[15] See Wittrick (1962), Zarghamee (1968), and Kapoor (1969).

Premultiplying by the transpose of the matrix on the left, we obtain the square system

$$\underset{n \times n}{[\mathbf{F}_i\mathbf{F}_i + 2\mathbf{M}Y_iY_i^T\mathbf{M}]}\underset{n \times 1}{\frac{\partial Y_i}{\partial d_j}} = -\underset{n \times n}{\left[\mathbf{F}_i\frac{\partial \mathbf{F}_i}{\partial d_j} + \mathbf{M}Y_iY_i^T\frac{\partial \mathbf{M}}{\partial d_j}\right]}\underset{n \times 1}{Y_i}, \tag{5.54}$$

where the term in square brackets on the left is now an $n \times n$ nonsingular matrix and we can obtain the desired quantities from the inversion

$$\frac{\partial Y_i}{\partial d_j} = -[\mathbf{F}_i\mathbf{F}_i + 2\mathbf{M}Y_iY_i^T\mathbf{M}]^{-1}\left[\mathbf{F}_i\frac{\partial \mathbf{F}_i}{\partial d_j} + \mathbf{M}Y_iY_i^T\frac{\partial \mathbf{M}}{\partial d_j}\right]Y_i. \tag{5.55}$$

A difficulty which sometimes arises in applying this method is that the inversion of the matrix indicated in Eq. (5.55) may present numerical problems. If the order of magnitude of the elements $2\mathbf{M}Y_iY_i^T\mathbf{M}$ is small or large compared to $\mathbf{F}_i\mathbf{F}_i$, then the resulting matrix, while not theoretically singular, will be uninvertible in the finite digit computation of the computer. The solution is simply to note that Eq. (5.48) can be multiplied by a scalar $\mu$, giving

$$\mu Y_i^T\mathbf{M}Y_i = \mu, \tag{5.56}$$

and thus Eq. (5.55) would be

$$\frac{\partial Y_i}{\partial d_j} = -[\mathbf{F}_i\mathbf{F}_i + 2\mu\mathbf{M}Y_iY_i^T\mathbf{M}]^{-1}\left[\mathbf{F}_i\frac{\partial \mathbf{F}_i}{\partial d_j} + \mu\mathbf{M}Y_iY_i^T\frac{\mathbf{M}}{\partial d_j}\right]Y_i, \tag{5.57}$$

where $\mu$ can be chosen to balance the magnitudes of the two parts of the matrix to be inverted.

The most serious disadvantage of the method is that we may need to solve a large system of equations (or invert a large matrix). A second method will now be presented which avoids this difficulty but which, at least for an exact solution, requires the complete eigensolution.

Since the eigenvectors form a complete set of vectors, any $n$-component vector can be represented as a linear combination of them. In particular, $\partial Y_i/\partial d_j$ can be represented as

$$\partial Y_i/\partial d_j = \sum_{k=1}^{n} a_{ijk}Y_k. \tag{5.58}$$

Substituting Eq. (5.58) into Eq. (5.51), we get

$$\mathbf{F}_i\sum_{k=1}^{n} a_{ijk}Y_k = -\frac{\partial \mathbf{F}_i}{\partial d_j}Y_i. \tag{5.59}$$

Premultiplying both sides by $Y_l^T$, $l \neq i$, gives

$$\sum_{k=1}^{n} a_{ijk}Y_l^T\mathbf{F}_iY_k = -Y_l^T\frac{\partial \mathbf{F}_i}{\partial d_j}Y_i \tag{5.60}$$

or, solving for $a_{ijl}$,

$$a_{ijl} = \frac{Y_l^T \left[ \dfrac{\partial \mathbf{K}}{\partial d_j} - \lambda_i \dfrac{\partial \mathbf{M}}{\partial d_j} \right] Y_i}{(\lambda_i - \lambda_l)}, \qquad i \neq l, \tag{5.61}$$

because the **M**-orthonormal vectors are also **K**-orthogonal. In order to get $a_{iji}$, we substitute Eq. (5.58) into Eq. (5.52), which gives

$$2Y_i^T \mathbf{M} \sum_{k=1}^{m} a_{ijk} Y_k = - Y_i^T \frac{\partial \mathbf{M}}{\partial d_j} Y_i. \tag{5.62}$$

Using the **M**-orthogonality of the eigenvectors, we get

$$a_{iji} = \frac{- Y_i^T \dfrac{\partial \mathbf{M}}{\partial d_j} Y_i}{2}. \tag{5.63}$$

Note that in contrast to Eq. (5.55), the expression of Eq. (5.58) requires that the complete eigensolution be available, although it does not require the inversion of an additional matrix. On the other hand, it is natural to speculate that, as in solving dynamics problems, we should be able to approximate the derivative of an eigenvector in Eq. (5.58) by the partial sum

$$\frac{\partial Y_i}{\partial d_j} \simeq \sum_{k=1}^{r} a_{ijk} Y_k, \tag{5.64}$$

where $r < k$.

This approach, while not completely verified at present, has been used with some success by Kapoor (1969) to solve a structural dynamics optimization problem.

The preceding examples support the contention that exact formulas for derivatives of behavior quantities are attainable in many cases and should be sought whenever they might lead to a more efficient algorithm.

**Approximate Methods for Derivatives**

In the absence of exact or explicit formulas for the needed derivatives, some of the methods using derivatives are still applicable with the use of finite differencing. The basic idea behind these computations is very simple, but their application may require careful attention.

The technique is simply to use the well-known formulas for differencing to represent the derivatives. The simplest of these is the approximation

$$\frac{\partial g_j}{\partial d_k} \simeq \frac{g_j(D^{(k)}) - g_j(D)}{\Delta d_k}, \tag{5.65}$$

where

$$D^{(k)} = (d_1, d_2, \ldots, d_k + \Delta d_k, \ldots, d_n) \tag{5.66}$$

and $\Delta d_k$ is some small change in $d_k$. The so-called *truncation error* of this formula is quite large. Truncation error is the basic inaccuracy of the formula and is so named because it is related to the truncation of the Taylor series upon which the approximation is based. If we expand $g_j$,

$$g_j(\boldsymbol{D}^{(k)}) = g_j(\boldsymbol{D}) + \Delta d_k(\partial g_j/\partial d_k)_D + \tfrac{1}{2}\Delta d_k^2(\partial^2 g_j/\partial d_k^2)_D + \cdots, \tag{5.67}$$

then solving for $\partial g_j/\partial d_k$ we obtain

$$\frac{\partial g_j}{\partial d_k} = \frac{g_j(\boldsymbol{D}^{(k)}) - g_j(\boldsymbol{D})}{\Delta d_k} + \mathcal{O}(\Delta d_k), \tag{5.68}$$

where $\mathcal{O}(\Delta d_k)$ means terms of *order* $\Delta d_k$ and higher. Thus the error in Eq. (5.65) decreases linearly with $\Delta d_k$ for sufficiently small $\Delta d_k$. The principal advantage of the formula is that it accomplishes an approximation to the derivative with respect to each $d_k$ with only one additional computation of $g_j$ beyond that at $\boldsymbol{D}$. If the computation of $g_j$ is lengthy, as we are assuming, then this is an important factor. The difficulty is that it is hard to know what value of $\Delta d_k$ is suitable for getting accurate results, since if it is taken too small, then roundoff error begins to dominate. This is because $g_j(\boldsymbol{D}^{(k)})$ and $g_j(\boldsymbol{D})$ may differ only minutely, say in the seventh place out of eight significant figures.

One way of ascertaining whether the step size is proper is to compute $\partial g_j/\partial d_k$, as in Eq. (5.65), for one value of $\Delta d_k$, recompute it for a smaller value, and then compare the results. If they agree sufficiently, then the approximation is probably sound; otherwise, the values $\Delta d_k$ may be too large or too small and will need adjustment.

Using the finite arithmetic of the computer, it is sometimes impossible to get sufficiently accurate results because the truncation error does not diminish rapidly enough to keep pace with the roundoff error.[16] In such cases we may need to go to the more accurate "central" formula:

$$\frac{\partial g_j}{\partial d_k} \simeq \frac{g_j(\boldsymbol{D}^{(k+)}) - g_j(\boldsymbol{D}^{(k-)})}{2\Delta d_k}, \tag{5.69}$$

where

$$\boldsymbol{D}^{(k+)} \equiv \boldsymbol{D}^{(k)}, \tag{5.70}$$

as defined in Eq. (5.66), and

$$\boldsymbol{D}^{(k-)} \equiv (d_1, \ldots, d_k - \Delta d_k, \ldots, d_n). \tag{5.71}$$

This formula is of order $(\Delta d_k)^2$, as we can see by taking the difference between two Taylor expansions similar to Eq. (5.67), one for $g_j(\boldsymbol{D}^{(k+)})$ and the other for $g_j(\boldsymbol{D}^{(k-)})$. While the formula is much more accurate, it does require, *a priori*, two function evaluations per derivative approximation and may still

[16] For a highly readable discussion of this subject, see Crandall (1956).

need to be repeated to determine a suitable $\Delta d_k$. We must ultimately determine the best approach on a heuristic basis, in the absence of other information.

An interesting and occasionally useful observation is that if $\nabla g_j$ is to be determined, the steps need not be taken in the coordinate directions. Consider a set of independent vectors $\boldsymbol{P}_k$ of sufficiently small magnitude that

$$\frac{dg_j}{d\boldsymbol{P}_k} \simeq \frac{g_j(\boldsymbol{D}+\boldsymbol{P}_k) - g_j(\boldsymbol{D})}{|\boldsymbol{P}_k|}, \qquad k = 1, 2, \ldots, n, \tag{5.72}$$

or some other suitable difference approximation. Then since

$$dg_j/d\boldsymbol{P}_k = \boldsymbol{P}_k{}^T \nabla g_j, \tag{5.73}$$

we have $n$ equations in $n$ unknowns to solve for the components of $\nabla g_j$. Denoting

$$\boldsymbol{G} \equiv (dg_j/d\boldsymbol{P}_1, \ldots, dg_j/d\boldsymbol{P}_n), \tag{5.74}$$

$$\mathbf{P} \equiv [\boldsymbol{P}_1, \boldsymbol{P}_2, \ldots, \boldsymbol{P}_n], \tag{5.75}$$

we have

$$\nabla g_j = \mathbf{P}^{-1}\boldsymbol{G}. \tag{5.76}$$

The procedure thus requires a matrix inversion, in addition to the usual differencing. Its main advantage comes about if there are some directions $\boldsymbol{P}_k$ in which reanalysis of the design is particularly simple. In a structures problem, for example, groups of members may be related so that if they are changed in some proportional way the analysis of the new design is easy to obtain. The ultimate of this is in, for example, a truss problem where if the areas of all members are changed by some factor (i.e., $\boldsymbol{P}_k = \alpha \boldsymbol{D}$), then the new analysis is obtained simply by scaling the old one. Similar situations have been mentioned previously for other types of analysis problems.

Finally we note that when we are minimizing a penalty function and must obtain its derivatives by finite difference, it is much more accurate to difference the $g$ functions and assemble the derivative of the $\phi$ function as

$$\frac{\partial \phi}{\partial d_i} \simeq \frac{\widetilde{\partial F}}{\partial d_i} + r \sum \frac{1}{g_j{}^2} \frac{\widetilde{\partial g_j}}{\partial d_i} \tag{5.77}$$

for the interior penalty function, or as

$$\frac{\partial \phi}{\partial d_i} \simeq \frac{\widetilde{\partial F}}{\partial d_i} + r \sum 2\langle g_j \rangle \frac{\widetilde{\partial g_j}}{\partial d_i} \tag{5.78}$$

for the exterior form. Here $\widetilde{\partial F}/\partial d_i$ and $\widetilde{\partial g_j}/\partial d_i$ denote the approximate values of these quantities.

## 5.5 THE DISCRETE VALUED DESIGN VARIABLE

In many engineering situations, the design variables are available only in discrete sizes. This fact can pose some formidable problems for the optimist, because most of the well-studied methods apply particularly to continuous variables. The fundamental difficulty, of course, is that it is usually impractical, for reasons of computational cost, to check all possible designs for suitability.

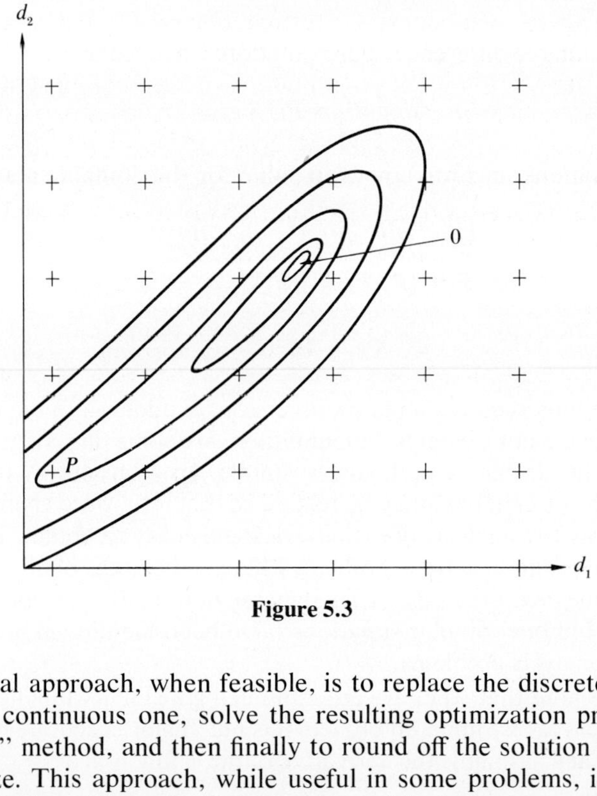


**Figure 5.3**

An initial approach, when feasible, is to replace the discrete valued variable with a continuous one, solve the resulting optimization problem with a "continuous" method, and then finally to round off the solution to the nearest available size. This approach, while useful in some problems, is not without pitfalls. Consider a hypothetical function with contours as shown in Fig. 5.3. The +'s represent available combinations of $d_1$ and $d_2$. The minimum of the continuous problem is at $O$, whereas that of the discrete problem is at $P$. Note that $P$ is not adjacent to $O$ in each variable. Thus the simple process of rounding would not produce the minimum. Furthermore, this example ignores constraints and in some problems we may find it difficult to obtain a feasible design simply by rounding. Finally, the approach may not be applicable in some cases, since there may not even exist a continuous analog of the discrete problem.

Other methods for the discrete problem are combinational in nature and are only applicable to special problem classes.[17] For example, if the problem is linear in all its variables, special methods are applicable for the discrete valued variable.

**An Example of a Continuous Approximation**[18]

A common type of structural element is the wide flange beam. In practical applications, standard rolled sections are used and, of course, these are available only in discrete sizes. To further complicate the problem of size selection, four dimensions are needed to specify the basic cross sections (see Fig. 5.4) and these all vary discontinuously from one standard section to another. Assuming that the objective is to design the structure for a minimum amount of material, we would ordinarily use the so-called economy sections, which have the "maximum" section modulus for least weight.[19] Denoting the in-plane moment of inertia of the section as $I$ and the depth as $2y$, we define the section modulus as

$$S \equiv \frac{I}{y}. \tag{5.79}$$

This expression roughly characterizes the load-carrying capacity of a beam.

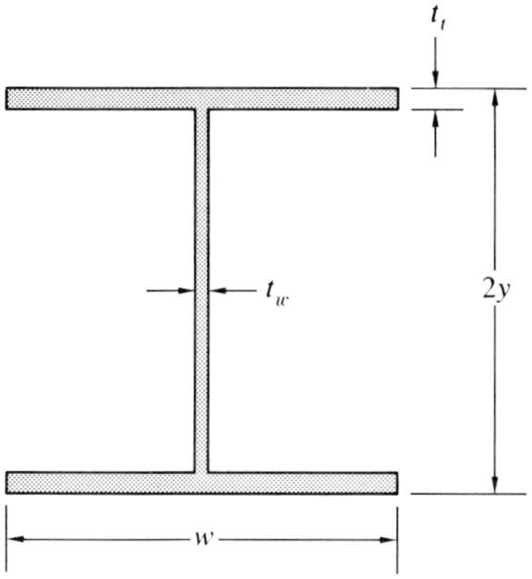


Figure 5.4

[17] See Bellman (1957), Nemhauser (1966), Dantzig (1963), Gomory (1962), or Balinski (1965).

[18] See Brown and Ang (1966) for a complete discussion of the work from which this example is taken.

[19] See *Manual of Steel Construction* (1964).

In order to analyze the displacements and stresses of a general indeterminant frame structure, it is a fundamental necessity that we know the moments of inertia, the areas, and the section moduli. There is some latitude in the choice of independent properties; for example, we can calculate the moment of inertia from the area and the radius of gyration, etc. For framed structures, the basic property of a member is usually its bending stiffness, which is directly proportional to the moment of inertia. In an attack on the problem of the minimum weight design of structures, Brown and Ang (1966) chose $I$ as the independent design variable for members of the structure. They established "empirical" relations for section modulus, weight per foot, and in-plane radius of gyration as functions of $I$. Figure 5.5 plots the section modulus of standard sections versus $I$ and also a piecewise smooth curve fitted through the discrete data. Figures 5.6 and 5.7 are similar plots for weight and radius of gyration. It is probably not mere happenstance that the points lie on such well-defined curves. The designers of the AISC sections probably did not seek

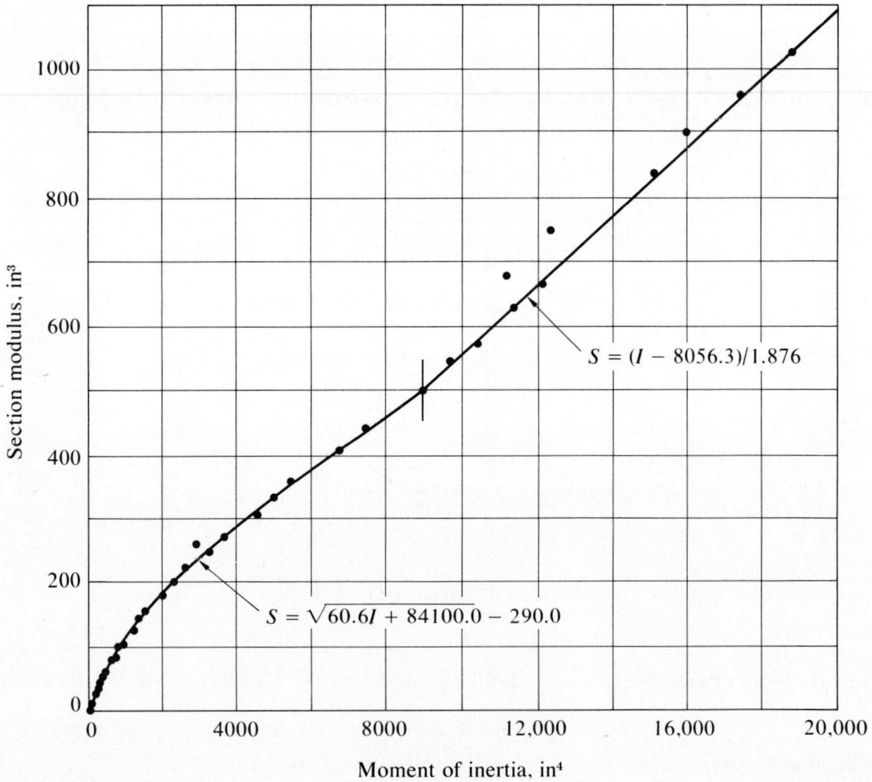


**Figure 5.5**

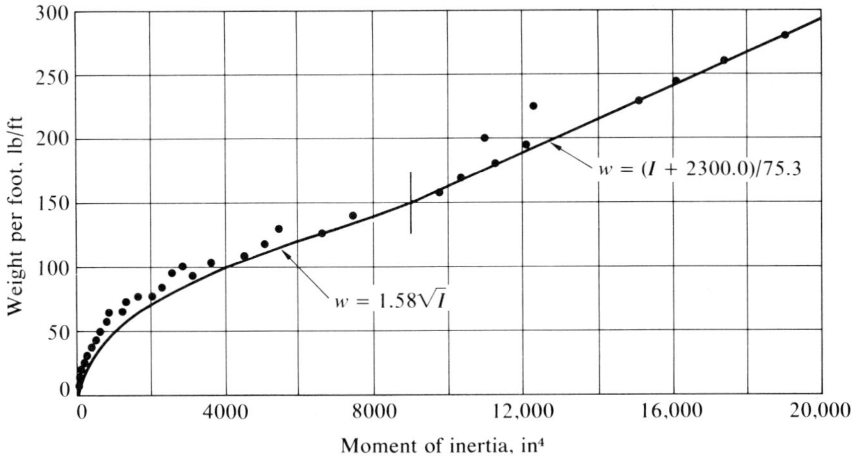


**Figure 5.6**

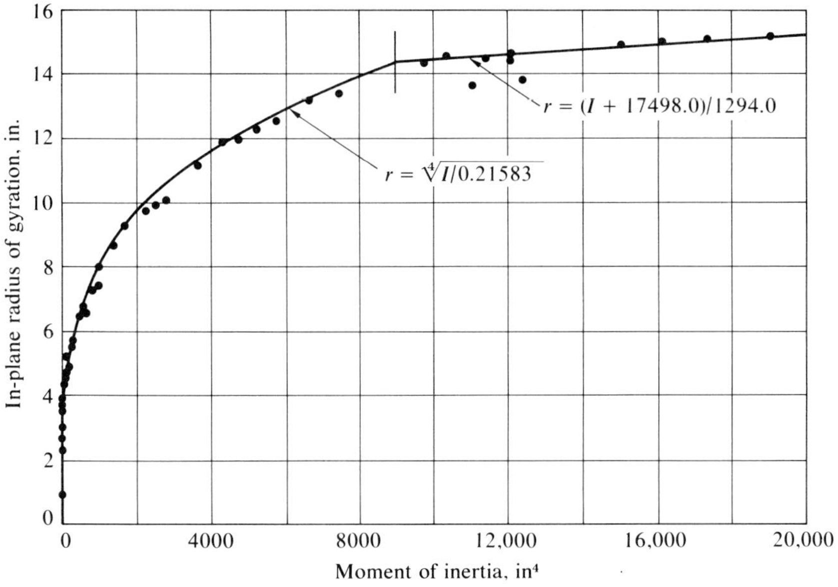


**Figure 5.7**

this continuity; rather, the physical problem of designing least-weight sections for a given moment of inertia in itself produced a sort of smoothness.

Using the fitted curves, we can apply a continuous optimization method (Brown and Ang used gradient projection) and then round off the "continuous solution" to an "available solution." There are various possibilities for the latter step. For example, Brown and Ang recommended that the next lighter available size for each member be chosen in turn until no further members can be changed without violating a constraint. Evidently, the reason the members can be reduced in size is that the fitted curves are somewhat conservative through most of their range.

This example is typical of many in structural design, although similar situations occur in machine design. Consider the picking of gear ratios in power transmission applications. Between the diametrical pitch and the tooth numbers, the speed ratios are available only in discrete values. We can probably pick various criteria so that for each of a discrete set of ratios the gear can be completely designed. Properties of these gear sets can then be plotted and reasonable curves fitted to this empirical data.

## 5.6 CONSIDERATIONS IN PICKING AN APPROACH AND SOME FINAL COMMENTS

When conditions warrant the inclusion of optimization as a step in the design process, a decision regarding the choice of a method must be faced. There are a number of factors which enter into this decision and it may be well to list some of them. We are specifically considering the development and use of the necessary computer program for the method selected:

1. The man-hours and other costs necessary to develop the program.
2. The calendar time necessary to develop the program.
3. The subsequent running-time costs to solve the desired optimization problems.
4. The expected reliability of the program in finding the desired solution.
5. The flexibility of the program: whether it can be used in different ways on the same general problem.
6. The generality of the program or parts of it: whether it can be used to solve other problems.
7. The ease with which the program can be used and its output interpreted.

Taking each of these briefly, we first note that the amount of funds to be allocated to the development of optimization programs (item 1), as with all such economic considerations, depends on the expected return. If it is only marginally important to improve designs with respect to the objective function selected, then only modest expenditure is justified in the development and application of the computer programs. The development part of these costs may be somewhat offset by the generality of the program (item 6) if it can solve whole classes of problems or even serve as part of a general library of optimization programs. In fact, many organizations have developed optimization programs only to find that their chief, and not inconsiderable, benefit is that they save man-hours on subsequent designs and shorten design calendar time.

In general, the unconstrained formulations are the easiest to program and debug. This is particularly true if a minimization algorithm is available in preprogrammed form. Except for the need to have a feasible starting point, the interior penalty functions are the least complicated. Other penalty function methods follow closely in this respect. Even if the minimization algorithm has to be programmed for the application, the penalty function methods are usually best from the point of view of programming cost.

Regarding item 2, there is very little difference between the development time requirements of the methods and their development costs. The small differences that do occur are primarily due to the fact that some methods can be broken down into more or less independent segments, so that several individuals can work on the segments simultaneously.

The running-time cost of optimization programs (item 3) has received a major share of the attention given to these techniques. In an abstract way, this is indeed the central question because, as we mentioned earlier, all optimization problems can be solved by analyzing all possible designs and choosing the best. What we seek in developing an optimization program is a practical alternative to the exhaustive search approach. However, most of the methods we have discussed, save the most primitive, are such enormous improvements over analyzing all possible designs that the point is somewhat academic. The preoccupation with efficiency appears equally academic to many of the people involved in the practical applications of optimization, since any program that solves the problem is usually sufficient, irrespective of running efficiency.

Nevertheless, efficiency is important in many cases. For design problems with explicit analyses [i.e., formulas for $g_j(X)$] and a moderate number of variables, the penalty function methods seem best. Of these, the interior penalty function is usually the most effective. It is particularly useful if an approximate analysis is being used. Of course, for linear problems the simplex method is without equal, and for problems with linear constraints and a nonlinear objective function, the gradient projection method is best.

For problems with difficult analyses, much depends on whether the derivatives of $g_j$ can be easily calculated; if they can, then some feasible direction method is probably the most efficient. If the only access to derivatives is complete finite difference, then perhaps penalty functions used with nongradient or finite difference minimizers are the best hope. (See Section 2.12 for a discussion of the relative merits of unconstrained minimizers.) For extremely difficult analyses in the form of solutions to nonlinear equations $l_j(W) = 0$, the last unconstrained formulation discussed in Section 3.7 seems the most promising. We should always try to reduce the difficulty of the analysis by some approximation technique in the early stages of any optimization process.

The reliability of an optimization program (item 4) is difficult to assess in advance because so much depends on the application. Reliability, in the present context, is rather loosely defined as the ability of a program to find global optimum design, or, should there be relative minima, to find at least one local optimum or, failing these, to at least significantly improve the design. Included in this concept of program reliability would be some assurance that when the program terminates there would be enough information to ascertain the nature of the termination point. For the general nonlinear programming problem, the interior penalty function appears to be the most reliable unconstrained method, because it provides numerous checks against false convergence and because the sequence of designs is feasible. The method of feasible directions with an optimum solution to the direction-finding problem seems to be the most reliable of the direct methods.

There exists no protection against convergence to suboptimal relative minima in the general problem. All the methods which we have discussed seek a local minimum, and there are no apparent methods of modifying the iteration to force convergence to the best minimum. In engineering problems, relative minima often correspond to different design subtypes of the main design type. In mechanical design, for example, each of the "cognate" linkages of the 4-bar mechanism produces the same coupler curve but, in the conceptual sense, they are distinctly different arrangements.[20] Another example, in structures, is the existence of several designs that transmit the load to the supports by distinctly different paths and that are locally optimal. In the structural sense, such designs constitute different design concepts.

Flexibility of an optimum design program (item 5), is of course a desirable feature. By flexibility (as distinguished from generality), we mean the program's capacity to be used in a variety of ways on a particular problem or modifications of a problem. Often this kind of flexibility is of central importance in new technological areas where behavior and performance characteristics are subject to considerable uncertainty. It is also important in an area with changing or uncertain product demands. When flexibility is important, the penalty function methods with nongradient minimizers generally excel because we can easily add or delete constraints, modify the objective function or constraints, and interchange the roles of various parts of the problem. This sort of manipulation is more difficult with the direct methods or gradient minimized penalty functions and, of course, any method based on special properties of the problem (simplex, gradient projection, etc.) restricts the range of changes that can be made in it.

Generality of a program (item 6) means the degree to which it or its subparts can be used for other problems. Here a great deal depends on the way a program is coded, because subroutines (FORTRAN) or procedures (ALGOL) that are properly constructed and documented can be used repeatedly for assembling optimization programs. One example is the packaging into a subroutine (or procedure) the code that solves the direction-finding problem

---

[20] See Hall (1961).

in the method of feasible directions; other examples are subroutines for the simplex method, gradient projection, 1-dimensional minimization methods, and the various multidimensional minimizers. We should always try to code programs so that some of the parts are reusable. This, of course, increases cost and effort. In fact, as much time may be spent in preparing a program for general use and documenting, on the average, as in doing the original development for a special application.

The ease or difficulty of using a program (item 7) consists of two parts: (1) the effort necessary to determine and feed in the required starting data, and (2) the effort required to interpret the final output. Of course, both depend on the actual computer program. There are, however, some irreducible factors; the interior penalty function method needs a feasible starting point, an initial value for $r$, and a convergence criterion; the method of feasible directions requires a feasible starting point, a constraint tolerance, and a number of other parameters. All methods have certain minimum initial data requirements.

If finding a feasible starting point is extremely difficult, then it may be wise to choose a different method. An alternative is to use an initialization technique to get a feasible point (see Section 3.5), but this process complicates the program and may cause large increases in running time.

The peripheral advantages of computerized design may sometimes overshadow the optimization aspect. In these cases, the computer can turn out in a few minutes or perhaps hours a reasonable design, completely checked against specifications and requirements, and even dimensionally detailed, whereas the traditional approach might require many tedious man-hours and weeks or months of delay. It is not reasonable to argue the use of optimization technology if "computerization" is the real objective unless optimization is a practical approach to attaining a feasible design. In such cases the penalty function methods are particularly useful.

### Concluding Comment

The maturation of computerized design methods will not revolutionize design or designers. It will change some of the things the designers want to know and some of the ways in which they do things, but the important advances in product design will still be conceptual and creative, rather than routine and mechanical. The competent engineer-designer must therefore be thoroughly familiar with the technology. He cannot depend on a vast computer library to supply all analysis programs because his needs will continuously outstrip the available software. He must thoroughly understand optimization methods for the same reason that he must understand his physical technology: first, to intelligently interpret his result, and second, to utilize the methods as an aid to discovering new kinds of design solutions. As Richard Hamming (1962) says in the motto to his book on numerical methods: "The purpose of computing is insight, not numbers."

## REFERENCES

Balinski, M. L., "Integer Programming: Methods, Uses, Computation," *Man. Sci.* **12** (3), 253–312 (Nov. 1965)

Bellman, R., *Dynamic Programming*, Princeton Univ. Press, Princeton, N.J. (1957)

Bradbury, W. W., and R. Fletcher, "New Iterative Methods for Solution of the Eigenproblem," *Num. Math.* **9**, 259–267 (1966)

Brown, D. M., and A. H. S. Ang, "A Nonlinear Programming Approach to the Minimum Weight Elastic Design of Steel Structures," Structural Research Series No. 298, Univ. of Illinois Civil Engineering Studies (1965)

Brown, D. M., and A. H. S. Ang, "Structural Optimization by Nonlinear Programming," *J. Struct. Div., ASCE*, **92** (ST6), 319–340 (1966)

Crandall, S. H., *Engineering Analysis—A Survey of Numerical Procedures*, McGraw-Hill, New York (1956)

Dantzig, G., *Linear Programming and Extensions*, Princeton Univ. Press, Princeton, N.J. (1963).

Fox, R. L., "Constraint Surface Normals for Structural Synthesis Techniques," *AIAA J.* **3** (8) 1517, 1518 (1965).

Fox, R. L., and M. P. Kapoor, "A Minimization Method for the Solution of the Eigenproblem Arising in Structural Dynamics," presented at the Second Air Force Conference on Matrix Methods in Structural Mechanics, Wright-Patterson AFB, Ohio, AFFDL-TR-68-150 (1968a)

Fox, R. L., and M. P. Kapoor, "Rates of Change of Eigenvalues and Eigenvectors," *AIAA J.* **6** (12), 2426–2429 (1968b)

Gomory, R. E., "Large and Non-convex Problems in Linear Programming," *IBM Res. Rep. RC-765* (1962)

Hadley, G., *Linear Programming*, Addison-Wesley, Reading, Mass. (1962)

Hadley, G., *Nonlinear and Dynamic Programming*, Addison-Wesley, Reading, Mass. (1964)

Hall, A. S., Jr., *Kinematics and Linkage Design*, Prentice Hall, Englewood Cliffs, N.J. (1961)

Hamming, R. W., *Numerical Methods for Scientists and Engineers*, McGraw-Hill, New York (1962).

Householder, A. S., *Principles of Numerical Analysis*, McGraw-Hill, New York (1953)

Isaacson, E., and H. B. Keller, *Analysis of Numerical Methods*, Wiley, New York (1966)

Kapoor, M. P., "Automated Optimum Designs of Structures under Dynamic Response Restrictions," Ph.D. Thesis, Case Western Reserve University (1969)

Lavi, A., and T. P. Vogl, *Recent Advances in Optimization Techniques*, Wiley, New York (1966)

*Manual of Steel Construction*, 6th ed., Amer. Inst. of Steel Construction, New York (1964)

Melosh, R. J., and R. Luik, "Approximate Multiple Configuration Analysis and Allocation for Least Weight Structural Design," AFFDL-TR-67-29 (1967)

Melosh, R. J., and R. Luik, "An Allocation Procedure for Structural Design," AIAA/ASME 9th Conference on Structures, Structural Dynamics, and Materials, Palm Springs, Calif., Preprint No. 68-329 (1968)

Nemhauser, G. L., "*Introduction to Dynamic Programming*, Wiley, New York (1966)

Sheu, C. Y., and W. Prager, "Recent Developments in Optimal Structural Design," *Applied Mechanics Reviews* **21** (10), 985–992 (1968)

Thornton, W. A., and L. A. Schmit, "Structural Synthesis of an Ablating Thermostructural Panel," AIAA/ASME 9th Conference on Structures, Structural Dynamics, and Materials, Palm Springs, Calif., Preprint No. 68–332 (1968a)

Thornton, W. A., and L. A. Schmit, "Structural Synthesis of an Ablating Thermostructural Panel," NASA CR-1215 (1968b)

Timko, C. A., "Determining Linkage Proportions," *Mach. Des.*, March 31, 127–130 (1966)

Wilkinson, J. H., *The Algebraic Eigenvalue Problem*, Clarendon Press, Oxford (1965)

Wittrick, W. H., "Rates of Change of Eigenvalues with Reference to Buckling and Vibration Problems," *J. of the Royal Aeronautical Soc.* **66**, 590 (1962)

Wright, P. M., "Behavior Gradient Matrices in the Weight Minimization of Structures," Ph.D. Thesis, University of Colorado (1968)

Zarghamee, M. S., "Optimum Frequency of Structures," *AIAA J.*, **6** (4), 749–750 (1968)

# INDEX

# INDEX